Contents

About this book... iv

Chapter 5 The complex plane
Introduction... 1
5.1   Further loci with complex numbers.......... 2
5.2   Transforming the Argand plane 9
Summary and review 14
Exploration.. 16
Assessment 17

Chapter 6 Recurrence relations
Introduction... 19
6.1   First-order recurrence relations 20
6.2   Second-order recurrence relations 32
Summary and review 42
Exploration 45
Assessment 46

Chapter 7 Further methods in calculus
Introduction... 49
7.1   Reduction formulae.................................. 50
7.2   Arc lengths... 56
7.3   Surface areas 65
Summary and review 72
Exploration.. 74
Assessment 75

Chapter 8 Further matrices
Introduction... 77
8.1   Eigenvalues and eigenvectors.................. 78
8.2   Matrix diagonalisation 91
Summary and review 100
Exploration.. 102
Assessment 103

Chapter 9 Number theory
Introduction... 105
9.1   Division and the Euclidean algorithm .. 106
9.2   Modular arithmetic 112
9.3   Congruence equations 119
9.4   Combinatorics 125
Summary and review 131
Exploration.. 134
Assessment 135

Chapter 10 Group theory
Introduction... 137
10.1   Groups 138
10.2   Subgroups.. 144
10.3   Isomorphism.. 149
Summary and review 153
Exploration.. 156
Assessment 157

Mathematical formulae.............................. 159

Mathematical formulae - to learn.............. 164

Mathematical notation 168

Answers 172

Index.. 215

About this book

This book has been specifically created for those studying the Edexcel 2017 Further Mathematics AS and A Level. It's been written by a team of experienced authors and teachers, and it's packed with questions, explanation and extra features to help you get the most out of your course.

Every section starts by covering the basic **Fluency and skills** (A01).

Key points highlight important concepts, and make the information easier to digest.

Worked examples provide a model answer and commentary to realistic practice questions.

There is a Fluency and skills exercise for each section, to practise the skills before moving on to the Reasoning and problem-solving section.

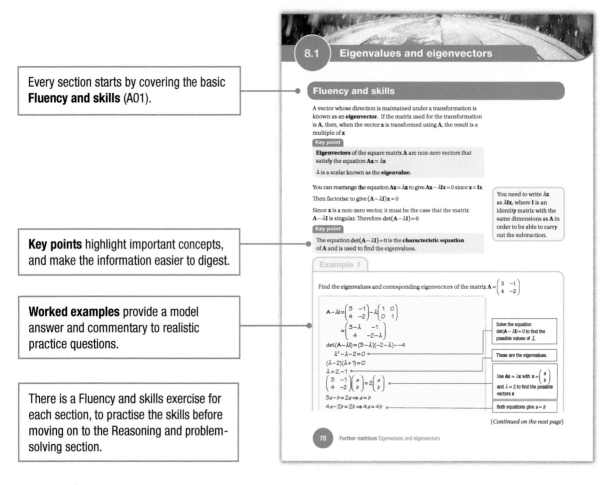

On the chapter **Introduction page**, the **Orientation box** explains what you should already know, what you will learn, and what this leads to.

At the end of every chapter, an **Exploration page** gives you an opportunity to explore the subject beyond the specification.

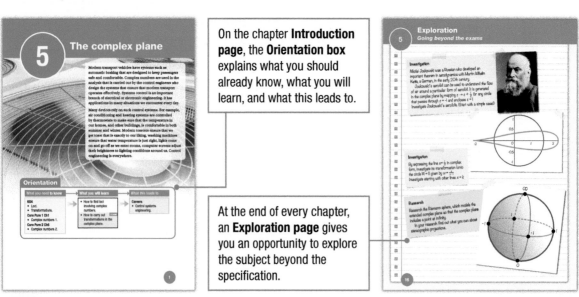

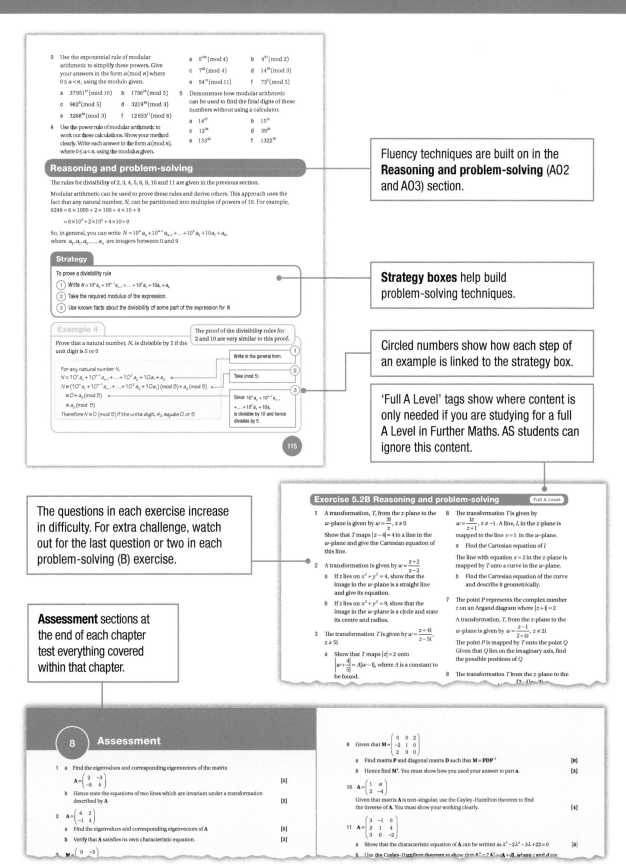

3 Use the exponential rule of modular arithmetic to simplify these powers. Give your answers in the form $a \pmod n$ where $0 \le a < n$, using the modulo given.

   a $5^{135} \pmod 4$ b $4^{87} \pmod 2$
   c $7^{92} \pmod 4$ d $14^{39} \pmod 3$
   e $54^{15} \pmod{11}$ f $73^5 \pmod 5$

5 Demonstrate how modular arithmetic can be used to find the final digits of these numbers without using a calculator.

   a 14^{27} b 15^{12}
   c 12^{36} d 39^{28}
   e 153^{32} f 1322^{30}

   a $37951^{57} \pmod{10}$ b $1736^{26} \pmod 5$
   c $982^9 \pmod 5$ d $3219^{40} \pmod 3$
   e $3268^{84} \pmod 3$ f $12653^{11} \pmod 6$

4 Use the power rule of modular arithmetic to work out these calculations. Show your method clearly. Write each answer in the form $a \pmod n$, where $0 \le a < n$, using the modulus given.

Reasoning and problem-solving

The rules for divisibility of 2, 3, 4, 5, 6, 9, 10 and 11 are given in the previous section.

Modular arithmetic can be used to prove these rules and derive others. This approach uses the fact that any natural number, N, can be partitioned into multiples of powers of 10. For example, $6249 = 6 \times 1000 + 2 \times 100 + 4 \times 10 + 9$

$= 6 \times 10^3 + 2 \times 10^2 + 4 \times 10 + 9$

So, in general, you can write $N = 10^n a_n + 10^{n-1} a_{n-1} + \ldots + 10^2 a_2 + 10 a_1 + a_0$, where $a_0, a_1, a_2, \ldots, a_n$ are integers between 0 and 9

Strategy

To prove a divisibility rule

① Write $N = 10^n a_n + 10^{n-1} a_{n-1} + \ldots + 10^2 a_2 + 10 a_1 + a_0$

② Take the required modulus of the expression.

③ Use known facts about the divisibility of some part of the expression for N

Example 4

Prove that a natural number, N, is divisible by 5 if the unit digit is 5 or 0.

The proof of the divisibility rules for 2 and 10 are very similar to this proof.

For any natural number N,
$N = 10^n a_n + 10^{n-1} a_{n-1} + \ldots + 10^2 a_2 + 10 a_1 + a_0$
$N \equiv (10^n a_n + 10^{n-1} a_{n-1} + \ldots + 10^2 a_2 + 10 a_1)\pmod 5 + a_0 \pmod 5$
$\equiv 0 + a_0 \pmod 5$
$\equiv a_0 \pmod 5$
Therefore $N \equiv 0 \pmod 5$ if the units digit, a_0, equals 0 or 5

Write in the general form. ①

Take $\pmod 5$ ②

Since $10^n a_n + 10^{n-1} a_{n-1} + \ldots + 10^2 a_2 + 10 a_1$, is divisible by 10 and hence divisible by 5 ③

115

Fluency techniques are built on in the **Reasoning and problem-solving** (AO2 and AO3) section.

Strategy boxes help build problem-solving techniques.

Circled numbers show how each step of an example is linked to the strategy box.

'Full A Level' tags show where content is only needed if you are studying for a full A Level in Further Maths. AS students can ignore this content.

The questions in each exercise increase in difficulty. For extra challenge, watch out for the last question or two in each problem-solving (B) exercise.

Assessment sections at the end of each chapter test everything covered within that chapter.

Exercise 5.2B Reasoning and problem-solving   Full A Level

1 A transformation, T, from the z-plane to the w-plane is given by $w = \dfrac{3i}{z}$, $z \ne 0$

Show that T maps $|z-4| = 4$ to a line in the w-plane and give the Cartesian equation of this line.

2 A transformation is given by $w = \dfrac{z+2}{z-2}$

  a If z lies on $x^2 + y^2 = 4$, show that the image in the w-plane is a straight line and give its equation.

  b If z lies on $x^2 + y^2 = 9$, show that the image in the w-plane is a circle and state its centre and radius.

3 The transformation T is given by $w = \dfrac{z+4i}{z-5i}$, $z \ne 5i$

  a Show that T maps $|z| = 2$ onto $\left| w + \dfrac{4}{5} \right| = A|w - 1|$, where A is a constant to be found.

6 The transformation T is given by $w = \dfrac{iz}{z+1}$, $z \ne -1$. A line, l, in the z-plane is mapped to the line $v = 1$ in the w-plane.

  a Find the Cartesian equation of l

The line with equation $x = 2$ in the z-plane is mapped by T onto a curve in the w-plane.

  b Find the Cartesian equation of the curve and describe it geometrically.

7 The point P represents the complex number z on an Argand diagram where $|z+1| = 2$

A transformation, T, from the z-plane to the w-plane is given by $w = \dfrac{z-1}{2+iz}$, $z \ne 2i$

The point P is mapped by T onto the point Q

Given that Q lies on the imaginary axis, find the possible positions of Q

8 The transformation T from the z-plane to the

---

8   Assessment

1 a Find the eigenvalues and corresponding eigenvectors of the matrix

    $\mathbf{A} = \begin{pmatrix} 2 & -3 \\ -8 & 4 \end{pmatrix}$ **[5]**

b Hence state the equations of two lines which are invariant under a transformation described by $\mathbf{A}$ **[2]**

2 $\mathbf{A} = \begin{pmatrix} 6 & 2 \\ -1 & 4 \end{pmatrix}$

  a Find the eigenvalues and corresponding eigenvectors of $\mathbf{A}$ **[5]**

  b Verify that $\mathbf{A}$ satisfies its own characteristic equation.   **[3]**

3 $\mathbf{M} = \begin{pmatrix} 0 & -3 \end{pmatrix}$

9 Given that $\mathbf{M} = \begin{pmatrix} 0 & 0 & 2 \\ -2 & 1 & 0 \\ 2 & 0 & 0 \end{pmatrix}$

  a Find matrix $\mathbf{P}$ and diagonal matrix $\mathbf{D}$ such that $\mathbf{M} = \mathbf{PDP}^{-1}$ **[8]**

  b Hence find $\mathbf{M}^4$. You must show how you used your answer to part **a**.   **[3]**

10 $\mathbf{A} = \begin{pmatrix} 1 & a \\ 2 & -4 \end{pmatrix}$

Given that matrix $\mathbf{A}$ is non-singular, use the Cayley–Hamilton theorem to find the inverse of $\mathbf{A}$. You must show your working clearly.   **[4]**

11 $\mathbf{A} = \begin{pmatrix} 3 & -1 & 0 \\ 2 & 1 & 4 \\ 3 & 0 & -2 \end{pmatrix}$

  a Show that the characteristic equation of $\mathbf{A}$ can be written as $\lambda^3 - 2\lambda^2 - 3\lambda + 22 = 0$ **[3]**

  b Use the Cayley–Hamilton theorem to show that $\mathbf{A}^4 = 7\mathbf{A}^2 + c\mathbf{A} + d\mathbf{I}$, where c and d are

5 The complex plane

Modern transport vehicles have systems such as automatic braking that are designed to keep passengers safe and comfortable. Complex numbers are used in the analysis that is carried out by the control engineers who design the systems that ensure that modern transport operates effectively. Systems control is an important branch of electrical or electronic engineering. It has applications in many situations we encounter every day.

Many devices rely on such control systems. For example, air conditioning and heating systems are controlled by thermostats to make sure that the temperature in our homes, and other buildings, is comfortable in both summer and winter. Modern toasters ensure that we get toast that is exactly to our liking, washing machines ensure that water temperature is just right, lights come on and go off as we enter rooms, computer screens adjust their brightness to lighting conditions around us. Control engineering is everywhere.

Orientation

What you need to know	What you will learn	What this leads to
KS4 • Loci. • Transformations. **Core Pure 1 Ch1** • Complex numbers 1. **Core Pure 2 Ch6** • Complex numbers 2.	• How to find loci involving complex numbers. • How to carry out transformations in the complex plane.	**Careers** • Control systems engineering.

A Level

Fluency and skills

See Core Pure 1 Ch1.4

For a reminder of loci.

You can draw loci such as:

- $|z - z_1| = r$ (circle, centre z_1, radius r)

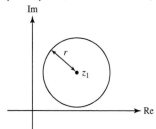

- $\arg(z - z_1) = \theta$ (half-line from z_1 at angle θ to positive real axis)

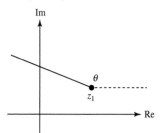

- $|z - z_1| = |z - z_2|$ (perpendicular bisector of line joining z_1 and z_2)

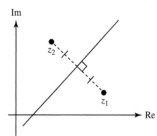

In this chapter you will see more loci involving multiple points and angles.

Consider the locus of points, z, satisfying $\arg\left(\dfrac{z - z_1}{z - z_2}\right) = \theta$

If you let $\arg(z - z_1) = \alpha$ and $\arg(z - z_2) = \beta$, then because

$\arg\left(\dfrac{z - z_1}{z - z_2}\right) = \arg(z - z_1) - \arg(z - z_2)$, you can write $\alpha - \beta = \theta$

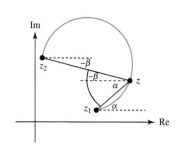

The locus of points satisfying $\arg\left(\dfrac{z - z_1}{z - z_2}\right) = \theta$ will be the sector of a

circle. As z moves around the sector, the values of α and β will change but $\alpha - \beta = \theta$ will remain constant since angles in a sector are equal.

The angle in a semicircle is always $\dfrac{\pi}{2}$ rad. An acute value of θ will lead to a **major arc** and an obtuse value of θ will give a **minor arc**.

Key point

$\arg\left(\dfrac{z-z_1}{z-z_2}\right)=\theta$ represents the arc of a circle drawn anticlockwise from z_1 to z_2

- $\theta > \dfrac{\pi}{2}$ leads to a minor arc
- $\theta = \dfrac{\pi}{2}$ leads to a semicircle
- $\theta < \dfrac{\pi}{2}$ leads to a major arc

A minor arc is an arc of a circle that is subtended by an angle of less than π radians and a major arc is an arc of a circle that is subtended by an angle of greater than π radians.

Example 1

Sketch the locus of points satisfying

a $\arg\left(\dfrac{z-2i}{z+3}\right)=\dfrac{\pi}{6}$ b $\arg\left(\dfrac{z+3}{z-2i}\right)=\dfrac{\pi}{6}$ c $\arg\left(\dfrac{z-2i}{z+3}\right)=\dfrac{5\pi}{6}$

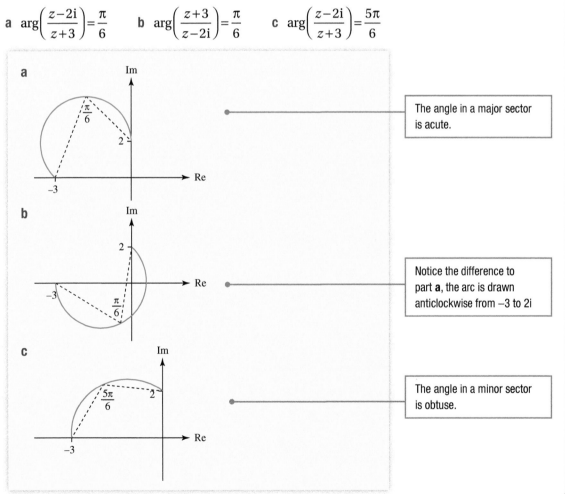

a

The angle in a major sector is acute.

b

Notice the difference to part **a**, the arc is drawn anticlockwise from −3 to 2i

c

The angle in a minor sector is obtuse.

Example 2

Sketch the locus of points satisfying $\arg\left(\dfrac{z+1-i}{z-2+2i}\right) = \dfrac{\pi}{2}$

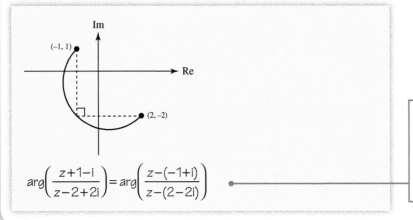

$\arg\left(\dfrac{z+1-i}{z-2+2i}\right) = \arg\left(\dfrac{z-(-1+i)}{z-(2-2i)}\right)$

So arc is drawn anti-clockwise from $(-1, 1)$ to $(2, -2)$

An angle of $\dfrac{\pi}{2}$ produces a semicircle.

To get the Cartesian equation of a locus, you can substitute for z. If you have an equation of the form $|z - z_1| = A|z - z_2|$, then substituting $z = x + iy$ into the equation gives

$$|x + iy - z_1| = A|x + iy - z_2|$$

Letting $z_1 = x_1 + iy_1$ and $z_2 = x_2 + iy_2$, and squaring both sides gives

$$|x + iy - (x_1 + iy_1)|^2 = A^2|x + iy - (x_2 + iy_2)|^2$$

Calculating the modulus and squaring gives

$$(x - x_1)^2 + (y - y_1)^2 = A^2(x - x_2)^2 + A^2(y - y_2)^2$$

This becomes the equation of a circle except in the case where $A = 1$ (when it becomes an equation of the form $|z - z_1| = |z - z_2|$, which you know is a straight line).

Key point

$|z - z_1| = A|z - z_2|$, $A \neq 1$ represents a circle. To find its centre and radius, substitute $z = x + iy$ into the equation.

Example 3

The point z satisfies $|z - 2i| = \sqrt{3}|z + 1 + 2i|$

a Show that the locus of z is a circle.

b Sketch the locus of z and state its centre and radius.

(Continued on the next page)

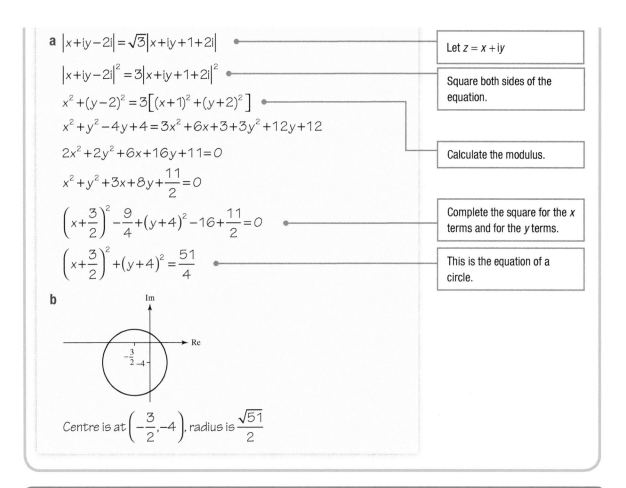

a $|x+iy-2i| = \sqrt{3}|x+iy+1+2i|$ Let $z = x+iy$

$|x+iy-2i|^2 = 3|x+iy+1+2i|^2$ Square both sides of the equation.

$x^2+(y-2)^2 = 3[(x+1)^2+(y+2)^2]$

$x^2+y^2-4y+4 = 3x^2+6x+3+3y^2+12y+12$ Calculate the modulus.

$2x^2+2y^2+6x+16y+11 = 0$

$x^2+y^2+3x+8y+\dfrac{11}{2} = 0$

$\left(x+\dfrac{3}{2}\right)^2-\dfrac{9}{4}+(y+4)^2-16+\dfrac{11}{2} = 0$ Complete the square for the x terms and for the y terms.

$\left(x+\dfrac{3}{2}\right)^2+(y+4)^2 = \dfrac{51}{4}$ This is the equation of a circle.

b

Centre is at $\left(-\dfrac{3}{2},-4\right)$, radius is $\dfrac{\sqrt{51}}{2}$

Exercise 5.1A Fluency and skills

1 Describe each of these loci in terms of z

a

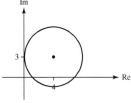

b

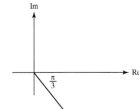

c

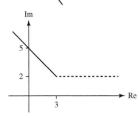

d

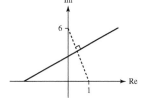

2 In each case

  i Sketch the locus of points satisfying the equation,

  ii Give the Cartesian equation of the locus.

  a $|z-8| = 6$ **b** $|z+3i| = 3$

  c $|z-1-4i| = 4$ **d** $|z+2-4i| = \sqrt{5}$

  e $|z-4i| = |z-4|$ **f** $|z+2| = |z-2i|$

  g $|z-3i| = |z-7i|$ **h** $|z-2+5i| = |z+1-i|$

  i $|z+i-3| = |z+4i-2|$

  j $|z+5-i| = |z-2+3i|$

5

3 Here are four equations and four loci.

A: $\arg\left(\dfrac{z-4i}{z-7}\right)=\dfrac{2\pi}{3}$

B: $\arg\left(\dfrac{z-7}{z-4i}\right)=\dfrac{\pi}{3}$

C: $\arg\left(\dfrac{z-7}{z-4i}\right)=\dfrac{2\pi}{3}$

D: $\arg\left(\dfrac{z-4i}{z-7}\right)=\dfrac{\pi}{3}$

Match each of these loci to its equation.

a

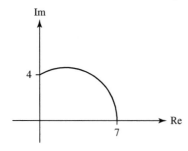

b

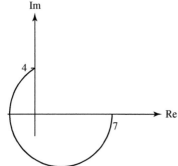

c

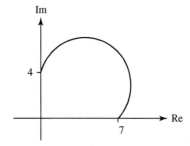

d

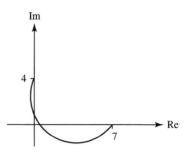

4 In each case

   i Sketch the locus of points satisfying the equation,

   ii Find the Cartesian equation of the line on which the locus lies.

   a $\arg z=\dfrac{\pi}{3}$

   b $\arg(z+5)=\dfrac{\pi}{2}$

   c $\arg(z-2i)=\dfrac{\pi}{4}$

   d $\arg(z+3-i)=\dfrac{5\pi}{6}$

   e $\arg(z-\sqrt{3}+6i)=-\dfrac{2\pi}{3}$

5 For each part

   i Find the Cartesian equation of the locus,

   ii State the coordinates of the centre and the length of the radius.

   a $|z+3|=2|z|$

   b $|z+4i|=3|z-2|$

   c $|z-2+5i|=\sqrt{5}|z+1|$

   d $|z+1-4i|=\sqrt{2}|z+i|$

   e $|z-2i+1|=\sqrt{3}|z-3+4i|$

Reasoning and problem-solving

Strategy

To find a region bounded by two loci

  (1) Sketch the locus or loci at the boundary of the region.

  (2) Test a point to see if it is inside the region or not.

  (3) Shade the correct area.

Example 4

Shade the region that satisfies both $|z-3i|<2$ and $-1 \le \text{Re}(z)<1$

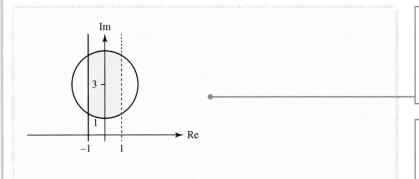

1 **2**

$|z-3i|=2$ a circle with centre 3i and radius 2

$|z-3i|<2$ represents the area inside and including the boundary of the circle.

1 **3**

Notice how the $\text{Re}(z)=1$ line is dotted since there is a strict inequality.

Shade the area inside the circle and between the two lines.

Example 5

Shade the region that is defined by the locus $|z-3i| \le |z-3| \le 2|z-3i|$

The locus $|z-3i|=|z-3|$ is the perpendicular bisector of the line joining the point 3 to the point 3i
$|z-3i| \le |z-3|$ is the region closer to 3i than 3

Consider each inequality separately.

1

Sketch the line.

Now consider $|z-3| \le 2|z-3i|$
$|x+iy-3| \le 2|x+iy-3i|$

$\sqrt{(x-3)^2+y^2} \le 2\sqrt{x^2+(y-3)^2}$

$(x-3)^2+y^2 \le 4(x^2+(y-3)^2)$ ⟵ Square both sides.

$x^2-6x+9+y^2 \le 4x^2+4y^2-24y+36$

$3x^2+3y^2+6x-24y+27 \ge 0$

$x^2+y^2+2x-8y+9 \ge 0$ ⟵ Divide by 3

$(x+1)^2-1+(y-4)^2-16+9 \ge 0$ ⟵ Complete the square.

$(x+1)^2+(y-4)^2 \ge 8$

So, $|z-3| \le 2|z-3i|$ is the region outside the circle with centre $(-1,4)$ and radius $\sqrt{8}$

2

You could check a point, e.g. if $z=3i$ then $|z-3i|=|0|=0$ and $|z-3|=|3i-3|=3\sqrt{2}$ so $|z-3i| \le |z-3|$

Substitute $z=x+iy$ to find the centre and radius.

3

Shade the region left of the line and outside the circle.

1 Sketch and shade the region satisfying

  a $|z+7\mathrm{i}|<7$ **b** $1\le \mathrm{Re}(z)\le 5$

  c $-3<\mathrm{Im}(z)<2$ **d** $\dfrac{\pi}{4}\le \arg(z-2)<\dfrac{\pi}{2}$

  e $|z-5+\mathrm{i}|\ge 1$ **f** $\mathrm{Im}(z-\mathrm{i})\le 4$

  g $-\dfrac{\pi}{6}<\arg(z+\mathrm{i})<\dfrac{\pi}{6}$

2 Shade the region satisfying both equations in each case.

  a $|z+2|<2$ and $-2\le \mathrm{Re}(z)\le 0$

  b $|z-4\mathrm{i}+1|\le 1$ and $\mathrm{Im}(z)<4$

  c $0\le \arg(z)\le \dfrac{\pi}{2}$ and $|z-3-2\mathrm{i}|<3$

  d $|z-3+4\mathrm{i}|>4$ and $\dfrac{\pi}{3}\le \arg(z-3+4\mathrm{i})\le \dfrac{2\pi}{3}$

  e $-\dfrac{\pi}{6}<\arg(z+1-\mathrm{i})<\dfrac{\pi}{6}$ and $0\le \mathrm{Re}(z)\le 2$

  f $|z+\mathrm{i}-2|>1$ and $|z-2|<1$

  g $|z-3-2\mathrm{i}|\ge 2$ and $|z-3-2\mathrm{i}|<3$

3 **a** On the same Argand diagram

  i Sketch the locus of points that satisfy $|z|=5$

  ii Sketch the locus of points that satisfy $|z-2\mathrm{i}|=\sqrt{2}|z+\mathrm{i}|$

  At the point A, z satisfies both $|z|=5$ and $|z-\mathrm{i}|=\sqrt{2}|z+\mathrm{i}|$

  b Find the complex coordinates of A

4 **a** On the same Argand diagram

  i Sketch the locus of points that satisfy $|z+2\mathrm{i}|=\sqrt{5}|z-2|$

  ii Sketch the locus of points that satisfy $|z+2|=|z-2\mathrm{i}|$

  At the point A, z satisfies both $|z+2\mathrm{i}|=\sqrt{5}|z+2|$ and $|z+2|=|z-2\mathrm{i}|$

  b Find the complex coordinates of A

5 Use set notation to describe each of the shaded regions in terms of the complex number z

  a

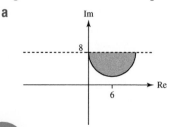

b

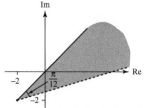

6 The arc of a circle is defined by the locus
$$\arg\!\left(\dfrac{z-5\mathrm{i}}{z+5}\right)=\dfrac{\pi}{4}$$

  a Sketch the locus of points z which satisfy
$$\arg\!\left(\dfrac{z-5\mathrm{i}}{z+5}\right)=\dfrac{\pi}{4}$$

  b Write down the complex number that represents the centre of the circle.

  c Find the complex number P that satisfies both $\arg\!\left(\dfrac{z-5\mathrm{i}}{z+5}\right)=\dfrac{\pi}{4}$ and $\mathrm{Re}(z)=-3$

7 P represents the complex number z such that $\arg\!\left(\dfrac{1}{z-\mathrm{i}}\right)=\dfrac{\pi}{4}$

  a Sketch the locus of P

  Q represents the complex number z where $|z+4|=\sqrt{2}|z|$

  b Show that the locus of Q is a circle and state its centre and radius.

  c Find the complex numbers that satisfy both loci.

8 The locus of points that satisfy $\arg\!\left(\dfrac{w}{z}\right)=\dfrac{2\pi}{3}$ is shown on the Argand diagram.

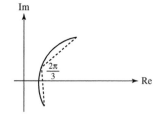

  Copy the diagram and add to it a sketch of the locus of points that satisfy $\arg\!\left(\dfrac{z}{w}\right)=\dfrac{2\pi}{3}$

9 **a** Prove that the locus of points, z, satisfying $|z|=k|z-(a+b\mathrm{i})|$, where $k\in \mathbb{R}, k\ne 1$ is a circle.

  b Find the coordinates of the centre of the circle in terms of k, a and b

  c State the radius of the circle in terms of k, a and b

Transforming the Argand plane

Fluency and skills

Full A Level

You can apply transformations to the complex plane. The convention is to apply a transformation to points in the **z-plane**, leading to the image of the points in the **w-plane**.

Example 1

Recall that $|zw| = |z||w|$, $\left|\dfrac{z}{w}\right| = \dfrac{|z|}{|w|}$ and

$$\arg(zw) = \arg(z) + \arg(w), \arg\left(\dfrac{z}{w}\right) = \arg(z) - \arg(w)$$

A transformation, T, from the z-plane to the w-plane is given by $w = 4 + 7z$

a Find the image of $z = 5 - i$ under T

b Show that the circle $|z| = 3$ is transformed by T to a circle in the w-plane and give its centre and radius.

c Find the image of $\arg(z - 1) = -\dfrac{\pi}{4}$ under T

a $w = 4 + 7(5 - i)$

    $= 39 - 7i$

| Substitute for z in the rule for T |

b $z = \dfrac{w - 4}{7}$

| Rearrange to make z the subject. |

$|z| = 3 \Rightarrow \left|\dfrac{w - 4}{7}\right| = 3$

$\dfrac{|w - 4|}{|7|} = 3 \Rightarrow |w - 4| = 21$

This is a circle with centre $(4, 0)$ and radius 21

c $\arg\left(\dfrac{w - 4}{7}\right) = -\dfrac{\pi}{4}$

| Since $\arg(z) = \arg\left(\dfrac{w - 4}{7}\right)$ and $\arg(z) = -\dfrac{\pi}{4}$ |

$\arg(w - 4) - \arg(7) = -\dfrac{\pi}{4}$

$\arg(w - 4) = -\dfrac{\pi}{4}$

This is a half-line from $(11, 0)$ at an angle of $-\dfrac{\pi}{4}$

| Use property of arguments that $\arg\left(\dfrac{w_1}{w_2}\right) = \arg(w_1) - \arg(w_2)$ |

| Since $\arg(7) = 0$ |

Example 2

A transformation from the z-plane to the w-plane is given by $w = z^2$. Find the locus of w when the locus of z is given by

a $|z| = 5$ **b** $\arg(zi) = \dfrac{\pi}{12}$

a $w = z^2 \Rightarrow |w| = |z^2|$

    $= |z||z|$

    $= 25$ •————————————————— Since $|z| = 5$

So the locus of w is $|w| = 25$ •————————————— Locus is a circle centre the origin, radius 25

b $\arg(zi) = \arg(z) + \arg(i)$

    $= \arg(z) + \dfrac{\pi}{2}$

So $\arg(z) + \dfrac{\pi}{2} = \dfrac{\pi}{12} \Rightarrow \arg(z) = -\dfrac{5\pi}{12}$

$\arg(w) = \arg(z^2) = 2\arg(z)$ •————————— Since $\arg(z \times z) = \arg(z) + \arg(z)$

Therefore, $\arg(w) = 2 \times -\dfrac{5\pi}{12} = -\dfrac{5\pi}{6}$

The locus is a half-line from the origin at angle of $-\dfrac{5\pi}{6}$ with the positive real axis.

Exercise 5.2A Fluency and skills

Full A Level

1 Find the image in the w-plane of the circle $|z| = 3$ under each of these transformations. Describe each locus in the w-plane geometrically.

    a $w = z - 1$

    b $w = 3z$

    c $w = 2z^2$

    d $w = iz$

    e $w = 2 + i - z$

    f $w = z^3$

2 Find the image in the w-plane of the circle $\arg(z) = \dfrac{\pi}{3}$ under each of these transformations. Describe each locus in the w-plane geometrically.

    a $w = z + 5i$

    b $w = 4z + 1 + i$

    c $w = z^3$

    d $w = iz$

    e $w = \dfrac{z^2 + 1}{2}$

    f $w = \dfrac{z - 1}{2z + i}$

3 A transformation, T, is given by $z = \dfrac{3}{w}$, $z \neq -1$. Find the locus of points in the w-plane when T is applied to each of these loci of points in the z-plane. Describe each locus in the w-plane geometrically.

   a $|z+i| = 1$ **b** $|2z-3| = 2$

   c $\arg(z) = -\dfrac{\pi}{12}$ **d** $\arg(z+i) = \dfrac{3\pi}{4}$

4 **a**   Find the locus of points in the w-plane when each of these transformations is applied to the half-line $\arg(z-2i) = \dfrac{\pi}{6}$

       i $w = 3z$ **ii** $w = z+3-2i$

  b   Show that the locus of points in the w-plane when the transformation $w = \dfrac{2}{z}$, $z \neq 0$ is applied to the half-line $\arg(z-2i) = \dfrac{\pi}{6}$ can be written as $\arg\left(\dfrac{w+i}{w}\right) = \dfrac{2\pi}{3}$

5 The transformation $w = \dfrac{3+z}{z-3i}$, $z \neq i$ is applied to points in the z-plane. Show that the locus of points in the w-plane when this transformation is applied to the half-line $\arg(z+3) = -\dfrac{\pi}{3}$ is $\arg\left(\dfrac{w}{w-1}\right) = -\dfrac{7\pi}{12}$

6 A transformation, T, is given by $w = \dfrac{z}{1+z}$, $z \neq -1$. Find the locus of points in the w-plane when T is applied to each of these loci of points in the z-plane. Describe each locus in the w-plane geometrically.

   a $|z+3| = 2$ **b** $|z-i+1| = 1$

   c $\arg(z) = -\dfrac{2\pi}{3}$ **d** $\arg(z-3) = -\dfrac{\pi}{4}$

7 A transformation, T, is given by $w = \dfrac{z+3i}{z-4}$, $z \neq 4$. Find the locus of points in the w-plane when T is applied to each of these loci of points in the z-plane. Describe each locus in the w-plane geometrically.

   a $\arg(z) = \dfrac{\pi}{3}$

   b $\arg(z+i-4) = 1.2$ rad

Reasoning and problem-solving

You can find the equation of the object or the image of a transformation. By convention, points in the z-plane are written as $z = x+iy$ and points in the w-plane are written as $w = u+iv$

Strategy

To find a Cartesian equation of an image in the w-plane

  (1) Rearrange the transformation to make z the subject.

  (2) Use properties of modulus or arguments.

  (3) Substitute $u+iv$ for w or $x+iy$ for z

  (4) Consider real or imaginary components separately.

Example 3

A transformation, T, is given by $w = \dfrac{2z+1}{z-i}$

a Given that z lies on the circle $x^2 + y^2 = 2$, give a Cartesian equation of its image under T in the w-plane.

b The line l is mapped by T onto the line with equation $u = 2$. Find a Cartesian equation of l

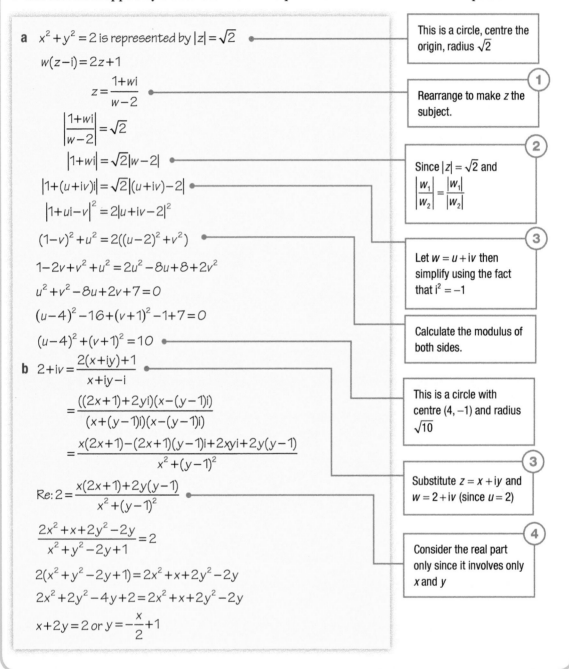

a $x^2 + y^2 = 2$ is represented by $|z| = \sqrt{2}$

This is a circle, centre the origin, radius $\sqrt{2}$

$w(z-i) = 2z+1$

$z = \dfrac{1+wi}{w-2}$

(1) Rearrange to make z the subject.

$\left| \dfrac{1+wi}{w-2} \right| = \sqrt{2}$

$|1+wi| = \sqrt{2}\,|w-2|$

(2) Since $|z| = \sqrt{2}$ and $\left| \dfrac{w_1}{w_2} \right| = \dfrac{|w_1|}{|w_2|}$

$|1+(u+iv)i| = \sqrt{2}\,|(u+iv)-2|$

$|1+ui-v|^2 = 2|u+iv-2|^2$

$(1-v)^2 + u^2 = 2((u-2)^2 + v^2)$

(3) Let $w = u+iv$ then simplify using the fact that $i^2 = -1$

$1-2v+v^2+u^2 = 2u^2 - 8u + 8 + 2v^2$

$u^2 + v^2 - 8u + 2v + 7 = 0$

$(u-4)^2 - 16 + (v+1)^2 - 1 + 7 = 0$

Calculate the modulus of both sides.

$(u-4)^2 + (v+1)^2 = 10$

b $2 + iv = \dfrac{2(x+iy)+1}{x+iy-i}$

This is a circle with centre $(4, -1)$ and radius $\sqrt{10}$

$= \dfrac{((2x+1)+2yi)(x-(y-1)i)}{(x+(y-1)i)(x-(y-1)i)}$

$= \dfrac{x(2x+1)-(2x+1)(y-1)i+2xyi+2y(y-1)}{x^2+(y-1)^2}$

(3) Substitute $z = x+iy$ and $w = 2+iv$ (since $u = 2$)

$\text{Re}: 2 = \dfrac{x(2x+1)+2y(y-1)}{x^2+(y-1)^2}$

$\dfrac{2x^2+x+2y^2-2y}{x^2+y^2-2y+1} = 2$

(4) Consider the real part only since it involves only x and y

$2(x^2+y^2-2y+1) = 2x^2+x+2y^2-2y$

$2x^2+2y^2-4y+2 = 2x^2+x+2y^2-2y$

$x+2y = 2$ or $y = -\dfrac{x}{2}+1$

1   A transformation, T, from the z-plane to the w-plane is given by $w = \dfrac{3i}{z}$, $z \neq 0$

Show that T maps $|z-4| = 4$ to a line in the w-plane and give the Cartesian equation of this line.

2   A transformation is given by $w = \dfrac{z+2}{z-2}$

a   If z lies on $x^2 + y^2 = 4$, show that the image in the w-plane is a straight line and give its equation.

b   If z lies on $x^2 + y^2 = 9$, show that the image in the w-plane is a circle and state its centre and radius.

3   The transformation T is given by $w = \dfrac{z+4i}{z-5i}$, $z \neq 5i$

a   Show that T maps $|z| = 2$ onto $\left| w + \dfrac{4}{5} \right| = A|w-1|$, where A is a constant to be found.

b   Show this represents a circle in the w-plane and find its centre and radius.

4   A transformation, T, from the z-plane to the w-plane is given by $w = \dfrac{z+2}{z}$, $z \neq 0$. T maps points on the imaginary axis in the z-plane onto a line in the w-plane. Find the equation of this line.

5   A transformation, T, from the z-plane to the w-plane is given by $w = \dfrac{z+3i}{4+iz}$, $z \neq 4i$. The point P in the z-plane is mapped by T onto the point Q in the w-plane. Given that Q lies on the real axis, show that the locus of P is a circle and find its centre and radius.

6   The transformation T is given by $w = \dfrac{iz}{z+1}$, $z \neq -1$. A line, l, in the z-plane is mapped to the line $v = 1$ in the w-plane.

a   Find the Cartesian equation of l

The line with equation $x = 2$ in the z-plane is mapped by T onto a curve in the w-plane.

b   Find the Cartesian equation of the curve and describe it geometrically.

7   The point P represents the complex number z on an Argand diagram where $|z+1| = 2$

A transformation, T, from the z-plane to the w-plane is given by $w = \dfrac{z-1}{2+iz}$, $z \neq 2i$

The point P is mapped by T onto the point Q Given that Q lies on the imaginary axis, find the possible positions of Q

8   The transformation T from the z-plane to the w-plane is given by $w = \dfrac{(2-i)z-3i}{z-i}$

Show that T maps the points on the line with equation $y = x$ in the z-plane to a circle in the w-plane and find the centre and radius of the circle.

9   The transformation T is given by $w = \dfrac{z+3i}{z-3i}$

a   Find the value of k for which T maps $|z| = k$, $k > 0$ onto a line in the w-plane.

b   i   Show that, for all other values of $k > 0$, T maps $|z| = k$ onto a circle.

ii   Find the centre and the radius of this circle for all possible values of k

Chapter summary

- $|z - z_1| = r$ represents a circle, centre z_1, radius r

- $\arg(z - z_1) = \theta$ represents a half-line from z_1 at angle θ to positive real axis.

- $|z - z_1| = |z - z_2|$ represents the perpendicular bisector of line joining z_1 and z_2

- $\arg\left(\dfrac{z - z_1}{z - z_2}\right) = \theta$ represents the arc of a circle drawn anticlockwise from z_1 to z_2

  - $\theta > \dfrac{\pi}{2}$ leads to a minor arc

  - $\theta = \dfrac{\pi}{2}$ leads to a semicircle

  - $\theta < \dfrac{\pi}{2}$ leads to a major arc

- $|z - z_1| = A|z - z_2|$, $A \neq 1$ represents a circle. To find its centre and radius, substitute $z = x + iy$ into the equation.

- Points, lines and curves in the z-plane can be mapped onto the w-plane using a transformation.

Check and review

You should now be able to...	Review Questions
✔ Construct loci of the form $\|z - z_1\| = r$ and $\|z - z_1\| = \|z - z_2\|$ on an Argand diagram and give their Cartesian equations.	1
✔ Construct loci of the form $\arg(z - z_1) = \theta$ and give the Cartesian equation of the line it lies on.	2
✔ Construct loci of the form $\arg\left(\dfrac{z - z_1}{z - z_2}\right) = \theta$ on an Argand diagram.	3
✔ Construct loci of the form $\|z - z_1\| = A\|z - z_2\|, A \neq 1$ on an Argand diagram and give the Cartesian equation of the curve.	4
✔ Sketch and shade regions satisfying loci on an Argand diagram.	5–7
✔ Transform the complex plane. **Full A Level**	8, 9
✔ Find the Cartesian equation of the image on the w-plane under a transformation from the z-plane.	10, 11

1 a Sketch the locus of points satisfying

   i $|z-2+3i|=4$

   ii $|z-7i|=|z+7|$

   iii $|z|=|z+6i|$

   b State the Cartesian equation of the curves in part **a**.

2 a Sketch the locus of points satisfying

   i $\arg(z+5)=\dfrac{\pi}{3}$

   ii $\arg(z+3+3i)=\dfrac{\pi}{4}$

   b State the Cartesian equation of the line on which each half-line lies.

3 Sketch the locus of points satisfying

   a $\arg\left(\dfrac{z+4i}{z-2}\right)=\dfrac{\pi}{3}$

   b $\arg\left(\dfrac{z-2}{z+4i}\right)=\dfrac{\pi}{3}$

   c $\arg\left(\dfrac{z+4i}{z-2}\right)=\dfrac{2\pi}{3}$

   d $\arg\left(\dfrac{z-2}{z+4i}\right)=\dfrac{2\pi}{3}$

4 a Work out the Cartesian equation of each of these curves.

   i $|z+1|=2|z-2i|$

   ii $|z-i+3|=\sqrt{3}|z+2|$

   b State the centre and radius of the curves in part **a**.

5 Shade the region satisfying $|z-3|\le\sqrt{2}|z+i|$ and $-4<\mathrm{Re}(z)\le0$

6 Shade the region satisfying
   $0<\arg(z+i-1)<\dfrac{\pi}{2}$ and $-2\le\mathrm{Im}(z)\le2$

7 Shade the region satisfying $|z|\ge\sqrt{3}|z+1-2i|$ and $|z-4i|\ge1$

8 a Find the image in the w-plane of the circle $|z|=5$ under each of these transformations.

   i $w=z^2$

   ii $w=\dfrac{z+2}{z-2i}$

   b Describe each of these images in the w-plane geometrically.

9 Find and sketch the image in the w-plane of the half-line $\arg(z)=-\dfrac{\pi}{4}$ under the transformation

   a $w=4iz^3$

   b $w=\dfrac{i-z}{z+4}$

10 A transformation T from the z-plane to the w-plane is given by $w=\dfrac{6}{z+1}$. Show that T maps $|z+5|=4$ to a line in the w-plane and give the Cartesian equation of this line.

11 The transformation, T, is given by $w=\dfrac{z+6i}{z+3}$, $z\ne-3$. Find the image in the w-plane of $|z|=5$

Investigation

Nikolai Joukowski was a Russian who developed an important theorem in aerodynamics with Martin Wilhelm Kutta, a German, in the early 20th century.

Joukowski's aerofoil can be used to understand the flow of air around a particular form of aerofoil. It is generated in the complex plane by mapping $z \to z + \frac{1}{z}$ for any circle that passes through $z = -1$ and encloses $z = 1$

Investigate Joukowski's aerofoils. (Start with a simple case!)

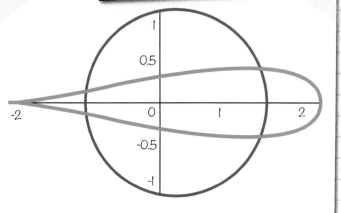

Investigation

By expressing the line $x = \frac{1}{2}$ in complex form, investigate its transformation (onto the circle $|z| = 1$) given by $w = \frac{z}{z-1}$

Investigate starting with other lines $x = k$

Research

Research the Riemann sphere, which models the extended complex plane so that the complex plane includes a point at infinity.

In your research find out what you can about stereographic projections.

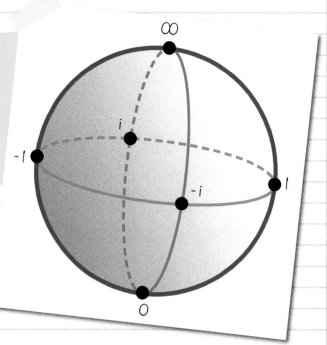

1 A curve, C, is described by the equation $|z-3\mathrm{i}|=2$

    a Sketch C on an Argand diagram. **[2]**

    b Write down the Cartesian equation of C **[2]**

2 **a** Sketch the locus of points satisfying the equation $|z+2|=|z-2\mathrm{i}|$ **[2]**

    b Give the Cartesian equation of the locus drawn in part **a**. **[1]**

3 A half-line, l, is given by the equation $\arg(z+\mathrm{i})=\dfrac{\pi}{4}$

    a Sketch l on an Argand diagram. **[2]**

    b Find the Cartesian equation of the line on which the half-line lies. **[2]**

    c Find the complex number z that satisfies $\arg(z+\mathrm{i})=\dfrac{\pi}{4}$ and $|z|=2$ **[5]**

4 A curve, C, has equation $|z+7|=\sqrt{2}|z-4\mathrm{i}+1|$

    a Show that C is a circle and state its centre and radius. **[5]**

    b Shade the region satisfying $|z+7|\geq\sqrt{2}|z-4\mathrm{i}+1|$ on an Argand diagram. **[3]**

Given that w lies on C,

    c Find the range of possible values of $\operatorname{Im}(w)$. Give your answer in the form $a\leq\operatorname{Im}(w)\leq b$ where a and b are given as exact values. **[2]**

5 Sketch the locus of the point satisfying $\arg\left(\dfrac{z-6}{z-6\mathrm{i}}\right)=\dfrac{5\pi}{6}$ **[3]**

6 The complex number z satisfies $\left|z-\sqrt{3}+3\mathrm{i}\right|=\sqrt{3}$

    a Sketch the locus of P which represents z on an Argand diagram. **[2]**

    b Work out the range of possible values of $|z|$ **[3]**

7 **a** On the same Argand diagram, sketch the locus of points that satisfy

      i $\arg(z+3)=-\dfrac{\pi}{3}$

      ii $|z+3|=3$ **[4]**

At the point P, z satisfies both $\arg(z+3)=-\dfrac{\pi}{3}$ and $|z+3|=3$

    b Find the coordinates of P **[6]**

8 A complex number z is represented by the point P in the Argand diagram. P is such that z satisfies $0\leq\arg(z-2\mathrm{i})<\dfrac{3\pi}{4}$ and $|z-2\mathrm{i}|\geq2$. Shade the region in which P must lie. **[5]**

9 A complex number z is represented by the point P in the Argand diagram.

    a Given that $|z+4\mathrm{i}|=|z|$, sketch the locus of P and state its Cartesian equation. **[2]**

    b Find the complex number z which satisfies both $|z-2+5\mathrm{i}|=3$ and $|z+4\mathrm{i}|=|z|$ **[3]**

10 The arc of a circle, C, is given by the locus $\arg\left(\dfrac{z-6\mathrm{i}}{z+6}\right)=\dfrac{\pi}{2}$

    a   Sketch the locus of points satisfying $\arg\left(\dfrac{z-6\mathrm{i}}{z+6}\right)=\dfrac{\pi}{2}$ **[2]**

    b   The centre of C is at the point P. State the complex number represented by P. Justify your answer.   **[2]**

11 A transformation from the z-plane to the w-plane is given by $w=4-2z$

    a   Find the image of $z=5+3\mathrm{i}$ under the transformation.   **[2]**

    b   Show that the circle $|z+1|=2$ is transformed to a circle in the w-plane and find its centre and radius.   **[3]**

12 The transformation T from the z-plane to the w-plane is given by $w=\dfrac{\mathrm{i}}{z}$

Show that T maps $|z-4|=4$ to a line in the w-plane and give its Cartesian equation.   **[5]**

13 A transformation, T, from the z-plane to the w-plane is given by $w=z^2$

    a   Show that the line with equation $\mathrm{Re}(z)=1$ in the z-plane is mapped to a parabola in the w-plane.   **[4]**

    b   Sketch the parabola on an Argand diagram.   **[2]**

14 A transformation, T, from the z-plane to the w-plane is given by $w=\mathrm{i}z^4$. Sketch the image in the w-plane when $\arg(z)=-\dfrac{\pi}{6}$ is transformed by T **[5]**

15 A transformation from the z-plane to the w-plane is a translation by vector $\begin{pmatrix}-4\\3\end{pmatrix}$ followed by an enlargement centre the origin and scale factor 2. Write down the transformation in the form $w=az+b$, where a and b are complex numbers.   **[3]**

16 Show that the transformation from the z-plane to the w-plane given by $w=\dfrac{z-3}{z+3\mathrm{i}}$ maps $|z|=3$ onto a line in the w-plane and find its Cartesian equation.   **[6]**

17 The transformation T is given by $w=\dfrac{1-z}{\mathrm{i}z+2}$, $z\neq 2\mathrm{i}$. The point P in the z-plane is mapped by T onto the point Q in the w-plane. Given that Q lies on the imaginary axis, show that the locus of P is a line and find its Cartesian equation.   **[5]**

18 Show that the transformation $w=\dfrac{z-\sqrt{2}\mathrm{i}}{z+\sqrt{2}\mathrm{i}}$ maps $|z|=2$ onto a circle in the w-plane and find the centre and the radius of the circle.   **[7]**

19 A transformation, T, maps points from the z-plane to the w-plane and is given by $w=z^2$

The point P in the z-plane lies on the line with equation $y=x+1$

Show that the locus of this point in the w-plane satisfies $2v=u^2-1$ **[6]**

20 A transformation, T, of the z-plane to the w-plane is given by $w=\dfrac{1}{z}+z$, $z\neq 0$

The point P in the z-plane is represented by z where $|z|=3$

Use the exponential form of z to show that the locus when the locus of P is mapped by T to the w-plane is given by

$144u^2+225v^2=1600$ **[6]**

6 Recurrence relations

Internet shopping and banking are used widely. Internet security is important so that criminals cannot access someone else's money. Cryptography is important to make sure that communication between customers and retailers or banks cannot be intercepted.

Information is typically encrypted at the customer's device, passed over the internet, and then decoded at either the retailer or bank, so that the desired transaction can take place. The encryption and decryption are carried out by processes and software that rely on programs that incorporate the use of recurrence relations in ways that help to ensure that, even if the information is intercepted, it cannot be stolen and misused.

Orientation

What you need to know	What you will learn	What this leads to
Maths Ch13 • Introduction to sequences. • Arithmetic sequences. **Core Pure 1 Ch2** • Algebra and series.	• How to use first-order recurrence relations. • How to use second-order recurrence relations. **A Level**	**Careers** • Computer programming.

Fluency and skills

Imagine you open a bank account with a £500 deposit which pays 1% interest per year and you also pay an additional £100 into the account at the end of each year.

You can work out the amount in the account at the end of each year as follows.

End of year 1: $500 \times 1.01 + 100 = £605$

End of year 2: $605 \times 1.01 + 100 = £711.05$

End of year 3: $711.05 \times 1.01 + 100 = £818.1605$

If you wanted to work out how much money would be in the account after 10 years, it would take quite a while and you would need to make several calculations.

Notice, however, that each term is the previous term multiplied by 1.01 plus 100. This can be expressed as a **recurrence relation**.

> The recurrence relation for this problem can be written as $u_{n+1} = 1.01u_n + 100$, $n \geq 1$ or $u_n = 1.01u_{n-1} + 100$, $n \geq 2$. The initial condition is the first term, $u_1 = 500$

Key point

A **first-order recurrence relation** is a recursive relationship between two consecutive terms of a sequence.

It is necessary to also provide the **initial condition** which is the value of the first term of the sequence.

First-order recurrence relations can occur in many contexts, for example those relating to finance (as in the bank account example) and the growth or decline of populations.

Example 1

A town has a birth rate of 16 per 1000 of population and a death rate of 6 per 1000 of population. Each year, 1200 people move to the town and 400 people leave the town.

At the start of 2015, the population of the town is 20 000

a Explain in the context of the problem why the population of the town n years after the start of 2015 is modelled by the recurrence relation $u_n = 1.01u_{n-1} + 800$, $u_1 = 20\,000$, $n \geq 2$

(Continued on the next page)

b Use the recurrence relation to find the population of the town at the start of 2017

c Why might this not be a realistic model over the long term?

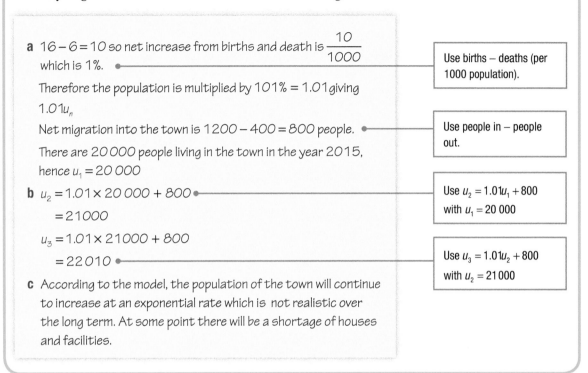

a $16 - 6 = 10$ so net increase from births and death is $\dfrac{10}{1000}$ which is 1%.

Therefore the population is multiplied by $101\% = 1.01$ giving $1.01u_n$

Net migration into the town is $1200 - 400 = 800$ people.

There are 20 000 people living in the town in the year 2015, hence $u_1 = 20\,000$

Use births – deaths (per 1000 population).

b $u_2 = 1.01 \times 20\,000 + 800$

$\quad = 21\,000$

$u_3 = 1.01 \times 21\,000 + 800$

$\quad = 22\,010$

Use people in – people out.

Use $u_2 = 1.01u_1 + 800$ with $u_1 = 20\,000$

Use $u_3 = 1.01u_2 + 800$ with $u_2 = 21\,000$

c According to the model, the population of the town will continue to increase at an exponential rate which is not realistic over the long term. At some point there will be a shortage of houses and facilities.

In this chapter, you will learn how to solve recurrence relations to find a **closed-form solution.**

Key point

A **closed-form solution** to a recurrence relation is a non-recursive formula for the nth term of the sequence.

Consider the sequence 5, 10, 20, 40, … where each term is double the previous term.

A recurrence relation for this sequence is $u_n = 2u_{n-1}$, $n \geq 2$

The **initial condition** is $u_1 = 5$

Consider the 6th term, u_6

$u_6 = 2u_5$ but $u_5 = 2u_4$, so

$u_6 = 2u_5$

$\quad = 2 \times 2u_4$

$\quad = 2 \times 2 \times 2u_3$

$\quad = 2 \times 2 \times 2 \times 2u_2$

$\quad = 2 \times 2 \times 2 \times 2 \times 2u_1$

$\quad = 2 \times 2 \times 2 \times 2 \times 2 \times 5$

$\quad = 5(2^5)$

Therefore the **closed-form solution** is $u_n = 5(2^{n-1})$

The closed-form solution of a recurrence relation of the form $u_n = ku_{n-1}$ is $u_n = u_1 k^{n-1}$

The recurrence relation can be a bit trickier, such as in the bank account example where a constant is also added to a multiple of the previous term.

For example, look at the recurrence relation

$u_n = 4u_{n-1} + 7$, $n \geq 2$ with $u_1 = 2$

Consider the nth term, u_n

$u_n = 4u_{n-1} + 7$

$\quad = 4(4u_{n-2} + 7) + 7$

$\quad = 4(4(4u_{n-3} + 7) + 7) + 7$

and so on

$\quad = 4^{n-1}u_1 + 7 + 4(7) + 4^2(7) + \ldots + 4^{n-2}(7)$

$\quad = 4^{n-1}u_1 + \sum_{r=1}^{n-1} 7(4^{r-1})$

Consider the 4th term, u_4

$u_4 = 4u_3 + 7$

$\quad = 4(4u_2 + 7) + 7$

$\quad = 4(4(4u_1 + 7) + 7) + 7$

$\quad = 4^3 u_1 + (7 + 28 + 112)$

$\quad = 4^{4-1}u_1 + \sum_{r=1}^{3} 7(4^{r-1})$

$\quad = 4^3 u_1 + \dfrac{7}{3}(4^3 - 1)$

$\quad = 128 + 147$

$\quad = 275$

$\sum_{r=1}^{n-1} 7(4^{r-1})$ is a geometric series, with first term 7 and common ratio 4

The sum of a geometric series is given by $S_n = \dfrac{a(r^n - 1)}{r - 1}$, so in this case

$S_{n-1} = \dfrac{7(4^{n-1} - 1)}{4 - 1} = \dfrac{7}{3}(4^{n-1} - 1)$

Therefore you can see that the closed-form solution is

$u_n = u_1(4^{n-1}) + \dfrac{7}{3}(4^{n-1} - 1)$

You can generalise this result to any recurrence relation of the form $u_n = ku_{n-1} + c$

Instead of memorising this formula, another method is to recognise that the solution above can be written as

$$u_n = \left(\frac{u_1 + \dfrac{7}{3}}{4} \right) 4^n - \frac{7}{3} \text{ or, in other words, } u_n = A(4^n) + B \text{ for some}$$

constants A and B that you can find by solving simultaneous equations.

Example 2

The first 5 terms of a sequence are 1, 4, 13, 40 and 121

a Write down a first-order recurrence relation whose first five terms are these numbers.

b Solve the recurrence relation in part **a** to find a closed-form solution.

c Calculate the 10th term of the sequence.

a $u_n = 3u_{n-1} + 1$, $n \geq 2$, $u_1 = 1$ ●————

Each term is the previous number multiplied by 3 plus 1

Remember to give the initial condition.

b $u_n = A(3^n) + B$ ●————

$u_1 = A(3^1) + B = 1$ leads to the equation $3A + C = 1$

$u_2 = A(3^2) + B = 4$ leads to the equation $9A + C = 4$

$6A = 3$ so $A = \dfrac{1}{2}$

Since the recurrence relation involves multiplying the previous term by 3 to get the next term.

$3 \times \dfrac{1}{2} + B = 1$ so $B = -\dfrac{1}{2}$

So the closed-form solution is $u_n = \dfrac{1}{2}(3^n) - \dfrac{1}{2}$

c $u_{10} = \dfrac{1}{2}(3^{10}) - \dfrac{1}{2}$

$= 29524$

The linear recurrence relation $u_n = ku_{n-1} + c$ is **homogeneous** if $c = 0$ and **non-homogeneous** if $c \neq 0$

Example 3

Find the solution to the recurrence relation $u_{n+1} = u_n + c, \ n \geq 1$ in terms of u_1

$u_n = u_{n-1} + c$

$\quad = u_{n-2} + c + c$

$\quad = u_{n-3} + c + c + c$ and so on

$\quad = u_1 + (n-1)c$

So the solution is $u_n = u_1 + (n-1)c$

Write out the sequence.

You can't use the general form

$u_n = u_1(k^{n-1}) + \dfrac{c}{k-1}(k^{n-1} - 1), \ k \neq 1$

since $k = 1$

Notice the slightly different form of the equation; this is equivalent to writing $u_n = u_{n-1} + c, \ n \geq 2$

Key point

The special case of the first-order linear recurrence relation
$u_n = ku_{n-1} + c, \ n \geq 2$, where $k = 1$ has closed-form solution

$u_n = u_1 + (n-1)c$

The general form of first-order linear recurrence relation is
$u_n = f(n)u_{n-1} + g(n)$, where $f(n)$ and $g(n)$ are functions of n

The linear recurrence equation $u_n = f(n)u_{n-1} + g(n)$ is
homogeneous if $g(n) = 0$ and **non-homogeneous** if $g(n) \neq 0$

If $c \neq 0$, then it is a **non-homogeneous** first-order linear
recurrence relation.

You only need to solve first-order recurrence relations where $f(n)$ is
a constant. However, $g(n)$ could be a simple function of n

Consider the non-homogeneous recurrence relation
$u_n = ku_{n-1} + g(n), \ n \geq 2$

The nth term is

$u_n = ku_{n-1} + g(n)$

$\quad = k(ku_{n-2} + g(n-1)) + g(n)$

$\quad = k(k(ku_{n-3} + g(n-2)) + g(n-1)) + g(n)$ and so on

$\quad = k^{n-1}u_1 + k^{n-1}g(2) + k^{n-2}g(3) + \ldots + g(n)$

$\quad = k^{n-1}u_1 + \displaystyle\sum_{r=2}^{n} k^{n-r}g(r)$

Try considering a specific term.

$$u_4 = ku_3 + g(4)$$
$$= k(ku_2 + g(3)) + g(4)$$
$$= k(k(ku_1 + g(2)) + g(3)) + g(4)$$
$$= k^3 u_1 + k^2 g(2) + kg(3) + g(4)$$

Key point

The non-homogeneous linear recurrence relation

$u_n = ku_{n-1} + g(n)$, $n \geq 2$ has solution $u_n = k^{n-1} u_1 + \displaystyle\sum_{r=2}^{n} k^{n-r} g(r)$

When $k = 1$, the solution becomes $u_n = u_1 + \displaystyle\sum_{r=2}^{n} g(r)$

Then if $g(r)$ is a linear, quadratic or cubic polynomial, you can

replace $\displaystyle\sum_{r=2}^{n} g(r)$ with the appropriate sum.

Example 4

> You could rewrite the recurrence relation as
> $u_n = u_{n-1} + (n-1)^2, n \geq 2$

A sequence has recurrence relation $u_{n+1} = u_n + n^2$, $n \geq 1$ with $u_1 = -3$.

a Write down the first 3 terms of the sequence.

b Solve the recurrence relation.

c Use your closed-form solution to find the 4th term of the sequence.

a $u_1 = -3$
$u_2 = u_1 + 1^2$
$= -3 + 1$
$= -2$
$u_3 = u_2 + 2^2$
$= -2 + 4$
$= 2$

> Use $u_n = u_{n-1} + n^2$ with $n = 1$

> Use $u_n = 2u_{n-1} + n^2$ with $n = 2$

b $u_n = u_{n-1} + (n-1)^2$
$= u_{n-2} + (n-2)^2 + (n-1)^2$
$= u_{n-3} + (n-3)^2 + (n-2)^2 + (n-1)^2$ and so on
$= u_1 + 1^2 + 2^2 + 3^2 + \ldots + (n-2)^2 + (n-1)^2$
$= u_1 + \displaystyle\sum_{r=2}^{n} (r-1)^2$

(Continued on the next page)

$$\sum_{r=2}^{n}(r-1)^2 = \frac{(n-1)}{6}(n-1+1)(2(n-1)+1)-0^2$$

Since $\sum_{r=0}^{n}r^2 = \frac{n}{6}(n+1)(2n+1)$

$$= \frac{n}{6}(n-1)(2n-1)$$

So $u_n = -3 + \frac{n}{6}(n-1)(2n-1)$

$$= -3 + \frac{n}{6}(n-1)(2n-1)$$

$$= \frac{1}{6}(2n^3 - 3n^2 + n - 18)$$

c $u_4 = \frac{1}{6}(2 \times 4^3 - 3 \times 4^2 + 4 - 18)$

$$= \frac{1}{6} \times 66$$

$$= 11$$

You could verify this using the recurrence relation: $u_4 = 2 + 3^2 = 11$

When $k \neq 1$, $u_n = ku_{n-1} + g(n)$, where g(n) is a polynomial, will have a solution of the form $Ak^n + h(n)$, where the degree of h(n) is equal to the degree of g(n)

Key point

A recurrence relation of the form $u_n = ku_{n-1} + g(n)$, $n \geq 2$, where $k \neq 1$ is a constant, has closed-form solutions of the form

$u_n = A(k^n) + B$, where g(n) is a constant

$u_n = A(k^n) + Bn + C$, where g(n) is linear

$u_n = A(k^n) + Bn^2 + Cn + D$, where g($n$) is a quadratic

$u_n = A(k^n) + Bn^3 + Cn^2 + Dn + E$, where g($n$) is a cubic.

The values of the coefficients can be found by substituting $n = 1, 2, 3, \ldots$ into the equation and solving the resulting equations simultaneously.

Example 5

A sequence has recurrence relation $u_n = 5u_{n-1} + n + 1$, $n \geq 2$ with $u_1 = 6$

a Write down the first 3 terms of the sequence.

b Find a closed-form solution.

a $u_1 = 6$
$u_2 = 5 \times 6 + 2 + 1$
$\quad = 33$
$u_3 = 5 \times 33 + 3 + 1$
$\quad = 169$

Use $u_2 = 5u_1 + 2 + 1$

Use $u_3 = 5u_2 + 3 + 1$

(Continued on the next page)

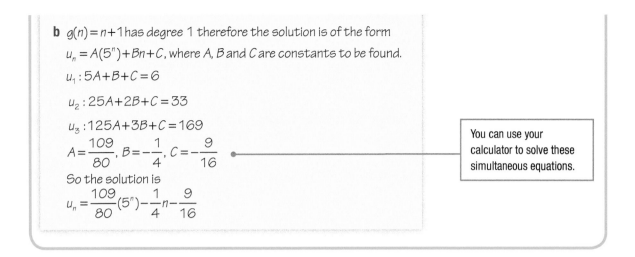

b $g(n) = n+1$ has degree 1 therefore the solution is of the form

$u_n = A(5^n) + Bn + C$, where A, B and C are constants to be found.

$u_1 : 5A + B + C = 6$

$u_2 : 25A + 2B + C = 33$

$u_3 : 125A + 3B + C = 169$

$A = \dfrac{109}{80}, B = -\dfrac{1}{4}, C = -\dfrac{9}{16}$

So the solution is

$u_n = \dfrac{109}{80}(5^n) - \dfrac{1}{4}n - \dfrac{9}{16}$

> You can use your calculator to solve these simultaneous equations.

Exercise 6.1A Fluency and skills

1   A person saves £1000 per year in a bank account that pays interest of 2% per annum. They initially deposit £2000 in the account.

  a   Form a recurrence relation for the amount of money in the account after n years.

  b   Use your recurrence relation to write down the amount in the account after two years.

2   The population of a species of animal in a particular region is estimated to be 18 000 Each week the birth rate is 40% and the death rate is 30%. In addition to this, it is estimated that 1950 of the animals leave the region each week.

  a   Form a recurrence relation for the population of the animal at the beginning of the nth week.

  b   Use your recurrence relation to find the number of the animals in the region at the beginning of the 3rd week.

  c   What does this model predict about the size of the population in the long term?

3   A town has a birth rate of 6 per 1000 of population and a death rate of 4 per 1000 of population. Each year 200 people move to the town and 1800 people leave the town.

At the start of 2010, the population of the town is 17 000

  a   Explain in the context of the problem why the population of the town n years after the start of 2010 is modelled by the recurrence relation

$$u_n = 1.002u_{n-1} - 1600, \; u_1 = 17\,000, \; n \geq 2$$

  b   Use the recurrence relation to find the population of the town at the start of 2012

  c   Why might this not be a realistic model over the long term?

4   Find the closed-form solution to each of these recurrence relations.

  a $u_n = 9u_{n-1}, \; n \geq 2, \; u_1 = 15$

  b $u_n = -3u_{n-1}, \; n \geq 2, \; u_1 = 8$

  c $u_{n+1} = 10u_n, \; n \geq 1, \; u_1 = 5$

  d $u_{n+1} = -\dfrac{1}{2}u_n, \; n \geq 1, \; u_1 = 128$

  e $u_n = 3u_{n-1}, \; n \geq 1, \; u_0 = 1$

  f $u_n = 7u_{n-1}, \; n \geq 1, \; u_0 = \dfrac{1}{49}$

5 Solve these recurrence relations.

a $u_n = 2u_{n-1} + 1, n \geq 2, u_1 = 3$

b $u_n = 3u_{n-1} - 4, n \geq 2, u_1 = 6$

c $u_{n+1} = 6u_n + 5, n \geq 1, u_1 = 2$

d $u_{n+1} = \frac{1}{2}u_n - 1, n \geq 1, u_1 = 48$

e $u_n = -3u_{n-1} - 8, n \geq 1, u_0 = 2$

f $u_n = \frac{1}{4}u_{n-1} + 3, n \geq 1, u_0 = -1$

6 Show that the recurrence relation
$u_n = u_{n-1} + 8n, n \geq 2, u_1 = 5$
has closed-form solution
$u_n = 4n^2 + 4n - 3$

7 Show that the recurrence relation
$u_n = u_{n-1} + 2n^2, n \geq 2, u_1 = -2$
has closed-form solution
$u_n = \frac{1}{3}(2n^3 + 3n^2 + n - 12)$

8 Show that the recurrence relation
$u_{n+1} = u_n + 3n(n+1), n \geq 1, u_1 = 0$
has closed-form solution
$u_n = n(n-1)(n+1)$

9 Show that the recurrence relation
$u_{n+1} = u_n + n^3, n \geq 1, u_1 = 2$
has closed-form solution
$u_n = \frac{1}{4}(8 + n^4 - 2n^3 + n^2)$

10 Show that the recurrence relation
$u_n = u_{n-1} + n^2 - 2n, n \geq 1, u_0 = -3$
has closed-form solution
$u_n = \frac{1}{6}(2n^3 - 3n^2 - 5n - 18)$

11 Solve these recurrence relations.

a $u_n = 2u_{n-1} + n, n \geq 2, u_1 = 4$

b $u_n = 3u_{n-1} + (n-2), n \geq 2, u_1 = 2$

c $u_n = -2u_{n-1} + 3n^2, n \geq 1, u_1 = 0$

d $u_{n+1} = -u_n + (n-1)^2, n \geq 1, u_1 = 5$

12 A couple take out a mortgage of £200 000 on their house. The mortgage company charges interest at a fixed rate of 3% per annum. The couple pay £12 000 to the mortgage company each year.

a Write down a recurrence relation for the size of the mortgage after n years.

b Use your recurrence relation to find the size of the mortgage after 3 years.

c Solve the recurrence relation to find a closed-form solution for u_n. Write your answer in the form $u_n = A(1.03^n) + B$ for some constants A and B

d Hence, find the term (length) of the mortgage to the nearest month.

13 The towers of Hanoi is a puzzle where a number of circular discs have to be moved from one rod to another without ever placing a larger disc on top of a smaller one. Only one disc can be moved at a time and the puzzle starts with all n discs in descending size order on the first rod, as shown. a_n is the number of moves required to complete the puzzle when there are n discs.

a Write down a_1 and a_2

A recurrence relation for the number of moves required is $a_n = 2a_{n-1} + 1$

b Find the closed-form solution for this problem and use it to find the number of moves required to complete this puzzle for 10 discs.

Reasoning and problem-solving

So far, you have used iteration and substitution into a general form to find solutions of recurrence relations. In this section, you will use proof by induction to actually prove the results.

Strategy

To prove the closed-form solution of a recurrence relation using proof by induction

① Substitute $n = 1$ into the closed-form solution to show it is equal to the value given for u_1

② Assume the closed-form solution is true for $n = k$ and use the recurrence relation to write out the $(k + 1)$th term.

③ Substitute the closed-form of the kth term into the closed-form solution and show that this leads to the required expression.

④ Write a conclusion.

Example 6

Prove by induction that the solution to the recurrence relation $u_n = 2u_{n-1} + 3$, $n \geq 2$, $u_1 = 4$ is $u_n = 7(2^{n-1}) - 3$

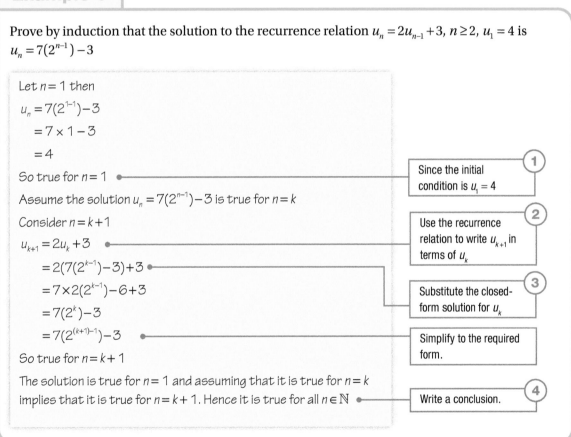

Let $n = 1$ then

$$u_n = 7(2^{1-1}) - 3$$
$$= 7 \times 1 - 3$$
$$= 4$$

So true for $n = 1$ —— Since the initial condition is $u_1 = 4$ ①

Assume the solution $u_n = 7(2^{n-1}) - 3$ is true for $n = k$

Consider $n = k + 1$

$$u_{k+1} = 2u_k + 3$$ —— Use the recurrence relation to write u_{k+1} in terms of u_k ②

$$= 2(7(2^{k-1}) - 3) + 3$$ —— Substitute the closed-form solution for u_k ③

$$= 7 \times 2(2^{k-1}) - 6 + 3$$

$$= 7(2^k) - 3$$

$$= 7(2^{(k+1)-1}) - 3$$ —— Simplify to the required form.

So true for $n = k + 1$

The solution is true for $n = 1$ and assuming that it is true for $n = k$ implies that it is true for $n = k + 1$. Hence it is true for all $n \in \mathbb{N}$ —— Write a conclusion.   ④

1 Prove by induction that the solution to the recurrence relation
   $u_n = 4u_{n-1}$, $n \geq 2$, $u_1 = 1$ is $u_n = 4^{n-1}$

2 Prove by induction that the solution to the recurrence relation
   $u_{n+1} = u_n + 7$, $n \geq 1$, $u_1 = 3$ is $u_n = 7n - 4$

3 Prove by induction that the solution to the recurrence relation
   $u_n = 5u_{n-1} - 2$, $n \geq 2$, $u_1 = 1$ is $u_n = \dfrac{1}{2}(5^{n-1} + 1)$

4 Prove by induction that the solution to the recurrence relation
   $u_n = \dfrac{1}{2}u_{n-1} + 1$, $n \geq 2$, $u_1 = -1$ is $u_n = 2 - 3(2^{1-n})$

5 Prove by induction that the solution to the recurrence relation
   $u_n = u_{n-1} + n$, $n \geq 2$, $u_1 = 0$ is $u_n = \dfrac{1}{2}(n^2 + n - 2)$

6 Prove by induction that the solution to the recurrence relation
   $u_{n+1} = u_n + n^2 - 3n$, $n \geq 1$, $u_1 = 0$ is $u_n = \dfrac{1}{3}n(n-1)(n-5)$

7 Prove by induction that the solution to the recurrence relation
   $u_{n+1} = u_n + 5n^2 - 4$, $n \geq 0$, $u_0 = -1$ is $u_n = \dfrac{1}{6}(10n^3 - 15n^2 - 19n - 6)$

8 Prove by induction that the solution to the recurrence relation
   $u_{n+1} = 3u_n + 2n$, $n \geq 0$, $u_0 = 2$ is $u_n = \dfrac{1}{2}(5(3^n) - 2n - 1)$

9 Prove by induction that the solution to the recurrence relation
   $u_{n+1} = nu_n$, $n \geq 1$, $u_1 = 3$ is $u_n = 3(n-1)!$

10 Prove by induction that the solution to the recurrence relation
   $u_n = n^2 u_{n-1}$, $n \geq 2$, $u_1 = 1$ is $u_n = (n!)^2$

11 A sequence is given by the recurrence relation $u_1 = 1$, $u_n = 1 + \dfrac{1}{2}u_{n-1}$
   Solve the recurrence relation and find the value that u_n tends towards.

12 A sequence is given by the recurrence relation $u_1 = 2$, $u_n = 3 - ku_{n-1}$, $k > 0$

Describe the behaviour of the sequence for

a $\quad 0 < k < 1$

b $\quad k > 1$

c $\quad k = 1$

Give your answers in terms of k, where appropriate.

13 A 'maze' has paths arranged in a grid of $2n$ squares, as shown. A mouse enters the maze at point S and an edible treat is placed at T. Each square is 20 cm long.

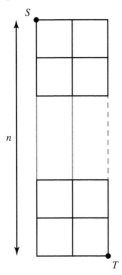

a State the shortest distance the mouse must walk to reach the treat.

Given that there are R_n possible routes of this shortest length,

b Write a recurrence relation for R_n

c Use proof by induction to show that the solution to this recurrence relation is

$$R_n = \frac{1}{2}(n^2 + 3n + 2)$$

6.2 Second-order recurrence relations

Fluency and skills

Some recurrence relations relate a term to the previous two terms, for example, in the Fibonacci sequence each term is the sum of the previous two terms:

1, 1, 2, 3, 5, 8, 13, ...

So the recurrence relation is

$$u_n = u_{n-1} + u_{n-2}$$

In this case, it is necessary to give the values of the first two terms as an **initial condition**: $u_1 = 1$, $u_2 = 1$

When a term is related to the previous two terms, the recurrence relation is known as a second-order recurrence relation.

> **Key point**
>
> A **second-order recurrence relation** is a recursive relationship between three consecutive terms of a sequence.
>
> It is necessary to provide the value of the first two terms of the sequence as an **initial condition**.

Let s be a root of the equation $x^2 - px - q = 0$ and then consider the sequence A, As, As^2, As^3, ..., As^n, $n \geq 0$

Then letting $u_n = As^n$,

$$u_n - pu_{n-1} - qu_{n-1} = As^n - pAs^{n-1} - qAs^{n-2}$$
$$= As^{n-2}(s^2 - ps - q)$$
$$= 0$$

since s is a solution to the equation $x^2 - px - q = 0$

Therefore $u_n = As^n$ satisfies the recurrence relationship

$$u_n - pu_{n-1} - qu_{n-2}$$

Since quadratic equations in general have two roots, it is necessary to consider the second root, t, in the same way, leading to the solution $u_n = As^n + Bt^n$

Therefore, in order to solve a second-order homogeneous recurrence relation with constant coefficients you must first find s and t by solving the equation $x^2 - px - q = 0$. This is known as the **auxiliary equation**.

Second-order recurrence relations with constant coefficients are **homogeneous** when $u_n - pu_{n-1} - qu_{n-2} = 0$ and **non-homogeneous** when $u_n - pu_{n-1} - qu_{n-2} = f(n)$

The **general solution** to the homogeneous second-order recurrence relation $u_n - pu_{n-1} - qu_{n-2} = 0$ is

$$u_n = As^n + Bt^n$$

where s and t are the distinct roots of the **auxiliary equation**

$$x^2 - px - q = 0$$

If you have initial conditions for the recurrence relation, then you can use this to find the values of A and B

Example 1

Solve the recurrence relation $u_n = 2u_{n-1} + 3u_{n-2}$, $n \geq 2$, $u_0 = 1$, $u_1 = 7$

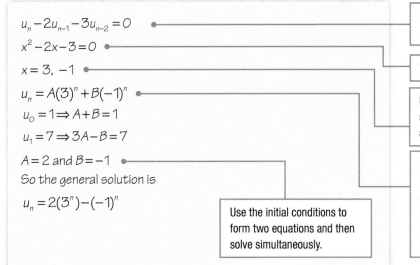

$u_n - 2u_{n-1} - 3u_{n-2} = 0$ First rearrange to the form $u_n - pu_{n-1} - qu_{n-2} = 0$

$x^2 - 2x - 3 = 0$ This is the auxiliary equation.

$x = 3, -1$ Use your calculator or any suitable method to solve the auxiliary equation.

$u_n = A(3)^n + B(-1)^n$

$u_0 = 1 \Rightarrow A + B = 1$

$u_1 = 7 \Rightarrow 3A - B = 7$

$A = 2$ and $B = -1$

So the general solution is

$$u_n = 2(3^n) - (-1)^n$$

Use the initial conditions to form two equations and then solve simultaneously.

Remember: the general solution is of the form $u_n = As^n + Bt^n$, where s and t are the solutions to the auxiliary equation and A and B are constants to be found.

Key point

If the auxiliary equation has equal roots, s, then the general solution can be shown to be of the form $u_n = (A + Bn)s^n$

You can use a similar method to before to show that Bns^n will satisfy the recurrence relation.

Example 2

Find the general solution to the recurrence relation

$u_n = 6u_{n-1} - 9u_{n-2}$, $n \geq 2$, $u_0 = 1$, $u_1 = 12$ First rearrange to the form $u_n - pu_{n-1} - qu_{n-2} = 0$

$u_n - 6u_{n-1} + 9u_{n-2} = 0$ This is the auxiliary equation $x^2 - 6x + 9 = 0$

$x^2 - 6x + 9 = 0$

(*Continued on the next page*)

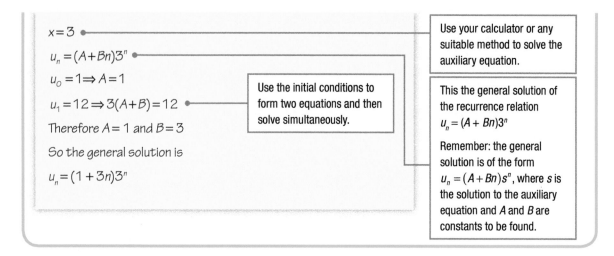

$x = 3$

$u_n = (A + Bn)3^n$

$u_0 = 1 \Rightarrow A = 1$

Use the initial conditions to form two equations and then solve simultaneously.

$u_1 = 12 \Rightarrow 3(A + B) = 12$

Therefore $A = 1$ and $B = 3$

So the general solution is

$u_n = (1 + 3n)3^n$

Use your calculator or any suitable method to solve the auxiliary equation.

This the general solution of the recurrence relation
$u_n = (A + Bn)3^n$

Remember: the general solution is of the form
$u_n = (A + Bn)s^n$, where s is the solution to the auxiliary equation and A and B are constants to be found.

If the auxiliary equation has complex roots, $s = \alpha + \beta i$, $t = \alpha - \beta i$ then the general solution can still be written as $u_n = As^n + Bt^n$, however, you don't want complex numbers in the solution so recall that $\alpha + \beta i = re^{i\theta}$ where r is the modulus of the complex number and θ is its argument.

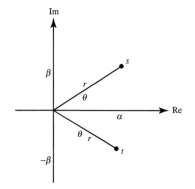

Therefore $As^n + Bt^n$ can be written as

$A(r_1 e^{i\theta_1})^n + B(r_2 e^{i\theta_2})^n = Ar_1^n e^{in\theta_1} + Br_2^n e^{in\theta_2}$

but $r_1 = r_2 = r$ since the moduli of $s = \alpha + \beta i$ and $t = \alpha - \beta i$ are equal.

Also, $\theta_1 = -\theta_2$ so

$Ar^n e^{in\theta} + Br^n e^{-in\theta} = r^n(Ae^{in\theta} + Be^{-in\theta})$

Consider the sum

$(A + B)e^{in\theta} + (A + B)e^{-in\theta} + (A - B)e^{in\theta} - (A - B)e^{-in\theta}$

$= Ae^{in\theta} + Be^{in\theta} + Ae^{-in\theta} + Be^{-in\theta} + Ae^{in\theta} - Be^{in\theta} - Ae^{-in\theta} + Be^{-in\theta}$

$= Ae^{in\theta} + Be^{-in\theta} + Ae^{in\theta} + Be^{-in\theta}$

$= 2(Ae^{in\theta} + Be^{-in\theta})$

Also $(A + B)e^{in\theta} + (A + B)e^{-in\theta} = 2(A + B)\cos(n\theta)$

and $(A - B)e^{in\theta} - (A - B)e^{-in\theta} = 2(A - B)i\sin(n\theta)$

So $2(Ae^{in\theta} + Be^{-in\theta}) = 2(A + B)\cos(n\theta) + 2(A - B)i\sin(n\theta)$

$\Rightarrow Ae^{in\theta} + Be^{-in\theta} = k_1 \cos(n\theta) + k_2 \sin(n\theta)$

(where $k_1 = A + B$ and $k_2 = (A - B)i$)

Key point

If the auxiliary equation has complex roots, z and z^*, then the general solution can be shown to be of the form

$u_n = r^n(k_1 \cos(n\theta) + k_2 \sin(n\theta))$, where r is the modulus and θ is the argument of z

Example 3

Solve the recurrence relation $u_n - 2u_{n-1} + 2u_{n-2} = 0, n \geq 2, u_0 = 2, u_1 = 1$

$x^2 - 2x + 2 = 0$

$x = 1 \pm i$ •————————————————————————————

| Use your calculator or any suitable method to solve the auxiliary equation. |

$\arg(1+i) = \dfrac{\pi}{4}$ and $r = \sqrt{1^2 + 1^2} = \sqrt{2}$ •————

| Find the argument and modulus of $1 + i$ (or $1 - i$) |

Therefore the general solution of the recurrence relation is

$u_n = (\sqrt{2})^n \left(k_1 \cos\left(\dfrac{\pi}{4}n\right) + k_2 \sin\left(\dfrac{\pi}{4}n\right) \right)$ •———

$u_0 = 2 \Rightarrow k_1 = 2$

| Remember, the general solution is of the form $u_n = r^n(k_1 \cos(n\theta) + k_2 \sin(n\theta))$, where r is the modulus and θ is the argument of z |

$u_1 = 1 \Rightarrow \sqrt{2}k_1\left(\dfrac{\sqrt{2}}{2}\right) + \sqrt{2}k_2\left(\dfrac{\sqrt{2}}{2}\right) = 1$ •———

Therefore $k_1 = 2$ and $k_2 = -1$

So the general solution is

$u_n = (\sqrt{2})^n \left(2\cos\left(\dfrac{\pi}{4}n\right) - \sin\left(\dfrac{\pi}{4}n\right) \right)$

| Use the initial conditions to form two equations and then solve simultaneously. |

Now consider a second-order non-homogeneous recurrence relation with linear coefficients, $u_n - pu_{n-1} - qu_{n-2} = \mathrm{f}(n)$ for some $\mathrm{f}(n) \neq 0$

In order to solve this non-homogeneous recurrence relation you need to first find the solution to the homogenous recurrence relation $u_n - pu_{n-1} - qu_{n-2} = 0$. This part is known as the **complementary function**. Then you must find a **particular solution** that satisfies the non-homogeneous recurrence relation $u_n - pu_{n-1} - qu_{n-2} = \mathrm{f}(n)$. Finally, these are combined to give the **general solution**.

Key point

A non-homogeneous recurrence relation has a solution of the form **general solution = complementary function + particular solution**

You should notice the similarity with second-order differential equations.

This **particular solution** will be of a similar form to the function $\mathrm{f}(n)$

If $f(n)$ is a constant, then try the particular solution $u_n = a$

If $f(n)$ is linear, then try the particular solution $u_n = an + b$

If $f(n)$ is quadratic, then try the particular solution $u_n = an^2 + bn + c$

If $f(n)$ is an exponential function λ^n, then try the particular solution $u_n = a(\lambda^n)$

Therefore the strategy for solving a non-homogeneous equation $u_n - pu_{n-1} - qu_{n-2} = f(n)$ is

1   Solve the auxiliary equation $x^2 - px - q = 0$

2   Form the complementary function as

   - $As^n + Bt^n$ if the auxiliary equation has distinct roots, s and t
   - $(A + Bn)s^n$ if the auxiliary equation has coincidental roots, s
   - $u_n = r^n(k_1 \cos(n\theta) + k_2 \sin(n\theta))$ if the auxiliary equation has complex roots, $re^{\pm i\theta}$

3   Find a particular solution of a similar form to $f(n)$

4   Form the general solution using
    complementary function + particular solution

5   Use the initial conditions to find the values of the constants A and B

Example 4

Solve the recurrence relation $u_n - 5u_{n-1} + 6u_{n-2} = n^2 + 1$, $n \geq 2$, $u_0 = 1$ and $u_1 = 2$

$x^2 - 5x + 6 = 0$ — This is the auxilliary equation.

$x = 2, 3$

Therefore the complementary function is

$A(2^n) + B(3^n)$ — Remember: the general solution is of the form $u_n = As^n + Bt^n$, where s and t are the solutions to the auxiliary equation and A and B are constants to be found.

$f(n) = n^2 + 1$ so try $u_n = an^2 + bn + c$

$u_{n-1} = a(n-1)^2 + b(n-1) + c$

$\qquad = an^2 - 2an + a + bn - b + c$

$\qquad = an^2 + (b - 2a)n + (a - b + c)$ — Find and simplify u_{n-1}

$u_{n-2} = a(n-2)^2 + b(n-2) + c$

$\qquad = an^2 - 4an + 4a + bn - 2b + c$

$\qquad = an^2 + (b - 4a)n + (4a - 2b + c)$ — Find and simplify u_{n-2}

(Continued on the next page)

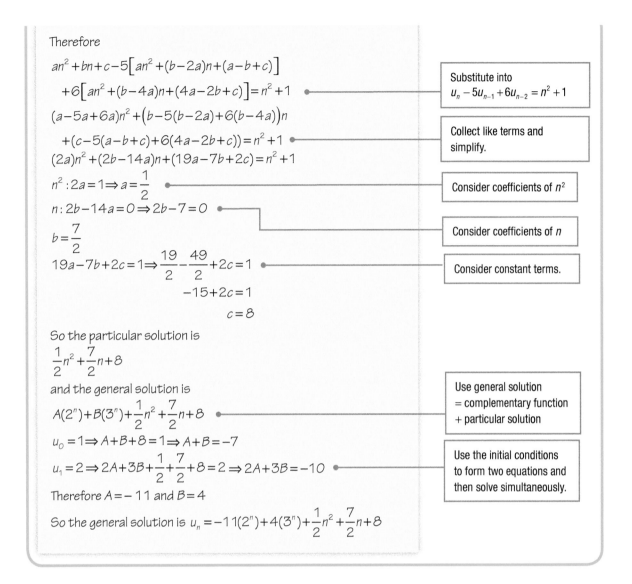

Therefore

$$an^2 + bn + c - 5\left[an^2 + (b-2a)n + (a-b+c)\right]$$

$$+6\left[an^2 + (b-4a)n + (4a-2b+c)\right] = n^2 + 1$$

Substitute into
$u_n - 5u_{n-1} + 6u_{n-2} = n^2 + 1$

$$(a - 5a + 6a)n^2 + \left(b - 5(b-2a) + 6(b-4a)\right)n$$

$$+(c - 5(a-b+c) + 6(4a-2b+c)) = n^2 + 1$$

Collect like terms and simplify.

$$(2a)n^2 + (2b - 14a)n + (19a - 7b + 2c) = n^2 + 1$$

$$n^2 : 2a = 1 \Rightarrow a = \frac{1}{2}$$

Consider coefficients of n^2

$$n : 2b - 14a = 0 \Rightarrow 2b - 7 = 0$$

Consider coefficients of n

$$b = \frac{7}{2}$$

$$19a - 7b + 2c = 1 \Rightarrow \frac{19}{2} - \frac{49}{2} + 2c = 1$$

Consider constant terms.

$$-15 + 2c = 1$$

$$c = 8$$

So the particular solution is

$$\frac{1}{2}n^2 + \frac{7}{2}n + 8$$

and the general solution is

$$A(2^n) + B(3^n) + \frac{1}{2}n^2 + \frac{7}{2}n + 8$$

Use general solution
= complementary function
+ particular solution

$$u_0 = 1 \Rightarrow A + B + 8 = 1 \Rightarrow A + B = -7$$

$$u_1 = 2 \Rightarrow 2A + 3B + \frac{1}{2} + \frac{7}{2} + 8 = 2 \Rightarrow 2A + 3B = -10$$

Use the initial conditions to form two equations and then solve simultaneously.

Therefore $A = -11$ and $B = 4$

So the general solution is $u_n = -11(2^n) + 4(3^n) + \frac{1}{2}n^2 + \frac{7}{2}n + 8$

Exercise 6.2A Fluency and skills

Full A Level

1 Solve each of these second-order homogeneous recurrence relations.

a $u_n - 2u_{n-1} - 3u_{n-2} = 0, n \geq 2, u_0 = 1, u_1 = 19$

b $u_n + 6u_{n-1} + 5u_{n-2} = 0, n \geq 2, u_0 = 0, u_1 = 4$

c $u_n - 4u_{n-1} + 4u_{n-2} = 0, n \geq 2, u_0 = 2, u_1 = 10$

d $u_n + 8u_{n-1} + 16u_{n-2} = 0, n \geq 2, u_0 = 1, u_1 = -2$

e $u_n + 9u_{n-2} = 0, n \geq 2, u_0 = 1, u_1 = 6$

f $u_n - 2u_{n-1} + 2u_{n-2} = 0, n \geq 2, u_0 = 2, u_1 = 0$

2 Solve each of these second-order homogeneous recurrence relations.

a $u_n = 2u_{n-1} + 15u_{n-2}, n \geq 2, u_0 = 2, u_1 = 18$

b $u_n + 49u_{n-2} = 14u_{n-1}, n \geq 2, u_0 = 3, u_1 = 14$

c $u_n = -4u_{n-1} - 8u_{n-2}, n \geq 2, u_0 = 1, u_1 = 2$

3 Solve each of these second-order homogeneous recurrence relations.

a $u_{n+1} = 7u_n - 10u_{n-1}, n \geq 1, u_0 = 3, u_1 = 0$

b $u_{n+2} = 15u_n - 2u_{n+1}, n \geq 1, u_1 = 14, u_2 = 2$

c $64u_{n-1} + u_{n+1} - 16u_n = 0, n \geq 1, u_0 = 2, u_1 = -24$

4 Solve the second-order non-homogeneous recurrence relation $u_n + 7u_{n-1} - 18u_{n-2} = f(n)$, $n \geq 2$ when

  a $f(n) = 5$, $u_0 = 4$, $u_1 = 14$

  b $f(n) = 10n+1$, $u_0 = 2$, $u_1 = -28$

  c $f(n) = 4n(5n-4)$, $u_0 = -13$, $u_1 = 0$

5 Solve the second-order non-homogeneous recurrence relation

$u_n - 10u_{n-1} + 25u_{n-2} = g(n)$, $n \geq 2$ when

  a $g(n) = 32$, $u_0 = 7$, $u_1 = 12$

  b $g(n) = 8n$, $u_0 = 1$, $u_1 = 3$

  c $g(n) = 16n^2 - 80n$, $u_0 = \dfrac{3}{8}$, $u_1 = \dfrac{3}{8}$

6 Solve each of these second-order non-homogeneous recurrence relations.

  a $u_n - 5u_{n-1} + 4u_{n-2} = 3^n$, $n \geq 2$,
  $u_0 = \dfrac{1}{2}$, $u_1 = \dfrac{1}{4}$

  b $u_n + 12u_{n-1} + 36u_{n-2} = 2^n$, $n \geq 2$,
  $u_0 = 1$, $u_1 = \dfrac{25}{8}$

  c $u_n + 4u_{n-2} = 2^n$, $n \geq 2$,
  $u_0 = 1$, $u_1 = -1$

Reasoning and problem-solving

Consider the recurrence relation

$u_n - 6u_{n-1} - 7u_{n-2} = (-1)^n$

The auxiliary equation is $x^2 - 6x - 7 = 0$, which has solutions $x = -1$ and $x = 7$. Therefore you know that the complementary function is of the form $A(-1)^n + B(7^n)$

Now consider the particular solution. Normally you would try using $c(-1)^n$ as the particular solution, but there is already a term of this form in the complementary function. So, instead, use $cn(-1)^n$

$cn(-1)^n - 6c(n-1)(-1)^{n-1} - 7c(n-2)(-1)^{n-2} = (-1)^n$

$(-1)^{n-2}\left[cn(-1)^2 - 6c(n-1)(-1) - 7c(n-2)\right] = (-1)^n$

$\qquad cn(-1)^2 - 6c(n-1)(-1) - 7c(n-2) = 1$ (divide both sides by $(-1)^n$ and use fact that $(-1)^{-2} = 1$)

$\qquad\qquad cn + 6cn - 6c - 7cn + 14c = 1$

$\qquad\qquad\qquad 8c = 1$ (since $cn + 6cn - 7cn = 0$)

$\qquad\qquad\qquad c = \dfrac{1}{8}$

So the general solution is $u_n = A(-1)^n + B(7^n) + \dfrac{1}{8}n(-1)^n$ and you could use the initial conditions to find the values of A and B

To solve second-order non-homogenous recurrence relations $u_n - pu_{n-1} - qu_{n-2} = f(n)$

(1) Solve the auxiliary equation and form the complementary function.

(2) Choose a function of the same form as f(n) for the particular solution.

- If f(n) is of the same form as part of the complementary function, then choose a function of the form nf(n) for the particular solution.

- If f(n) and nf(n) are of the same form as part of the complementary function, then choose a function of the form n^2f(n) for the particular solution.

(3) Substitute into the recurrence relation to find the values of the constants in the particular solution.

(4) Use general solution = complementary function + particular solution.

(5) Use initial conditions to find the values of the constants.

Example 5

Find the general solution to the second-order non-homogeneous recurrence relation

$u_n + 10u_{n-1} + 25u_{n-2} = -4(-5)^n$, $n \geq 3$, $u_1 = 5$, $u_2 = 50$

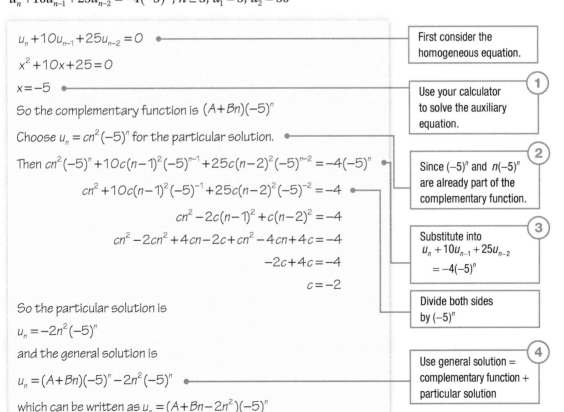

$u_n + 10u_{n-1} + 25u_{n-2} = 0$ — First consider the homogeneous equation.

$x^2 + 10x + 25 = 0$

$x = -5$ — Use your calculator to solve the auxiliary equation. (1)

So the complementary function is $(A + Bn)(-5)^n$

Choose $u_n = cn^2(-5)^n$ for the particular solution. (2)

Then $cn^2(-5)^n + 10c(n-1)^2(-5)^{n-1} + 25c(n-2)^2(-5)^{n-2} = -4(-5)^n$ — Since $(-5)^n$ and $n(-5)^n$ are already part of the complementary function.

$cn^2 + 10c(n-1)^2(-5)^{-1} + 25c(n-2)^2(-5)^{-2} = -4$

$cn^2 - 2c(n-1)^2 + c(n-2)^2 = -4$ — Substitute into $u_n + 10u_{n-1} + 25u_{n-2} = -4(-5)^n$ (3)

$cn^2 - 2cn^2 + 4cn - 2c + cn^2 - 4cn + 4c = -4$

$-2c + 4c = -4$

$c = -2$ — Divide both sides by $(-5)^n$

So the particular solution is

$u_n = -2n^2(-5)^n$

and the general solution is

$u_n = (A + Bn)(-5)^n - 2n^2(-5)^n$ — Use general solution = complementary function + particular solution (4)

which can be written as $u_n = (A + Bn - 2n^2)(-5)^n$

(*Continued on the next page*)

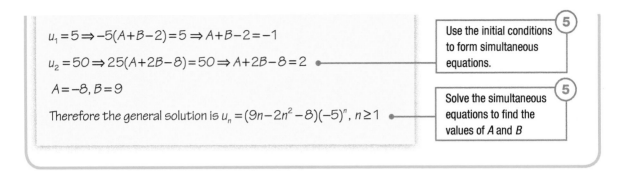

$u_1 = 5 \Rightarrow -5(A+B-2) = 5 \Rightarrow A+B-2 = -1$

$u_2 = 50 \Rightarrow 25(A+2B-8) = 50 \Rightarrow A+2B-8 = 2$

$A = -8, B = 9$

Therefore the general solution is $u_n = (9n - 2n^2 - 8)(-5)^n$, $n \geq 1$

⑤ Use the initial conditions to form simultaneous equations.

⑤ Solve the simultaneous equations to find the values of A and B

As with first-order recurrence relations, you can use proof by induction to prove the closed-form solution of second-order recurrence relations.

Strategy 2

To prove the closed-form solution of a recurrence relation using proof by induction

① Substitute $n = 0$ and $n = 1$ into the closed-form solution to show that they are equal to the values given for u_0 and u_1

② Assume that the closed-form solution is true for $n = k$ and $n = k + 1$ and use the recurrence relation to write out the $(k + 2)$th term.

③ Substitute the closed-form of the kth term and $(k + 1)$th term into the closed-form solution and show that this leads to the required expression.

④ Write a conclusion.

Example 6

Prove that the solution of the recurrence relation

$u_n = 4u_{n-1} - 3u_{n-2} + 3^n$, $n \geq 2$, $u_0 = 1$, $u_1 = 0$ is $u_n = \frac{1}{4}((6n-11)3^n + 15)$, $n \geq 0$

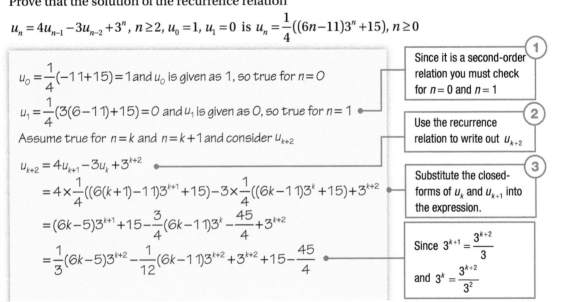

$u_0 = \frac{1}{4}(-11+15) = 1$ and u_0 is given as 1, so true for $n = 0$

$u_1 = \frac{1}{4}(3(6-11)+15) = 0$ and u_1 is given as 0, so true for $n = 1$

Assume true for $n = k$ and $n = k+1$ and consider u_{k+2}

$u_{k+2} = 4u_{k+1} - 3u_k + 3^{k+2}$

$= 4 \times \frac{1}{4}((6(k+1)-11)3^{k+1}+15) - 3 \times \frac{1}{4}((6k-11)3^k+15) + 3^{k+2}$

$= (6k-5)3^{k+1} + 15 - \frac{3}{4}(6k-11)3^k - \frac{45}{4} + 3^{k+2}$

$= \frac{1}{3}(6k-5)3^{k+2} - \frac{1}{12}(6k-11)3^{k+2} + 3^{k+2} + 15 - \frac{45}{4}$

① Since it is a second-order relation you must check for $n = 0$ and $n = 1$

② Use the recurrence relation to write out u_{k+2}

③ Substitute the closed-forms of u_k and u_{k+1} into the expression.

Since $3^{k+1} = \frac{3^{k+2}}{3}$

and $3^k = \frac{3^{k+2}}{3^2}$

(Continued on the next page)

$$= \left(2k - \frac{5}{3} - \frac{1}{2}k + \frac{11}{12} + 1\right)3^{k+2} + \frac{15}{4}$$

Collect terms in 3^{k+2}

$$= \left(\frac{3}{2}k + \frac{1}{4}\right)3^{k+2} + \frac{15}{4}$$

$$= \frac{1}{2}((6k+1)3^{k+2} + 15)$$

$$= \frac{1}{2}((6(k+2) - 11)3^{k+2} + 15) \text{ as required so true for } n = k+2$$

The solution is true for $n = 0$ and $n = 1$ and assuming that it is true for $n = k$ and $n = k+1$ implies that it is true for $n = k+2$. Hence it is true for all integers $n \geq 0$

Write a conclusion. ④

Exercise 6.2B Reasoning and problem-solving　　Full A Level

1 Solve these second-order non-homogeneous recurrence relations.

 a $u_n + 5u_{n-1} - 14u_{n-2} = 2^n$, $n \geq 2$,
 $u_0 = 3$, $u_1 = \frac{4}{9}$

 b $u_n - 11u_{n-1} + 18u_{n-2} = 2(9^n)$, $n \geq 2$,
 $u_0 = 0$, $u_1 = \frac{6}{7}$

 c $u_{n+1} = 25u_{n-1} + 5^n$, $n \geq 1$, $u_0 = 5$, $u_1 = \frac{1}{2}$

2 Solve these second-order non-homogeneous recurrence relations.

 a $u_n - 20u_{n-1} + 100u_{n-2} = 4(10^n)$, $n \geq 2$,
 $u_0 = 1$, $u_1 = 10$

 b $u_n + 6u_{n-1} + 9u_{n-2} = -2(-3)^n$, $n \geq 2$,
 $u_0 = 3$, $u_1 = 6$

 c $u_{n+1} - 24u_n + 144u_{n-1} = 5(12^n)$, $n \geq 1$
 $u_0 = 0$, $u_1 = 6$

3 Prove by induction that the closed-form solution of the recurrence relation

$$u_n = 2u_{n-1} + 3u_{n-2} + 3, n \geq 2,$$

$$u_0 = 1, u_1 = 3$$

is $u_n = \frac{1}{8}(3(-1)^n + 11(3)^n - 6), n \geq 0$

4 Prove by induction that the closed-form solution of the recurrence relation

$$u_n = 4u_{n-2}, n \geq 2, \ u_0 = 1, u_1 = 3$$

is $u_n = \frac{1}{4}(5 + (-1)^{n+1})2^n$, $n \geq 0$

5 Prove by induction that the closed-form solution of the recurrence relation

$$u_n - u_{n-1} - 30u_{n-2} = 0, n \geq 2, u_0 = 1, u_1 = -1$$

is $u_n = \frac{1}{11}(7(-5)^n + 4(6)^n)$, $n \geq 0$

6 The Fibonacci sequence, beginning 1, 1, 2, 3, 5, 8, is formed by adding the two previous terms to find the next term.

 a Fully define this sequence as a recurrence relation.

 b Find a closed-form solution for u_n, the nth term of the Fibonacci sequence.

 c Use proof by induction to prove your result from part **b**.

Chapter summary

- The closed-form solution of a recurrence relation of the form
  $u_n = ku_{n-1}$ is $u_n = u_1 k^{n-1}$

- The closed-form solution of a recurrence relation of the form
  $u_n = ku_{n-1} + c$, $n \geq 2$ is $u_n = u_1(k^{n-1}) + \dfrac{c}{k-1}(k^{n-1} - 1)$, for $k \neq 1$

- Recurrence relations of the form $u_n = ku_{n-1} + c$, $n \geq 2$, where
  $k \neq 1$ and c are constants, have closed-form solutions of the form
  $u_n = A(k^n) + B$, where A and B are constants to be found.

- The special case of the first-order linear recurrence relation
  $u_n = ku_{n-1} + c$, $n \geq 2$, where $k = 1$ has closed-form solution
  $u_n = u_1 + (n-1)c$

- The non-homogeneous linear recurrence relation
  $u_n = ku_{n-1} + g(n)$, $n \geq 2$ has solution $u_n = k^{n-1}u_1 + \displaystyle\sum_{r=2}^{n} k^{n-r} g(r)$

- Recurrence relations of the form $u_n = ku_{n-1} + g(n)$, $n \geq 2$, where
  $k \neq 1$ is a constant, have closed-form solutions of the form
  - $u_n = A(k^n) + B$, where $g(n)$ is a constant
  - $u_n = A(k^n) + Bn + C$, where $g(n)$ is linear
  - $u_n = A(k^n) + Bn^2 + Cn + D$, where $g(n)$ is a quadratic
  - $u_n = A(k^n) + Bn^3 + Cn^2 + Dn + E$, where $g(n)$ is a cubic.

  The values of the coefficients can be found by substituting
  $n = 1, \; 2, \; 3, \ldots$ into the equation and solving the resulting
  equations simultaneously.

- The general solution to the homogeneous second-order   **Full A Level**
  recurrence relation $u_n - pu_{n-1} - qu_{n-2} = 0$ is
  $u_n = As^n + Bt^n$, where s and t are the distinct roots of the
  auxiliary equation $x^2 - px - q = 0$

- If the auxiliary equation has equal roots, s, then the general
  solution can be shown to be of the form $u_n = (A + Bn)s^n$

- If the auxiliary equation has complex roots, z and z^*,
  then the general solution can be shown to be of the form
  $u_n = r^n(k_1 \cos(n\theta) + k_2 \sin(n\theta))$, where r is the modulus and θ is
  the argument of z

- A non-homogeneous recurrence relation has solution given by
  general solution = complementary function + particular
  solution

- The particular solution will be of a similar form to the function $f(n)$.
  - If $f(n)$ is a constant, then try particular solution $u_n = a$
  - If $f(n)$ is linear, then try particular solution $u_n = an + b$
  - If $f(n)$ is quadratic, then try particular solution $u_n = an^2 + bn + c$
  - If $f(n)$ is an exponential function λ^n, then try particular solution $u_n = a(\lambda^n)$
  - However, if $f(n)$ is of the same form of part of the complementary function, then choose a function of the form $nf(n)$ for the particular solution.
  - If $f(n)$ and $nf(n)$ are of the same form as part of the complementary function, then choose a function of the form $n^2f(n)$ for the particular solution.

Check and review

You should now be able to...	Review questions
✔ Use first-order recurrence relations to model real-life situations.	1
✔ Solve first-order recurrence relations.	1–4
✔ Use proof by induction to prove the closed-form solutions of first-order recurrence relations.	4, 5
✔ Use second-order recurrence relations to model real-life situations.	6
✔ Solve homogenous second-order recurrence relations. Full A Level	7
✔ Solve non-homogenous second-order recurrence relations.	8, 9
✔ Use proof by induction to prove the closed-form solutions of first-order recurrence relations.	9, 10

1 The population of a species in a particular area is recorded over time. The population is initially estimated to be 450. Half of the population are female and give birth to an average of one offspring each year. In addition, each year 40% of the population dies of natural causes or predation by other animals and 35 are killed by humans.

   a Write a recurrence relation for the size of the population, P_n, n years after the study begins.

   b Solve your recurrence relation to find a closed-form solution for P_n

   c Do you think that this model is suitable for estimating the population of the species in the long term? Explain your answer.

2 A sequence is defined by the recurrence relation $u_{k+1} = u_k + 2$, $k \geq 1$, $u_1 = -2$

   a Write down the first three terms of the sequence.

   b Find a closed-form solution for u_n

3 A sequence is defined by the recurrence relation $u_n = 3u_{n-1} + n$, $n \geq 2$, $u_1 = 2$

   a Write down the first three terms of the sequence.

   b Find a closed-form solution for u_n

4 A sequence has recurrence relation $u_{n+1} = u_n + n^2$, $n \geq 1$, $u_1 = 4$

   a Find a closed-form solution to the recurrence relation.

   b Use your closed-form solution to find the 4th term of the sequence and verify your answer using the recurrence relation.

   c Use proof by induction to prove the closed-form solution.

5 Prove by induction that the solution to the recurrence relation $u_n = nu_{n-1}$, $n \geq 1$, $u_1 = 5$ is $u_n = 5n!$

6 An investor purchases 2000 shares in a company at the beginning of each year. Investors receive a 5% dividend for shares they have owned for 1 year and 6% interest on shares they have owned for longer than 1 year. The dividend is paid by the issue of more shares to the investor.

   a Write a recurrence relation for the number of shares owned by the investor after n years, S_n

   b Use your recurrence relation to find the number of shares owned by the investor after 2 years.

7 Solve these homogeneous second-order recurrence relations.

   a $u_{n+1} = 19u_n - 88u_{n-1}$, $n \geq 1$, $u_0 = 1$, $u_1 = -4$

   b $u_n + 12u_{n-1} + 36u_{n-2} = 0$, $n \geq 2$, $u_0 = 4$, $u_1 = 12$

   c $u_{n+1} + 2u_n + 2u_{n-1} = 0$, $n \geq 1$, $u_0 = 2$, $u_1 = 3$

8 Solve the second-order non-homogeneous recurrence relation

$u_n + 5u_{n-1} - 14u_{n-2} = f(n)$, $n \geq 2$ when

   a $f(n) = 2$, $u_0 = 1$, $u_1 = -\dfrac{9}{2}$

   b $f(n) = 3 - 8n$, $u_0 = 1$, $u_1 = 36.5$

   c $f(n) = 3^n$, $u_0 = 0$, $u_1 = 9.9$

9 A sequence is defined by the recurrence relation

$u_n = 5u_{n-1} - 6u_{n-2} + 2^n$, $n \geq 2$,

$u_0 = 2$, $u_1 = -1$

   a Find the closed-form solution to the recurrence relation,

   b Prove your result from part **a** using proof by induction.

10 A sequence is defined by the recurrence relation

$u_{n+1} - 4u_n + 4u_{n-1} = n^2$, $n \geq 1$,

$u_0 = 0$, $u_1 = 0$

Prove that the closed-form solution to the recurrence relation is

$u_n = n^2 + 6n + 13 + (3n - 13)2^n$

Research

The logistic map has been used in Biology to model population growth. It is written using the recurrence relation $x_{n+1} = rx_n(1 - x_n)$, where x_n is the decimal fraction of the existing population out of the maximum possible population.

Graph the values of x when r takes a value between 0 and 1, 1 and 2, 2 and 3 or various values between 3 and 4. Try to explain what is happening to the population in each situation.

Research

The lagged Fibonacci generator creates a sequence of numbers whose properties approximate the properties of sequences of random numbers. Pseudo-random numbers are important in many applications, including simulations, electronic games and cryptography.

The Fibonacci sequence can be described by the recurrence relation $S_n = S_{n-1} + S_{n-2}$, which can be generalised to $S_n = S_j \circ S_k \pmod m$, $0 < j < k$, where $\circ$ represents a binary operation such as addition or multiplication. In other words, the new term is some combination of any two previous terms.

For example, let $j = 3$, $k = 7$, with mod 10 addition, using the first 7 digits of π as the seed.

1. 3141592
2. 1415926
3. 4159267
4. ....

$$4 + 2 = 6 \bmod 10$$
$$1 + 6 = 7 \bmod 10$$
$$5 + 7 = 2 \bmod 10$$

This gives the generated sequence of numbers 6, 7, 2, ...

Find the next three numbers in the sequence.

See what you can find out about the Mersenne twister algorithm.

Did you know?

An example of a multidimensional recurrence relationship can be found in the binomial coefficients $\binom{n}{k} = \binom{n-1}{k-1} + \binom{n-1}{k}$, where $\binom{n}{0} = 1$ and $\binom{n}{n} = 1$

1 A sequence is defined by the first-order recurrence relation $u_n = 3u_{n-1} + 5, n \geq 2, u_1 = 8$

    a   Write out the first 5 terms of this sequence. **[1]**

    b   Given that $u_n = A \times 3^n + B$, show that $A = \dfrac{7}{2}$ and $B = -\dfrac{5}{2}$ **[3]**

    c   Use mathematical induction to prove that $u_n = \dfrac{7}{2} \times 3^n - \dfrac{5}{2}$ **[5]**

2 A sequence is defined by the formula $u_n = 5 \times 4^n - 2$

    a   Write down the first 5 terms from u_0 to u_4 **[1]**

    b   Given that the sequence also satisfies a recurrence relation
$u_n = pu_{n-1} + q, u_0 = r$
find the constants p, q, and r **[4]**

3 A sequence is defined by the first-order recurrence relation
$u_n = 2u_{n-1}, n \geq 1, u_0 = 3$

    a   Write out the first 5 terms of this sequence. **[1]**

    b   Write down a closed-form solution for u_n in terms of n **[1]**

    c   If $S_n = \displaystyle\sum_{r=0}^{n} u_r$ show that $S_n = S_{n-1} + 3 \times 2^n$ **[1]**

    d   By writing $S_n = A \times 2^n + B$, find a closed-form solution for S_n, simplifying your answer as far as possible. **[4]**

4   a   Find a closed-form solution for u_n in terms of n for the sequence given by the recurrence relation $u_n = 7u_{n-1} + 5, n \geq 1, u_0 = 2$ **[5]**

    b   Use mathematical induction to prove that your formula is correct for all integers $n \geq 0$ **[5]**

5 A sequence is given by the recurrence relation $u_n = 5u_{n-1} - 3, n \geq 1, u_2 = 57$

    a   Find u_1 and u_0 **[3]**

    b   Find a closed-form solution for u_n in terms of n for the sequence. **[4]**

6 A sequence is given by the recurrence relation $u_n = u_{n-1} + 2n, n \geq 1, u_0 = 3$

    a   Write out the first 5 terms of this sequence. **[1]**

    b   Find a closed-form solution for u_n in terms of n **[3]**

7 A sequence is given by the recurrence relation $u_n = 3u_{n-1} - 2n + 5, n \geq 1, u_0 = 1$

    a   Write out the first 5 terms of this sequence. **[1]**

    b   Find a closed-form solution for u_n in terms of n **[5]**

    c   Use mathematical induction to prove that your formula is correct for all integers $n \geq 0$ **[5]**

8 a You decide to invest £1000 on January 1st every year in a savings account that pays 2% interest on December 31st each year. If u_n is the amount you have on December 31st of the nth year of the plan, write down a recurrence relation for u_n **[2]**

b Use your recurrence relation to find a closed-form solution for u_n in terms of n **[4]**

9 A king decides to reward his most faithful servant with anything he asks for. The servant decides to ask for a single grain of rice on the first day, and then, on each day after that, double the number of grains he received the day before. 'I will gladly do as you say,' replied the king, 'but that doesn't seem much, so I will do better: on each day I will give you 2 extra grains of rice over and above what you have asked for.' 'What, even on the very first day?' asked the servant. 'No,' snapped the king, rather crossly. 'Don't be greedy. You can have 1 grain of rice today, and, from tomorrow onwards, I will give you double the amount of rice I gave you the previous day, plus a 2-grain bonus.'

a Write down a recurrence relation for the amount of rice, u_n, that the servant receives on the nth day. **[2]**

b Use your recurrence relation to find a closed-form solution for u_n in terms of n **[4]**

c On the 20th day, how much rice does the servant receive? **[1]**

d After 20 days, how much rice has the servant received altogether? **[4]**

e Over the first 20 days, how much did the king save by not beginning the bonus until the second day? **[4]**

10 A sequence is given by the recurrence relation $u_n = u_{n-1} + 6u_{n-2}$, $n \geq 1$, $u_0 = 0$, $u_1 = 1$

a Write down the first 5 terms of the sequence. **[1]**

b By trying the solution $u_n = \lambda^n$, show that $\lambda^2 - \lambda - 6 = 0$ **[2]**

c Show that the general solution of the recurrence relation is of the form $u_n = A \times 3^n + B \times (-2)^n$ **[2]**

d Use the initial conditions to show that $u_n = \dfrac{3^n - (-2)^n}{5}$ **[3]**

11 In this question, u_n is the number of ways of making an n-digit number using the digits 1, 2, 3, 4, where you are not allowed to have two 1s together.

a Explain, in the context of the question, why $u_n = 3u_{n-1} + 3u_{n-2}$, $n \geq 1$, $u_0 = 1$, $u_1 = 4$ **[5]**

b Show that the solution of the recurrence relation is of the form
$$u_n = A\left(\frac{3+\sqrt{21}}{2}\right)^n + B\left(\frac{3-\sqrt{21}}{2}\right)^n$$ **[4]**

c Hence find a closed-form solution for the number of ways of making an n-digit number using the digits 1, 2, 3, 4, where you are not allowed to have two 1s together. **[5]**

12 Vans, cars and motorcycles are being loaded in single file into a shipping container with n bays. Cars and motorcycles each take up a single bay, but vans take up two bays. All the cars are identical, as are all the motorcycles and all the vans.

    a Explain, in the context of the question, why the number, u_n, $n \geq 2$, of distinct sequences of vehicles satisfies the recurrence relation $u_n = 2u_{n-1} + u_{n-2}$, $u_0 = 0$, $u_1 = 2$ **[5]**

    b Show that the general solution of the recurrence relation is of the form
$u_n = A(1+\sqrt{2})^n + B(1-\sqrt{2})^n$ **[4]**

    c Use the initial conditions to show that $u_n = \dfrac{\sqrt{2}}{2}\left[(1+\sqrt{2})^n - (1-\sqrt{2})^n\right]$ **[3]**

    d Use mathematical induction to prove that this formula is true for all integer values of $n \geq 0$ **[7]**

13 A sequence is given by the recurrence relation $u_n = 6u_{n-1} - 9u_{n-2}$, $n \geq 2$, $u_0 = -1$, $u_1 = 0$

    a By trying the solution $u_n = \lambda^n$, show that $(\lambda - 3)^2 = 0$ **[2]**

    b Find a closed-form solution for u_n in terms of n **[3]**

    c Use mathematical induction to prove that this formula is true for all integers $n \geq 0$ **[5]**

14 A sequence is given by the recurrence relation $u_n = u_{n-1} + 2u_{n-2} - 2n^2$, $n \geq 2$, $u_0 = 8$, $u_1 = 5$

    a By finding a complementary function and a particular solution, show that
$u_n = 3\left[(-1)^n - 2^n\right] + n^2 + 5n + 8$ **[11]**

    b Verify that the first 5 terms of the sequence using the recurrence relation are the same as the first 5 terms of the sequence using the closed formula.   **[2]**

15 A sequence is given by the recurrence relation $u_n = 2u_{n-1} - 4u_{n-2}$, $n \geq 2$, $u_0 = 1$, $u_1 = 3$

    a Write out the first 6 terms of this sequence.   **[1]**

    b By trying the solution $u_n = \lambda^n$, show that $\lambda^2 - 2\lambda + 4 = 0$ **[2]**

    c Show that the general solution of the recurrence relation is of the form
$$u_n = 2^n\left(A\cos\left(\frac{n\pi}{3}\right) + B\sin\left(\frac{n\pi}{3}\right)\right)$$ **[4]**

    d Use the initial conditions to show that $u_n = 2^n\left(\cos\left(\dfrac{n\pi}{3}\right) + \dfrac{2\sqrt{3}}{3}\sin\left(\dfrac{n\pi}{3}\right)\right)$ **[3]**

    e Use mathematical induction to prove that this is the correct formula for all integers $n \geq 0$ **[8]**

7 Further methods in calculus

Architects are incorporating far more curves and complex shapes in their designs. New building materials allow structural engineers to ensure that such designs can be realised. The use of calculus and computer software allows the calculation of aspects of building design, that previously would have been very difficult, to be carried out successfully. The length of curved parts of the structure, volumes (of revolution), the stress in various parts of structures, and so on, can now be calculated with relative ease.

These techniques have allowed the design of major new public buildings, such as museums, galleries and railway stations, to be much more ambitious. Structures such as bridges can now be designed by architects in ways that are not only strong, safe and efficient, but also architecturally and aesthetically pleasing.

Orientation

What you need to know	What you will learn	What this leads to
Maths Ch4 **Core Pure 1 Ch3** • Integration.	• How to use reduction formulae. • How to use integration to calculate arc lengths. • How to calculate surface areas of revolution.	**Careers** • Architecture. • Structural engineering.

7.1 Reduction formulae

Fluency and skills

Integration by parts can be used to find integrals of the form $\int u \dfrac{dv}{dx} dx$ where you know how to find $\dfrac{du}{dx}$ and v. For example,

$$\int xe^{-x} dx = -xe^{-x} - \int -e^{-x} dx \qquad\qquad u = x, \frac{dv}{dx} = e^{-x}$$
$$= -xe^{-x} - e^{-x} + c$$

Key point

The formula for integration by parts is $\int u \dfrac{dv}{dx} dx = uv - \int v \dfrac{du}{dx} dx$

You can apply this formula twice, for example,

$$\int x^2 e^{-x} dx = -x^2 e^{-x} - \int -2xe^{-x} dx \qquad\qquad u = x^2, \frac{dv}{dx} = e^{-x}$$
$$= -x^2 e^{-x} + 2\int xe^{-x} dx$$

Then apply again to the new integral:

$$= -x^2 e^{-x} + 2\left(-xe^{-x} - \int -e^{-x} dx\right) \qquad u = x, \frac{dv}{dx} = e^{-x}$$
$$= -x^2 e^{-x} - 2xe^{-x} - 2e^{-x} + c$$

You could use a similar process for higher powers of x but it would be very time-consuming. Instead, you can find a **reduction formula** which relates $I_n = \int x^n e^{-x} dx$ to $I_{n-1} = \int x^{n-2} e^{-x} dx$

$$I_n = \int x^n e^{-x} dx = -x^n e^{-x} - \int -nx^{n-1} e^{-x} dx \qquad u = x^n, \frac{dv}{dx} = e^{-x}$$
$$= -x^n e^{-x} + n\int x^{n-1} e^{-x} dx$$
$$= -x^n e^{-x} + nI_{n-1}$$

You can now use this formula to find, for example, $I_3 = \int x^3 e^{-x} dx$

$I_3 = -x^3 e^{-x} + 3I_2$, then use the formula again for I_2
$$= -x^3 e^{-x} + 3(-x^2 e^{-x} + 2I_1)$$

You can continue to use the formula until you have an integrand which is simpler to integrate.

$$I_3 = -x^3 e^{-x} - 3x^2 e^{-x} + 6I_1$$
$$= -x^3 - 3x^2 e^{-x} + 6(-xe^{-x} + I_0)$$
$$= -x^3 - 3x^2 e^{-x} - 6xe^{-x} + 6I_0$$

$I_0 = \int e^{-x} dx = -e^{-x}$ so substitute this to find the solution for I_3

$$I_3 = -x^3 - 3x^2 e^{-x} - 6xe^{-x} - 6e^{-x} + c$$

Key point

A **reduction formula** for I_n is an equation that relates I_n to I_{n-1} and/or I_{n-2}
It can be repeatedly applied to reduce the integral to one not requiring integration by parts.

You can use a reduction formula for a definite or an indefinite integral.

Example 1

Given that $I_n = \int_0^1 (\ln x)^n \, dx$, prove that $I_n = -nI_{n-1}$ and use this formula to evaluate I_4

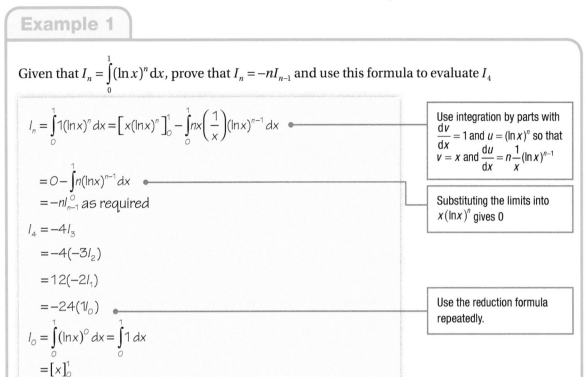

$$I_n = \int_0^1 1(\ln x)^n \, dx = \left[x(\ln x)^n \right]_0^1 - \int_0^1 nx\left(\frac{1}{x}\right)(\ln x)^{n-1} \, dx$$

Use integration by parts with $\frac{dv}{dx} = 1$ and $u = (\ln x)^n$ so that $v = x$ and $\frac{du}{dx} = n\frac{1}{x}(\ln x)^{n-1}$

$$= 0 - \int_0^1 n(\ln x)^{n-1} \, dx$$

$$= -nI_{n-1} \text{ as required}$$

Substituting the limits into $x(\ln x)^n$ gives 0

$$I_4 = -4I_3$$

$$= -4(-3I_2)$$

$$= 12(-2I_1)$$

$$= -24(1I_0)$$

Use the reduction formula repeatedly.

$$I_0 = \int_0^1 (\ln x)^0 \, dx = \int_0^1 1 \, dx$$

$$= [x]_0^1$$

$$= 1$$

Therefore $I_4 = -24I_0 = -24$

After you have used the integration by parts formula, you may need to rearrange the integrand so that it is clearly in the form of I_{n-1} and/or I_{n-2}

Example 2

Given that $I_n = \int_{-1}^0 x^n \sqrt{x+1} \, dx$, show that $I_n = -nI_{n-1}$ and use this formula to evaluate $\int_{-1}^0 x^3 \sqrt{x+1} \, dx$

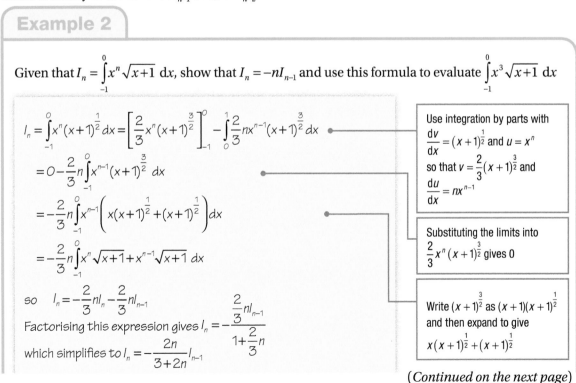

$$I_n = \int_{-1}^0 x^n (x+1)^{\frac{1}{2}} \, dx = \left[\frac{2}{3}x^n (x+1)^{\frac{3}{2}} \right]_{-1}^0 - \int_0^1 \frac{2}{3}nx^{n-1}(x+1)^{\frac{3}{2}} \, dx$$

Use integration by parts with $\frac{dv}{dx} = (x+1)^{\frac{1}{2}}$ and $u = x^n$ so that $v = \frac{2}{3}(x+1)^{\frac{3}{2}}$ and $\frac{du}{dx} = nx^{n-1}$

$$= 0 - \frac{2}{3}n \int_{-1}^0 x^{n-1}(x+1)^{\frac{3}{2}} \, dx$$

$$= -\frac{2}{3}n \int_{-1}^0 x^{n-1}\left(x(x+1)^{\frac{1}{2}} + (x+1)^{\frac{1}{2}} \right) dx$$

Substituting the limits into $\frac{2}{3}x^n (x+1)^{\frac{3}{2}}$ gives 0

$$= -\frac{2}{3}n \int_{-1}^0 x^n \sqrt{x+1} + x^{n-1}\sqrt{x+1} \, dx$$

so $I_n = -\frac{2}{3}nI_n - \frac{2}{3}nI_{n-1}$

Factorising this expression gives $I_n = -\dfrac{\frac{2}{3}nI_{n-1}}{1+\frac{2}{3}n}$

which simplifies to $I_n = -\dfrac{2n}{3+2n}I_{n-1}$

Write $(x+1)^{\frac{3}{2}}$ as $(x+1)(x+1)^{\frac{1}{2}}$ and then expand to give $x(x+1)^{\frac{1}{2}} + (x+1)^{\frac{1}{2}}$

(Continued on the next page)

51

$$\text{so } I_3 = -\frac{6}{9}I_2$$

$$= -\frac{6}{9}\left(-\frac{4}{7}\right)I_1$$

$$= -\frac{6}{9}\left(-\frac{4}{7}\right)\left(-\frac{2}{5}\right)I_0$$

$$= -\frac{16}{105}I_0$$

Use the reduction formula repeatedly.

$$I_0 = \int_{-1}^{0} (x+1)^{\frac{1}{2}}\,dx = \left[\frac{2}{3}(x+1)^{\frac{3}{2}}\right]_{-1}^{0}$$

$$= \frac{2}{3}$$

Therefore $\displaystyle\int_{-1}^{0} x^3\sqrt{x+1}\,dx = -\frac{16}{105}\left(\frac{2}{3}\right) = -\frac{32}{315}$

Exercise 7.1A Fluency and skills

1 $I_n = \int x^n e^x\,dx$

  a Show that $I_n = x^n e^x - nI_{n-1}$

  b Use the formula in part **a** to find I_4

2 $I_n = \int x^n e^{-\frac{x}{2}}\,dx$

  a Show that $I_n = 2nI_{n-1} - 2x^n e^{-\frac{x}{2}}$

  b Use the formula in part **a** to find $\int x^5 e^{-\frac{x}{2}}\,dx$

3 $I_n = \int_0^1 x^n e^{3x}\,dx$

  a Show that $I_n = \frac{1}{3}e^3 - \frac{n}{3}I_{n-1}$

  b Use the formula in part **a** to find $\int_0^1 x^4 e^{3x}\,dx$

4 $I_n = \int x(\ln x)^n\,dx$

  a Show that $I_n = \frac{x^2}{2}(\ln x)^n - \frac{n}{2}I_{n-1}$

  b Use the formula in part **a** to find $\int x(\ln x)^2\,dx$

5 $I_n = \int_0^1 \frac{x^n}{\sqrt{1-x}}\,dx$

  a Show that $I_n = \frac{2n}{1+2n}I_{n-1}$

  b Use the formula in part **a** to find $\int_0^1 \frac{x^6}{\sqrt{1-x}}\,dx$

6 $I_n = \int x^n \sin x\,dx$

  a Show that $I_n = -x^n \cos x + nx^{n-1}\sin x - n(n-1)I_{n-2}$

  b Use the formula in part **a** to find

    i $\int x^4 \sin x\,dx$

    ii $\int x^3 \sin x\,dx$

7 $I_n = \int_0^{\frac{\pi}{4}} x^n \cos 2x\,dx$

  a Show that $I_n = \frac{1}{2}\left(\frac{\pi}{4}\right)^n - \frac{n(n-1)}{4}I_{n-2}$ for $n > 1$

  b Use the formula in part **a** to evaluate

    i $\int_0^{\frac{\pi}{4}} x^6 \cos 2x\,dx$

    ii $\int_0^{\frac{\pi}{4}} x^5 \cos 2x\,dx$

Reasoning and problem-solving

Sometimes the integrand is not in the form of the product of two functions. In these cases, you can split up the integral yourself. For example, you can write $\sin^n x$ as $\sin x \sin^{n-1} x$

Strategy

To find and use a reduction formula

1. Split up the function if necessary and integrate.

2. Find an expression for I_n in terms of I_{n-1} and/or I_{n-2}

3. Use the formula repeatedly until you reach I_0 or I_1

4. Calculate I_0 or I_1 and use with your formula to find I_n for the required value of n

Example 3

Find a reduction formula for $I_n = \int_0^\pi \sin^n x\,dx$ and use it to find

a $\int_0^\pi \sin^8 x\,dx$ **b** $\int_0^\pi \sin^7 x\,dx$

$$I_n = \int_0^\pi \sin^n x\,dx = \int_0^\pi \sin x \, \sin^{n-1} x\,dx$$

Split the function. **1**

$$= [-\cos x \, \sin^{n-1} x]_0^\pi - \int_0^\pi -(n-1)\cos^2 x \, \sin^{n-2} x\,dx$$

Use integration by parts with **1**
$\dfrac{dv}{dx} = \sin x$ and $u = \sin^{n-1} x$
so that $v = -\cos x$ and
$\dfrac{du}{dx} = (n-1)\sin^{n-2} x \cos x$

$$= (n-1)\int_0^\pi \cos^2 x \, \sin^{n-2} x\,dx$$

$$= (n-1)\int_0^\pi \sin^{n-2} x - \sin^n x\,dx$$

Replace $\cos^2 x$ with $1 - \sin^2 x$

$$= (n-1)(I_{n-2} - I_n)$$

$$= (n-1)I_{n-2} - (n-1)I_n$$

Rearrange to give $I_n = \dfrac{n-1}{n} I_{n-2}$

This is the reduction formula. **2**

a Use to find I_8

$$I_8 = \frac{7}{8} I_6$$

$$= \frac{7}{8}\left(\frac{5}{6}\right) I_4$$

$$= \frac{7}{8}\left(\frac{5}{6}\right)\left(\frac{3}{4}\right) I_2$$

$$= \frac{7}{8}\left(\frac{5}{6}\right)\left(\frac{3}{4}\right)\left(\frac{1}{2}\right) I_0$$

Use the formula repeatedly until I_0 reached. **3**

(Continued on the next page)

$$= \frac{35}{128} I_0$$

$$I_0 = \int_0^{\pi} 1 \, dx$$

$$= [x]_0^{\pi}$$

$$= \pi$$

Substitute the value of I_0 into the formula for I_8 ④

So $I_8 = \frac{35}{128} \pi$

b Use to find I_7

$$I_7 = \frac{6}{7} I_5$$

$$= \frac{6}{7} \left(\frac{4}{5} \right) I_3$$

$$= \frac{6}{7} \left(\frac{4}{5} \right) \left(\frac{2}{3} \right) I_1$$

$$= \frac{16}{35} I_1$$

This time, I_1 is reached. ③

$$I_1 = \int_0^{\pi} \sin x \, dx = -[\cos x]_0^{\pi}$$

$$= -(\cos \pi - \cos 0)$$

$$= -(-1-1)$$

$$= 2$$

Substitute the value of I_1 into the formula for I_7 ④

So $I_7 = \frac{16}{35}(2)$

$$= \frac{32}{35}$$

Exercise 7.1B Reasoning and problem-solving

1 $I_n = \int_0^{\frac{\pi}{2}} \cos^n x \, dx$

    a Show that $I_n = \frac{n-1}{n} I_{n-2}$

    b Use the formula in part **a** to evaluate

        i $\int_0^{\frac{\pi}{2}} \cos^5 x \, dx$ **ii** $\int_0^{\frac{\pi}{2}} \cos^6 x \, dx$

2 $I_n = \int_{\frac{\pi}{2}}^{\pi} \sin^n x \, dx$

   a   Show that $I_n = \dfrac{n-1}{n} I_{n-2}$

   b   Use the formula in part **a** to evaluate

      i $\displaystyle\int_{\frac{\pi}{2}}^{\pi} \sin^7 x \, dx$ **ii** $\displaystyle\int_{\frac{\pi}{2}}^{\pi} \sin^8 x \, dx$

3 $I_n = \int \tan^n x \, dx$

   a   By writing $\tan^n x$ as $\tan^{n-2} x \tan^2 x$, find a reduction formula for I_n

   b   Use the formula in part **a** to find

      i $\displaystyle\int \tan^6 x \, dx$ **ii** $\displaystyle\int_0^{\frac{\pi}{4}} \tan^7 x \, dx$

4 $I_n = \int_0^1 x^n \sqrt{1+x^2} \, dx$

   a   Show that $I_n = \dfrac{2\sqrt{2} - (n-1)I_{n-2}}{2+n}$

   b   Use the formula in part **a** to evaluate

      i $\displaystyle\int_0^1 x^5 \sqrt{1+x^2} \, dx$

      ii $\displaystyle\int_0^1 x^4 \sqrt{1+x^2} \, dx$

5 $I_n = \int_0^{\pi} \dfrac{\cos nx}{\cos x} \, dx$

   a   Show that $I_n = -I_{n-2}$

   Hint: write $nx = (n-1)x + x$ and use the addition formula for cos.

   b   Use the reduction formula to find $\displaystyle\int_0^{\pi} \dfrac{\cos 7x}{\cos x} \, dx$

   c   Hence write down the value of

      i $\displaystyle\int_0^{\pi} \dfrac{\cos 27x}{\cos x} \, dx$

      ii $\displaystyle\int_0^{\pi} \dfrac{\cos 29x}{\cos x} \, dx$

   d   Show that $\displaystyle\int_0^{\pi} \dfrac{\cos nx}{\cos x} \, dx$ does not exist when n is an even number.

Fluency and skills

You can use integration to calculate the length of a curve between two points. Consider two points, A and B, that are close to each other on a curve. If you approximate the length of the curve, s, between these two points by a straight line, then you can use Pythagoras' theorem to see that the length of this line is

$$(\delta s)^2 = (\delta x)^2 + (\delta y)^2$$

Dividing by $(\delta x)^2$ gives $\dfrac{(\delta s)^2}{(\delta x)^2} = 1 + \dfrac{(\delta y)^2}{(\delta x)^2}$, which can be written as

$$\frac{\delta s}{\delta x} = \sqrt{1 + \left(\frac{\delta y}{\delta x}\right)^2}$$

As $\delta x \to 0$, $\dfrac{\delta s}{\delta x} \to \dfrac{ds}{dx}$ and $\dfrac{\delta y}{\delta x} \to \dfrac{dy}{dx}$ therefore $\dfrac{ds}{dx} = \sqrt{1 + \left(\dfrac{dy}{dx}\right)^2}$

You can integrate this to find the length of the curve:

$$s = \int \sqrt{1 + \left(\frac{dy}{dx}\right)^2}\, dx$$

Key point

The length of the arc of the curve $y = f(x)$ from x_1 to x_2

is given by $s = \displaystyle\int_{x_1}^{x_2} \sqrt{1 + \left(\dfrac{dy}{dx}\right)^2}\, dx$

Example 1

Calculate the length of the curve $y = 2x\sqrt{x}$ between the points $(0, 0)$ and $(4, 16)$

Write $y = 2x^{\frac{3}{2}}$, then $\dfrac{dy}{dx} = 3\sqrt{x}$

$$s = \int_0^3 \sqrt{1 + (3\sqrt{x})^2}\, dx$$

Use $s = \displaystyle\int_{x_1}^{x_2} \sqrt{1 + \left(\dfrac{dy}{dx}\right)^2}\, dx$

$$= \int_0^3 \sqrt{1 + 9x}\, dx$$

$$= \left[\frac{2}{27}(1 + 9x)^{\frac{3}{2}}\right]_0^3$$

You can check this result using differentiation.

$$= \frac{2}{27}(1 + 27)^{\frac{3}{2}} - \frac{2}{27}(1 + 0)^{\frac{3}{2}}$$

$$= \frac{2}{27}(56\sqrt{7} - 1)$$

If you are given a curve defined by parametric equations $x = f(t)$, $y = (t)$, then you need to divide by $(\delta t)^2$ instead.

So $\quad (\delta s)^2 = (\delta x)^2 + (\delta y)^2$ and divide by $(\delta t)^2$ to give

$$\left(\frac{\delta s}{\delta t}\right)^2 = \left(\frac{\delta x}{\delta t}\right)^2 + \left(\frac{\delta y}{\delta t}\right)^2 \text{ which can be written as}$$

$$\frac{\delta s}{\delta t} = \sqrt{\left(\frac{\delta x}{\delta t}\right)^2 + \left(\frac{\delta y}{\delta t}\right)^2}$$

As $\delta t \to 0$, $\dfrac{\delta s}{\delta t} \to \dfrac{ds}{dt}$, $\dfrac{\delta x}{\delta t} \to \dfrac{dx}{dt}$ and $\dfrac{\delta y}{\delta t} \to \dfrac{dy}{dt}$ therefore

$$\frac{ds}{dt} = \sqrt{\left(\frac{dx}{dt}\right)^2 + \left(\frac{dy}{dt}\right)^2}$$

You can then integrate this to find the length of the curve:

$$s = \int \sqrt{\left(\frac{dx}{dt}\right)^2 + \left(\frac{dy}{dx}\right)^2}\, dt$$

Key point

The length of the section of the curve $x = f(t)$, $y = g(t)$

from t_1 to t_2 is given by $s = \displaystyle\int_{t_1}^{t_2} \sqrt{\left(\frac{dx}{dt}\right)^2 + \left(\frac{dy}{dx}\right)^2}\, dt$

Example 2

Calculate the length of the arc of the curve $x = t^2 - 1$, $y = \dfrac{2}{3}t^3 + 1$ from $t = 0$ to $t = 2$

$$s = \int_0^2 \sqrt{(2t)^2 + (2t^2)^2}\, dt$$

Use the formula $= \displaystyle\int_{t_1}^{t_2} \sqrt{\left(\frac{dx}{dt}\right)^2 + \left(\frac{dy}{dx}\right)^2}\, dt$

$$= \int_0^2 \sqrt{4t^2 + 4t^4}\, dt$$

with $\dfrac{dx}{dt} = 2t$ and $\dfrac{dy}{dt} = 2t^2$

$$= \int_0^2 2t\sqrt{1 + t^2}\, dt$$

Take out a factor of $\sqrt{4t^2} = 2t$

$$= \left[\frac{2}{3}(1 + t^2)^{\frac{3}{2}}\right]_0^2$$

$$= \frac{2}{3}(1 + 2^2)^{\frac{3}{2}} - \frac{2}{3}(1)^{\frac{3}{2}}$$

Substitute in the limits.

$$= \frac{2}{3}(5\sqrt{5} - 1)$$

If you have a curve defined in polar coordinates as $r = f(\theta)$, $\theta_1 \le \theta \le \theta_2$, then the parametric equations for the curve are $x = r\cos\theta$, $y = r\sin\theta$

You will need to find the derivatives $\dfrac{dx}{d\theta}$ and $\dfrac{dy}{d\theta}$ by using the product rule, remembering that r is a function of θ, so

$$\frac{dx}{d\theta} = \frac{dr}{d\theta}\cos\theta - r\sin\theta \text{ and } \frac{dy}{d\theta} = \frac{dr}{d\theta}\sin\theta + r\cos\theta$$

The formula for arc length using these parametric equations is $s = \int\limits_{\alpha}^{\beta} \sqrt{\left(\dfrac{dx}{d\theta}\right)^2 + \left(\dfrac{dy}{d\theta}\right)^2}\,d\theta$

$$\left(\frac{dx}{d\theta}\right)^2 + \left(\frac{dy}{d\theta}\right)^2 = \left(\frac{dr}{d\theta}\cos\theta - r\sin\theta\right)^2 + \left(\frac{dr}{d\theta}\sin\theta + r\cos\theta\right)^2$$

$$= \left(\frac{dr}{d\theta}\right)^2 \cos^2\theta - 2r\frac{dr}{d\theta}\cos\theta\sin\theta + r^2\sin^2\theta + \left(\frac{dr}{d\theta}\right)^2 \sin^2\theta + 2r\frac{dr}{d\theta}\sin\theta\cos\theta + r^2\cos^2\theta$$

$$= \left(\frac{dr}{d\theta}\right)^2 (\cos^2\theta + \sin^2\theta) + r^2(\cos^2\theta + \sin^2\theta)$$

$$= r^2 + \left(\frac{dr}{d\theta}\right)^2 \text{ since } \cos^2\theta + \sin^2\theta \equiv 1$$

Therefore $s = \int\limits_{\theta_1}^{\theta_1} \sqrt{r^2 + \left(\dfrac{dr}{d\theta}\right)^2}\,d\theta$

Key point

The length of the section of the polar curve $r = f(\theta)$

from θ_1 to θ_2 is $s = \int\limits_{\theta_1}^{\theta_2} \sqrt{r^2 + \left(\dfrac{dr}{d\theta}\right)^2}\,d\theta$

Example 3

A polar curve has equation $r = \theta^2$

Calculate the exact length of the curve between the points $(0, 0)$ and $(2, 4)$

$$r^2 + \left(\frac{dr}{d\theta}\right)^2 = (\theta^2)^2 + (2\theta)^2$$

Since $\dfrac{dr}{d\theta} = 2\theta$

$$= \theta^4 + 4\theta^2$$

$$= \theta^2(\theta^2 + 4)$$

Therefore $s = \int\limits_0^4 \sqrt{\theta^2(\theta^2 + 4)}\,d\theta$

Use the formula
$$s = \int\limits_{\theta_1}^{\theta_2} \sqrt{r^2 + \left(\frac{dr}{d\theta}\right)^2}\,d\theta$$

$$= \int\limits_0^4 \theta\sqrt{\theta^2 + 4}\,d\theta$$

$$= \left[\frac{1}{3}(\theta^2 + 4)^{\frac{3}{2}}\right]_0^4$$

You can integrate by observation or use the substitution $u = \theta^2 + 4$

$$= \frac{1}{3}\left(20^{\frac{3}{2}} - 4^{\frac{3}{2}}\right)$$

$$= \frac{1}{3}(40\sqrt{5} - 8)$$

since $(\sqrt{20})^3 = (2\sqrt{5})^3 = 40\sqrt{5}$

1 Show that the length of the arc of the curve $y = \frac{2}{3}x^{\frac{3}{2}}$ between the points $x=0$ and $x=1$ is $A\sqrt{2}+B$, where A and B are constants to be found.

2 Calculate the arc length of the curve $y = x\sqrt{x}$ between $(4, 8)$ and $(9, 27)$, giving your answer to 3 significant figures.

3 Calculate the length of the curve with equation $y = \cosh x$, $\ln 2 \le x \le \ln 4$

4 Calculate the length of the arc of the curve $y = \frac{1}{2}\cosh 2x$ between the points $x=0$ and $x=\ln 2$

5 Calculate the length of the arc of the curve $y = (1+x)^{\frac{3}{2}}$ between $(-1, 0)$ and $\left(\frac{1}{3}, \frac{8}{9}\sqrt{3}\right)$

6 a Prove that $\frac{d(\ln(\sec x + \tan x))}{dx} = \sec x$

   b Hence calculate the length of the arc of the curve $y = \ln\left(\frac{1}{2}\cos 2x\right)$ between $x=0$ and $x=\frac{\pi}{6}$

7 A curve is given by the parametric equations $x = \frac{t^3}{6}+1$, $y = t^2$, $0 \le t \le 3$

   Calculate the arc length.

8 The curve C has polar equation $r = 3\sin\theta$. Use the formula for polar arc-length to show that the length of the curve from $\theta = \frac{\pi}{6}$ to $\theta = \pi$ is $\frac{5\pi}{2}$

9 A curve, C, has parametric equations $x = 5\cos t$, $y = 2+5\sin t$

   Calculate the length of C between the points $(5, 2)$ and $(0, 7)$

10 A circle has parametric equations $x = 4\sin t$, $y = 4\cos t$

   Use the formula for arc length for parametric equations to show that the length of the curve from $(0, 4)$ to $\left(2\sqrt{2}, 2\sqrt{2}\right)$ is π

11 Calculate the length of the polar curve $r = \theta^2 - 1$ from $\theta = 0$ to $\theta = 2$. You must show a full method.

12 a Show that $\frac{d}{dx}(x\sqrt{x^2+1}+\operatorname{arsinh}x) = 2\sqrt{x^2+1}$

   b Hence, show that the length of the polar curve $r = \theta$ from $\theta = 0$ to $\theta = 1$ is $\frac{1}{2}(\sqrt{2}+\ln(1+\sqrt{2}))$

13 A line has polar equation $r = \operatorname{cosec}\theta$

   Use the formula for polar arc-length to show that the length of the line from $\theta = \frac{\pi}{3}$ to $\theta = \frac{2\pi}{3}$ is $k\sqrt{3}$, where k is a constant to be found.

Reasoning and problem-solving

You may need to use substitution and other integration techniques to calculate arc lengths.

Strategy

To calculate the arc length

1. Choose the correct formula for arc length depending on whether the equation of the curve is in parametric, Cartesian or polar form.
2. Use a suitable substitution, and apply the correct limits.
3. Use trigonometric or hyperbolic identities.

Example 4

The hyperbolic identities $\cosh^2 x = \dfrac{1}{2}(\cosh 2x + 1)$ and $\sinh^2 x = \dfrac{1}{2}(\cosh 2x - 1)$ are particularly useful for integration.

The curve C has equation $y = 2x^2$. Calculate the length of the curve between $(0, 0)$ and $\left(\dfrac{1}{4}, \dfrac{1}{8}\right)$

$\dfrac{dy}{dx} = 4x$

So $s = \displaystyle\int_0^{\frac{1}{4}} \sqrt{1 + (4x)^2}\, dt$

1 Use the formula
$$s = \int_{x_1}^{x_2} \sqrt{1 + \left(\frac{dy}{dx}\right)^2}\, dx$$

$= \displaystyle\int_0^{\frac{1}{4}} \sqrt{1 + 16x^2}\, dt$

Let $x = \dfrac{1}{4}\sinh u$, then $\dfrac{dx}{du} = \dfrac{1}{4}\cosh u$

When $x = 0$, $u = 0$

When $x = \dfrac{1}{4}$, $u = \ln(1 + \sqrt{2})$

2 Choose a suitable substitution to use and change the limits.

$s = \displaystyle\int_0^{\ln(1+\sqrt{2})} \sqrt{1 + 16\left(\frac{1}{4}\sinh u\right)^2}\left(\frac{1}{4}\cosh u\right) du$

$= \dfrac{1}{4}\displaystyle\int_0^{\ln(1+\sqrt{2})} \sqrt{1 + \sinh^2 u}\,(\cosh u)\, du$

3 Use the hyperbolic identity $\cosh^2 x - \sinh^2 x = 1$

$= \dfrac{1}{4}\displaystyle\int_0^{\ln(1+\sqrt{2})} \sqrt{\cosh^2 u}\,(\cosh u)\, du$

$= \dfrac{1}{4}\displaystyle\int_0^{\ln(1+\sqrt{2})} \cosh^2 u\, du$

(Continued on the next page)

$$= \frac{1}{8} \int_{0}^{\ln(1+\sqrt{2})} \cosh(2u+1)\, du$$

Use the hyperbolic identity
$$\cosh^2 x = \frac{1}{2}(\cosh 2x + 1)$$

$$= \frac{1}{8}\left[\frac{1}{2}\sinh 2u + u\right]_{0}^{\ln(1+\sqrt{2})}$$

$$= \frac{1}{8}\left(\frac{1}{2}(2\sqrt{2}) + \ln(1+\sqrt{2})\right) - \frac{1}{8}(0+0)$$

$$= \frac{1}{8}(\sqrt{2} + \ln(1+\sqrt{2}))$$

Since
$$\sinh(2\ln(1+\sqrt{2})) = \frac{1}{2}\left(e^{2\ln(1+\sqrt{2})} - e^{-2\ln(1+\sqrt{2})}\right)$$
$$= \frac{1}{2}\left((1+\sqrt{2})^2 - \frac{1}{(1+\sqrt{2})^2}\right)$$
$$= 2\sqrt{2}$$

Give an exact answer if you can.

Example 5

The parametric equations of a curve are $x = 3t - 3\sin t,\ y = 7 + 3\cos t$

Calculate the length of the curve from the point where $t = 0$ to $t = \dfrac{\pi}{2}$

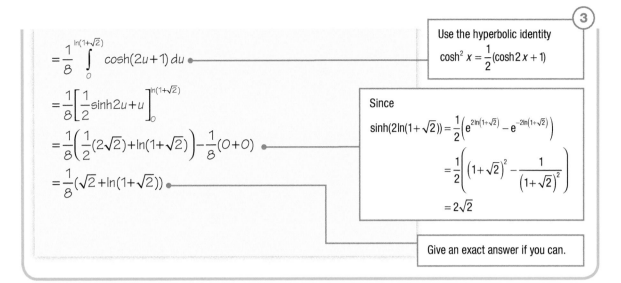

$$\left(\frac{dx}{dt}\right)^2 + \left(\frac{dy}{dt}\right)^2 = (3 - 3\cos t)^2 + (-3\sin t)^2$$
$$= 9 - 18\cos t + 9\cos^2 t + 9\sin^2 t$$
$$= 9 - 18\cos t + 9$$
$$= 18(1 - \cos t)$$

Since $\cos^2 t + \sin^2 t \equiv 1$

Therefore $s = \displaystyle\int_{0}^{\frac{\pi}{2}} \sqrt{18(1 - \cos t)}\, dt$

Use the formula
$$s = \int_{t_1}^{t_2} \sqrt{\left(\frac{dx}{dt}\right)^2 + \left(\frac{dy}{dt}\right)^2}\, dt$$

$$= \int_{0}^{\frac{\pi}{2}} \sqrt{18\left(2\sin^2\left(\frac{t}{2}\right)\right)}\, dt$$

Use the identity
$$2\sin^2\left(\frac{t}{2}\right) \equiv 1 - \cos t$$

$$= \int_{0}^{\frac{\pi}{2}} \sqrt{36\sin^2\left(\frac{t}{2}\right)}\, dt$$

$$= \int_{0}^{\frac{\pi}{2}} 6\sin\left(\frac{t}{2}\right) dt$$

$$= \left[-12\cos\left(\frac{t}{2}\right)\right]_{0}^{\frac{\pi}{2}}$$

$$= \left(-12\cos\left(\frac{\pi}{4}\right)\right) - (-12\cos(0))$$

$$= \left(-\frac{12}{\sqrt{2}}\right) - (-12)$$

$$= 12 - 6\sqrt{2}$$

The formulae $1 - \cos\theta \equiv 2\sin^2\left(\dfrac{\theta}{2}\right)$ and $1 + \cos\theta \equiv 2\cos^2\left(\dfrac{\theta}{2}\right)$ can be derived from the identity $\cos(2A) \equiv \cos^2 A - \sin^2 A$ using $A = \dfrac{\theta}{2}$

Example 6

The curve C has polar equation $r = \sqrt{2} - \sqrt{2}\sin\theta$

Calculate the exact length of C between $\theta = 0$ and $\theta = \dfrac{\pi}{2}$

$r^2 + \left(\dfrac{dr}{d\theta}\right)^2 = (\sqrt{2} - \sqrt{2}\sin\theta)^2 + (-\sqrt{2}\cos\theta)^2$

| Since $\dfrac{dr}{d\theta} = \sin\theta$ |

$\qquad = 2 - 4\sin\theta + 2\sin^2\theta + 2\cos^2\theta$

$\qquad = 4 - 4\sin\theta$

| Since $\cos^2\theta + \sin^2\theta \equiv 1$ |

$\qquad = 4(1 - \sin\theta)$

Therefore, $s = \displaystyle\int_0^{\frac{\pi}{2}} \sqrt{4(1-\sin\theta)}\,d\theta$

1

Use the formula

$$s = \int_{\theta_1}^{\theta_2} \sqrt{r^2 + \left(\dfrac{dr}{d\theta}\right)^2}\,d\theta$$

$= 2\displaystyle\int_0^{\frac{\pi}{2}} \sqrt{1 - \sin\theta}\,d\theta$

$= 2\displaystyle\int_0^{\frac{\pi}{2}} \sqrt{1 - \sin\theta} \cdot \dfrac{\sqrt{1 + \sin\theta}}{\sqrt{1 + \sin\theta}}\,d\theta$

Multiply the integrand by

$\dfrac{\sqrt{1 + \sin\theta}}{\sqrt{1 + \sin\theta}}$

$= 2\displaystyle\int_0^{\frac{\pi}{2}} \dfrac{\sqrt{1 - \sin^2\theta}}{\sqrt{1 + \sin\theta}}\,d\theta$

Since

$\sqrt{1 + \sin\theta}\sqrt{1 - \sin\theta}$

$\qquad = \sqrt{(1 - \sin\theta)(1 + \sin\theta)}$

$\qquad = \sqrt{1 - \sin^2\theta}$

$= 2\displaystyle\int_0^{\frac{\pi}{2}} \dfrac{\sqrt{\cos^2\theta}}{\sqrt{1 + \sin\theta}}\,d\theta$

$= 2\displaystyle\int_0^{\frac{\pi}{2}} \dfrac{\cos\theta}{\sqrt{1 + \sin\theta}}\,d\theta$

3

Use $1 - \sin^2\theta \equiv \cos^2\theta$

Let $u = 1 + \sin\theta$, then $\dfrac{du}{d\theta} = \cos\theta$

2

Use a substitution.

When $\theta = 0$, $u = 1$ and when $\theta = \dfrac{\pi}{2}$, $u = 2$

Remember to change the limits

$s = 2\left[2\sqrt{u}\right]_1^2$

so $s = 2\displaystyle\int_1^2 \dfrac{1}{\sqrt{u}}\,du$

$= 4(\sqrt{2} - 1)$

since $\cos\theta\,d\theta = du$

1 a Use a suitable substitution to show that

$$\int \sqrt{1+36x^2}\,dx = \frac{1}{2}x\sqrt{1+36x^2} + \frac{1}{12}\text{arsinh}\,6x + c$$

b Hence calculate the exact length of the arc of the curve $y = 3x^2 + 1$ between the points $(0, 1)$ and $(1, 4)$

2 A curve is defined by the parametric equations $x = t^2$, $y = 2t$. Calculate the exact arc length from $t = 0$ to $t = 1$

3 A curve has equation $y = 2\sqrt{x}$

a Show that the arc length of the curve between $x = 0$ and $x = 4$ is given by $s = \int_0^4 \sqrt{\frac{x+1}{x}}\,dx$

b Use the substitution $x = \sinh^2 u$ to calculate the exact value of s

4 A curve has parametric equations $x = \cos^3 t$, $y = \sin^3 t$

Calculate the arc length of the curve between $(1, 0)$ and $(0, 1)$

5 The parametric equations of a curve are $x = 3 + \cos t$, $y = t + \sin t$

Calculate the length of the curve between the points where $t = 0$ and $t = \frac{\pi}{2}$

6 Show that the length of the curve $y = 1 - x^2$ between $(0, 1)$ and $(1, 0)$ is $\frac{1}{2}\sqrt{5} + \ln(2 + \sqrt{5})$

7 A cardioid has polar equation $r = 1 + \cos\theta$

Show that the length of the arc of the curve from $\theta = \frac{\pi}{3}$ to $\theta = \frac{2\pi}{3}$ is $2(\sqrt{3} - 1)$

8 The polar equation of the curve C is $r = k(1 - \sin\theta)$. Calculate the exact length of C between $\theta = \frac{\pi}{2}$ and $\theta = \frac{3\pi}{2}$

9 The curve C has polar equation $r = 5 - 5\cos\theta$, $0 \le \theta \le 2\pi$

Show that the length of the curve is 40

10 A circle has radius r and centre the origin. Use the parametric equations of the circle to show that the circumference is $2\pi r$

11 A cardioid has polar equation

$r = k(1 + \cos\theta)$, $0 \le \theta \le 2\pi$

By splitting the cardioid into two symmetrical sections, or otherwise, find the length of the curve.

12 A piece of wire is supported at two ends, k metres apart and h metres above the ground. The wire forms a catenary with equation $y = 3\cosh\left(\dfrac{x}{3}\right)$, as shown.

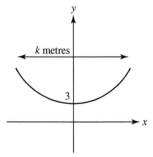

Given that the length of the wire is 4.5 metres

a Calculate the exact value of k

b Calculate the exact value of h

13 Show that the length of one 'petal' of the lemniscate $r = \sin 2\theta$ is given by $s = \displaystyle\int_{\alpha}^{\beta} \sqrt{1 + 3\cos^2 2\theta}\,d\theta$, where $0 \le \alpha, \beta \le \pi$

Give the values of α and β in terms of π where appropriate.

14 Show that the circumference of the ellipse with parametric equations

$x = a\cos\theta$, $y = b\sin\theta$, $a > b$ is given by $4\displaystyle\int_{0}^{\frac{\pi}{2}} \sqrt{1 - e^2 \cos^2\theta}\,d\theta$, where e is the eccentricity of the ellipse.

Fluency and skills

You can use the formula $V = \pi \int_{x_1}^{x_2} y^2 \, dx$ to calculate the volume of revolution when $f(x)$ between x_1 and x_2 is rotated through 2π radians around the x-axis.

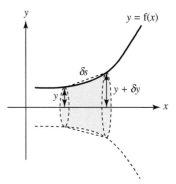

It is also possible to calculate the surface area of revolution. Consider a small section of the curve rotated through 2π radians around the x-axis. The shape can be approximated by a truncated cone (also known as a **frustum**).

The curved surface area of a truncated cone is given by $S = \pi(r_1 + r_2)l$, where r_1 is the radius of the base, r_2 is the radius of the top and l is the length of the slanted side of the frustum.

Therefore $\delta S = \pi(y + \delta y + y)\delta s = \pi(2y + \delta y)\delta s$

Divide by δx to give $\dfrac{\delta S}{\delta x} = \pi(2y + \delta y)\dfrac{\delta s}{\delta x}$

As $\delta x \to 0$, $\delta y \to 0$, $\dfrac{\delta s}{\delta x} \to \dfrac{ds}{dx}$ and $\dfrac{\delta S}{\delta x} \to \dfrac{dS}{dx}$

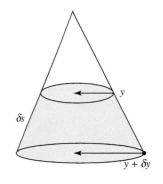

Therefore

$\dfrac{dS}{dx} = 2y\pi \dfrac{ds}{dx}$

You can then integrate both sides with respect to x to find the surface area of revolution:

$$S = \int 2y\pi \, ds$$

As $\dfrac{ds}{dx} = \sqrt{1 + \left(\dfrac{dy}{dx}\right)^2}$, you can write this as

$$S = \int 2y\pi \sqrt{1 + \left(\dfrac{dy}{dx}\right)^2} \, dx$$

Key point

The surface area of revolution when the curve $y = f(x)$ from x_1 through to x_2 is rotated through 2π radians around the x-axis is given by $S = 2\pi \int_{x_1}^{x_2} y \sqrt{1 + \left(\dfrac{dy}{dx}\right)^2} \, dx$

65

Example 1

The section of the curve with equation $y = x^3$ between $x = 0$ and $x = \dfrac{1}{2}$ is rotated through 2π radians around the x-axis. For the solid formed, calculate the exact value of

a The volume,

b The curved surface area of the solid formed.

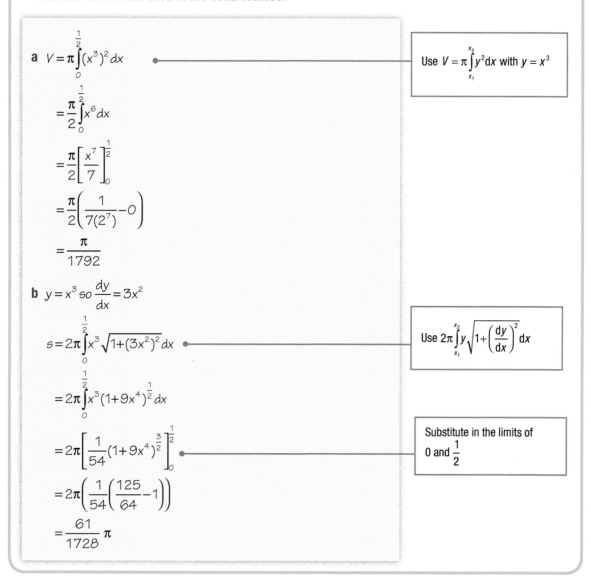

a $V = \pi \displaystyle\int_0^{\frac{1}{2}} (x^3)^2 \, dx$

> Use $V = \pi \displaystyle\int_{x_1}^{x_2} y^2 \, dx$ with $y = x^3$

$\quad = \dfrac{\pi}{2} \displaystyle\int_0^{\frac{1}{2}} x^6 \, dx$

$\quad = \dfrac{\pi}{2} \left[\dfrac{x^7}{7} \right]_0^{\frac{1}{2}}$

$\quad = \dfrac{\pi}{2} \left(\dfrac{1}{7(2^7)} - 0 \right)$

$\quad = \dfrac{\pi}{1792}$

b $y = x^3$ so $\dfrac{dy}{dx} = 3x^2$

$\quad s = 2\pi \displaystyle\int_0^{\frac{1}{2}} x^3 \sqrt{1 + (3x^2)^2} \, dx$

> Use $2\pi \displaystyle\int_{x_1}^{x_2} y \sqrt{1 + \left(\dfrac{dy}{dx} \right)^2} \, dx$

$\quad = 2\pi \displaystyle\int_0^{\frac{1}{2}} x^3 (1 + 9x^4)^{\frac{1}{2}} \, dx$

$\quad = 2\pi \left[\dfrac{1}{54} (1 + 9x^4)^{\frac{3}{2}} \right]_0^{\frac{1}{2}}$

> Substitute in the limits of 0 and $\dfrac{1}{2}$

$\quad = 2\pi \left(\dfrac{1}{54} \left(\dfrac{125}{64} - 1 \right) \right)$

$\quad = \dfrac{61}{1728} \pi$

You can also find a formula for the surface area of revolution when the curve is defined by parametric equations.

Using $\dfrac{ds}{dt} = \sqrt{\left(\dfrac{dx}{dt} \right)^2 + \left(\dfrac{dy}{dt} \right)^2}$ in the formula for surface area of revolution, $S = \displaystyle\int 2y\pi \, ds$, gives

$S = \displaystyle\int 2y\pi \sqrt{\left(\dfrac{dx}{dt} \right)^2 + \left(\dfrac{dy}{dt} \right)^2} \, dt$

Key point

The surface area of revolution when the curve
$x = f(t)$, $y = g(t)$ from t_1 to t_2 is rotated through 2π radians around
the x-axis is given by

$$S = 2\pi \int_{t_1}^{t_2} y \sqrt{\left(\frac{dx}{dt}\right)^2 + \left(\frac{dy}{dt}\right)^2}\, dt,\text{ where } y \text{ is replaced by } g(t)$$

Example 2

The curve C has parametric equations $x = 2t^2$, $y = 4t$

The section of the curve from $t = 0$ to $t = 1$ is rotated through 2π radians around the x-axis.

Calculate the exact surface area of the solid formed.

$$\left(\frac{dx}{dt}\right)^2 + \left(\frac{dy}{dt}\right)^2 = (4t)^2 + (4)^2$$

$$= 16t^2 + 16$$

$$= 16(t^2 + 1)$$

$$S = 2\pi \int_0^1 4t\sqrt{16(t^2 + 1)}\, dt$$

Use
$$S = 2\pi \int_{t_1}^{t_2} y \sqrt{\left(\frac{dx}{dt}\right)^2 + \left(\frac{dy}{dt}\right)^2}\, dt$$
and replace y with $4t$

$$= 2\pi \int_0^1 16t\sqrt{t^2 + 1}\, dt$$

$$= 2\pi \left[\frac{16}{3}(t^2 + 1)^{\frac{3}{2}} \right]_0^1$$

Use inspection or the substitution $u = t^2 + 1$ to integrate.

$$= \frac{32\pi}{3}(2\sqrt{2} - 1)$$

As with the arc length, you can use the formula for parametric equations to find a formula for a polar equation. The parametric equations of the curve $r = f(\theta)$, $\theta_1 \le \theta \le \theta_1$ are $x = r\cos\theta$, $y = r\sin\theta$

You have already seen that $\left(\frac{dx}{d\theta}\right)^2 + \left(\frac{dy}{d\theta}\right)^2 = r^2 + \left(\frac{dr}{d\theta}\right)^2$

Therefore the formula for surface area becomes

$$S = 2\pi \int_{\theta_1}^{\theta_2} r\sin\theta \sqrt{r^2 + \left(\frac{dr}{d\theta}\right)^2}\, d\theta$$

Key point

The surface area of revolution when the section of the polar curve $r = f(\theta)$ from θ_1 to θ_2 is rotated through 2π radians around the initial line is

$$S = 2\pi \int_{\theta_1}^{\theta_2} r\sin\theta \sqrt{r^2 + \left(\frac{dr}{d\theta}\right)^2}\, d\theta$$

Example 3

A polar curve has equation $r = \cos\theta$

Calculate the surface area of the solid formed when the section of the curve between $\theta = 0$ and $\theta = \dfrac{\pi}{2}$ is rotated through 2π radians around the initial line.

$$r^2 + \left(\frac{dr}{d\theta}\right)^2 = (\cos\theta)^2 + (\sin\theta)^2$$

$$= \cos^2\theta + \sin^2\theta$$

$$= 1$$

Use the formula

$$S = 2\pi \int_{\theta_1}^{\theta_2} r\sin\theta \sqrt{r^2 + \left(\frac{dr}{d\theta}\right)^2}\, d\theta$$

Therefore, $S = 2\pi \displaystyle\int_0^{\frac{\pi}{2}} \cos\theta\sin\theta\sqrt{1}\,d\theta$

$$= 2\pi \int_0^{\frac{\pi}{2}} \frac{1}{2}\sin 2\theta\, d\theta$$

Since $\sin 2\theta \equiv 2\sin\theta\cos\theta$

$$= \pi \int_0^{\frac{\pi}{2}} \sin 2\theta\, d\theta$$

$$= \pi\left[-\frac{1}{2}\cos 2\theta\right]_0^{\frac{\pi}{2}}$$

$$= -\frac{1}{2}\pi(\cos\pi - \cos 0)$$

$$= -\frac{1}{2}\pi(-1-1)$$

$$= \pi$$

Exercise 7.3A Fluency and skills

1   The section of the line $y = \dfrac{1}{5}x$ between the points $(5, 1)$ and $(25, 5)$ is rotated through 2π radians around the x-axis.

   a   Use calculus to find the surface area of the solid formed.

   b   Verify this result using the formula for the curved surface area of a cone, $S = \pi r l$, where l is the slant length of the cone.

2   The section of the curve $y = \sqrt{x}$ between $(0, 0)$ and $(1, 1)$ is rotated through 2π radians around the x-axis.

   a   Show that the surface area of revolution is given by $S = \pi \displaystyle\int_0^1 \sqrt{4x + 1}\,dx$

   b   Hence find the exact value of S

3   The curve C has parametric equations

$$x = t - e^t, \quad y = 4e^{\frac{t}{2}}$$

   Calculate the curved surface area of the solid formed when the section of C from $t = 0$ to $t = \ln 4$ is rotated through 2π radians around the x-axis. Give your answer in the form $k\pi$, where k is a constant to be found.

4   A circle has parametric equations

$$x = 1 + \cos t, \quad y = \sin t$$

   The section of the circle between $t = 0$ and $t = \dfrac{\pi}{3}$ is rotated through 2π radians to form part of a sphere.

   Use integration to calculate the curved surface area.

5 The curve C has equation $y = x^{\frac{1}{2}} - \frac{1}{3}x^{\frac{3}{2}}$

The arc of C between the points where $x = 0$ and $x = 2$ is rotated through 2π radians around the x-axis. Calculate the surface area of the solid formed.

6 A polar curve has equation $r = 3\sin\theta$

Calculate the surface area of the solid formed when the section of the curve between $\theta = 0$ and $\theta = \frac{\pi}{4}$ is rotated through 2π radians around the x-axis.

7 The curve C has polar equation $r = 1 - \cos\theta$

The arc of the curve between $\theta = 0$ and $\theta = \frac{\pi}{2}$ is rotated through 2π radians around the initial line. Show that the solid formed has a curved surface area of $\frac{4}{5}\sqrt{2}\pi$

8 A straight line has polar equation $r = 3\mathrm{cosec}\theta$

a Use integration to find the surface area of revolution when the section of the curve between $\theta = \frac{\pi}{4}$ and $\theta = \frac{\pi}{2}$ is rotated through 2π radians around the initial line.

b Use the formula for the curved surface area of a cylinder to verify your answer to part **a**.

9 The curve C is defined by the parametric equations $x = t^2$, $y = 2t$. The section of C between $t = 0$ and $t = 2$ is rotated through 2π radians about the x-axis. Calculate the surface area of revolution.

10 A curve, C, has equation $y = 4x^3, 0 \le x \le \frac{1}{2}$

The curve C is rotated through 2π radians around the x-axis. Calculate

a The volume of the solid formed,

b The curved surface area of the solid formed.

11 The arc of the curve with equation $y = \cosh x$ between $x = 0$ and $x = \ln 3$ is rotated through 2π radians around the x-axis. Calculate

a The volume of the solid formed,

b The curved surface area of the solid formed.

Reasoning and problem-solving

You will need to use techniques that you have previously learnt to find a surface area of revolution, such as simplifying the integrand using trigonometric or hyperbolic identities or using an integration method such as substitution.

Strategy

To calculate the surface area of revolution

① Choose the correct formula for arc length depending on whether the equation of the curve is in parametric, Cartesian or polar form.

② Use trigonometric or hyperbolic identities.

③ Use any known integration techniques.

Example 4

The curve C has parametric equations $x = t + \sin t$, $y = 1 + \cos t$

The section of the curve from $(0, 2)$ to $(\pi, 0)$ is rotated through 2π radians around the x-axis.

Calculate the exact surface area of the solid formed.

$$\left(\frac{dx}{dt}\right)^2 + \left(\frac{dy}{dt}\right)^2 = (1 + \cos t)^2 + (-\sin t)^2$$

$$= 1 + 2\cos t + \cos^2 t + \sin^2 t$$

$$= 2(1 + \cos t)$$

At $(0, 2)$, $t = 0$ and at $(\pi, 0)$, $t = \pi$

$$S = 2\pi \int_0^\pi (1 + \cos t)\sqrt{2(1 + \cos t)}\,dt$$

$$= 2\pi \int_0^\pi (1 + \cos t)\sqrt{4\cos^2\left(\frac{t}{2}\right)}\,dt$$

$$= 2\pi \int_0^\pi (1 + \cos t)\sqrt{4\cos^2\left(\frac{t}{2}\right)}\,dt$$

$$= 2\pi \int_0^\pi \left(2\cos^2\left(\frac{t}{2}\right)\right)\left(2\cos\left(\frac{t}{2}\right)\right)\,dt$$

$$= 8\pi \int_0^\pi \left(1 - \sin^2\left(\frac{t}{2}\right)\right)\left(\cos\left(\frac{t}{2}\right)\right)\,dt$$

$$= 8\pi \int_0^\pi \cos\left(\frac{t}{2}\right) - \sin^2\left(\frac{t}{2}\right)\cos\left(\frac{t}{2}\right)\,dt$$

$$= 8\pi \left[2\sin\left(\frac{t}{2}\right) - \frac{2}{3}\sin^3\left(\frac{t}{2}\right)\right]_0^\pi$$

$$= 8\pi \left(2\sin\left(\frac{\pi}{2}\right) - \frac{2}{3}\sin^3\left(\frac{\pi}{2}\right)\right) - 0$$

$$= 8\pi \left(2 - \frac{2}{3}\right)$$

$$= \frac{32}{3}\pi$$

1. Use the formula

$$S = 2\pi \int_{t_1}^{t_2} y \sqrt{\left(\frac{dx}{dt}\right)^2 + \left(\frac{dy}{dt}\right)^2}\,dt$$

2. Use the identity

$$1 + \cos t \equiv 2\cos^2\left(\frac{t}{2}\right)$$

2. Use the identity

$$1 - \sin^2 t \equiv 2\cos^2\left(\frac{t}{2}\right)$$

Expand the brackets.

3. Use inspection or integration by substitution to work out

$$\int \sin^2\left(\frac{t}{2}\right)\cos\left(\frac{t}{2}\right)\,dt = \frac{2}{3}\sin^3\left(\frac{t}{2}\right)$$

1 The section of the curve $y = 2e^{-x}$ between $(0, 2)$ and $(\ln 2, 1)$ is rotated through 2π radians around the x-axis.

   a Calculate the volume of revolution,

   b Show that the surface area of revolution is given by $4\pi \int_0^{\ln 2} e^{-x} \sqrt{1 + 4e^{-2x}} \, dx$

   c Use the substitution $e^{-x} = \frac{1}{2}\sinh u$ to calculate the surface area of revolution.

2 A circle is defined by the parametric equations $x = r\cos\theta$, $y = r\sin\theta$. Use integration to prove that

   a The volume of a sphere is $\frac{4}{3}\pi r^3$

   b The surface area of a sphere is $4\pi r^2$

3 A curve has parametric equation $x = \cosh 2\theta$, $y = 2\sinh\theta$, $0 < \theta \le 2\pi$

Calculate the surface area of revolution when the curve is rotated through 2π radians around the x-axis.

4 **a** Show that $\sqrt{1 - \cos\theta} = A\sin\frac{\theta}{2}$ where A is a constant to be found.

A curve is defined by the parametric equations $x = \theta - \sin\theta$, $y = 1 - \cos\theta$

   b Calculate the arc length between $\theta = 0$ and $\theta = \pi$

   c Calculate the surface area of revolution when the section of the curve between $\theta = 0$ and $\theta = \pi$ is rotated through 2π radians around the x-axis.

5 Part of the curve with equation $y = 2 - \cosh x$ is shown. The curve intersects the x-axis at the point A and the y-axis at the point B.

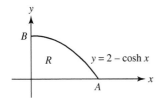

The region R is bounded by the curve $y = 2 - \cosh x$ and the coordinate axes.

R is rotated through 2π radians around the x-axis. Calculate

   a The exact volume of revolution,

   b The exact length of the arc AB

   c The exact surface area of revolution.

6 A curve has parametric equations
$$x = \ln t, \quad y = \frac{1}{2}t^2$$
The arc of the curve between $\left(0, \frac{1}{2}\right)$ and $(\ln 2, 2)$ is rotated through 2π radians around the x-axis.

   a Show that the surface area of revolution is given by $S = \pi \int_1^6 t\sqrt{1 + t^4} \, dt$

   b Hence use the substitution $t^2 = \sinh u$ to find the value of S

7 The arc of the curve $y = e^x$ between $(0, 1)$ and $(\ln 3, 3)$ is rotated through 2π radians around the x-axis. Find the exact surface area of the solid formed.

8 The curve C has polar equation $r = e^{-\theta}$

The section of C from $\theta = 0$ to $\theta = \frac{\pi}{2}$ is rotated a full turn around the initial line to form a solid.

Show that the surface area of the solid is $\frac{2}{5}\sqrt{2}(1 - 2e^{-\pi})\pi$

9 The curve C has equation $y = \frac{1}{2}x^2$

The section of C from $(0, 0)$ to $(2, 2)$ is rotated through 2π radians about the x-axis to form a solid. Show that the exact surface area of this solid is $\left(\frac{9}{4}\sqrt{5} - \frac{1}{8}\ln(2 + \sqrt{5})\right)\pi$

Chapter summary

- The formula for integration by parts is $\int u\dfrac{\mathrm{d}v}{\mathrm{d}x}\mathrm{d}x = uv - \int v\dfrac{\mathrm{d}u}{\mathrm{d}x}\mathrm{d}x$

- A reduction formula for I_n is an equation that relates I_n to I_{n-1} and/or I_{n-2}. It can be repeatedly applied to reduce the integral to one not requiring integration by parts.

- The length of the curve $y = \mathrm{f}(x)$ from x_1 to x_2 is given by $s = \displaystyle\int_{x_1}^{x_2}\sqrt{1+\left(\dfrac{\mathrm{d}y}{\mathrm{d}x}\right)^2}\,\mathrm{d}x$

- The length of the curve $x = \mathrm{f}(t)$, $y = \mathrm{g}(t)$ from t_1 to t_2 is given by $s = \displaystyle\int_{t_1}^{t_2}\sqrt{\left(\dfrac{\mathrm{d}x}{\mathrm{d}t}\right)^2+\left(\dfrac{\mathrm{d}y}{\mathrm{d}x}\right)^2}\,\mathrm{d}t$

- The length of the arc of the curve defined in polar coordinates as $r = \mathrm{f}(\theta)$ between θ_1 and θ_2 is given by $s = \displaystyle\int_{\theta_1}^{\theta_2}\sqrt{r^2+\left(\dfrac{\mathrm{d}r}{\mathrm{d}\theta}\right)^2}\,\mathrm{d}\theta$

- The surface area of revolution when the curve $y = \mathrm{f}(x)$ from x_1 to x_2 is rotated through 2π radians around the x-axis is given by $S = 2\pi\displaystyle\int_{x_1}^{x_2}y\sqrt{1+\left(\dfrac{\mathrm{d}y}{\mathrm{d}x}\right)^2}\,\mathrm{d}x$

- The surface area of revolution when the curve $y = \mathrm{f}(x)$ from y_1 to y_2 is rotated through 2π radians around the y-axis is given by $S = 2\pi\displaystyle\int_{y_1}^{y_2}x\sqrt{1+\left(\dfrac{\mathrm{d}x}{\mathrm{d}y}\right)^2}\,\mathrm{d}y$

- The surface area of revolution when the curve $x = \mathrm{f}(t)$, $y = \mathrm{g}(t)$ from t_1 to t_2 is rotated through 2π radians around the x-axis is given by $S = 2\pi\displaystyle\int_{t_1}^{t_2}y\sqrt{\left(\dfrac{\mathrm{d}x}{\mathrm{d}t}\right)^2+\left(\dfrac{\mathrm{d}y}{\mathrm{d}t}\right)^2}\,\mathrm{d}t$

- The surface area of revolution when the curve $x = \mathrm{f}(t)$, $y = \mathrm{g}(t)$ from t_1 to t_2 is rotated through 2π radians around the y-axis is given by $S = 2\pi\displaystyle\int_{t_1}^{t_2}x\sqrt{\left(\dfrac{\mathrm{d}x}{\mathrm{d}t}\right)^2+\left(\dfrac{\mathrm{d}y}{\mathrm{d}t}\right)^2}\,\mathrm{d}t$

- The surface area of revolution when the curve defined in polar coordinates as $r = \mathrm{f}(\theta)$ from θ_1 to θ_2 is rotated through 2π radians around the initial line is given by
$$S = 2\pi\int_{\theta_1}^{\theta_2}r\sin\theta\sqrt{r^2+\left(\dfrac{\mathrm{d}r}{\mathrm{d}\theta}\right)^2}\,\mathrm{d}\theta$$

Check and review

You should now be able to...	Review Questions
✔ Derive a reduction formula for indefinite and definite integrals.	1, 2
✔ Use a reduction formula for indefinite and definite integrals.	1, 2
✔ Calculate the length of the arc of a curve given by a Cartesian equation.	3
✔ Calculate the length of the arc of a curve given by parametric equations.	4
✔ Calculate the length of the arc of a curve given in polar coordinates.	5
✔ Calculate the surface area of revolution of a curve given by a Cartesian equation.	6
✔ Calculate the surface area of revolution of a curve given by parametric equations.	7, 8
✔ Calculate the surface area of revolution of a curve given in polar coordinates.	9

1 $I_n = \int x^n e^{-2x} dx$

   a Show that $I_n = -\dfrac{1}{2}x^n e^{-2x} + \dfrac{n}{2}I_{n-1}$

   b Use this formula to find I_3

2 $I_n = \int_0^{\pi} x^n \cos x \, dx$

   a Show that $I_n = -n\pi^{n-1} - n(n-1)I_{n-2}$

   b Use this formula to evaluate

     i $\displaystyle\int_0^{\pi} x^6 \cos x \, dx$

     ii $\int x^5 \cos x \, dx$

3 Calculate the length of the curve $y = (2x+1)^{\frac{3}{2}}$ between the points where $x = 3$ and $x = 5$

4 A curve is given by the parametric equations $x = 2t$, $y = t^2$, $0 \le t \le 2$. Calculate the length of the curve.

5 A curve is defined in polar coordinates as $r = 2\sin\theta$. Find the length of the arc from

   $\theta = 0$ to $\theta = \dfrac{\pi}{3}$

6 Calculate the surface area of revolution when the arc of the curve $y = \dfrac{1}{3}x^3$ between $(0, 0)$ and $\left(1, \dfrac{1}{3}\right)$ is rotated through 2π radians around the x-axis.

7 A curve is given by the parametric equations $x = \cos\theta$, $y = \sin\theta$, $\dfrac{\pi}{2} \le \theta \le \dfrac{3\pi}{4}$ Show that the surface area of revolution when the curve is rotated through 2π radians around the x-axis is $A\pi$, where A is a constant to be found.

8 A curve, C, has equation $y = x^2 - 3$. Calculate the surface area of revolution when the section of C between $x = 0$ and $x = 9$ is rotated through π radians around the y-axis.

9 Find the area of the surface formed by rotating the polar curve $r = 2\cos\theta$ from $\theta = 0$ to $\theta = \dfrac{\pi}{2}$ through 2π radians around the initial line $\theta = 0$

Research

A logarithmic spiral is also known as a self-similar spiral.

It is defined in polar coordinates by $r = ae^{b\theta}$

Alternatively, in parametric form

$x(t) = ae^{bt} \cos(t)$ $y(t) = ae^{bt} \sin(t)$

Use graph plotting software to investigate the form of such spirals.

Research how the length of the spiral can be found using integration techniques and how the length of the spiral grows with increasing angle of the spiral.

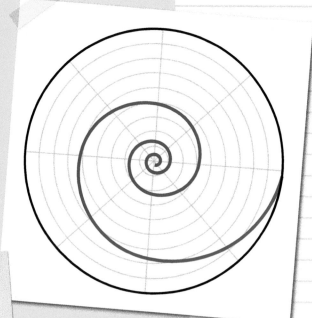

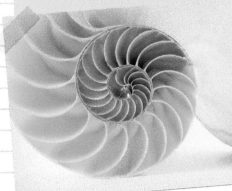

Investigation

A catenary is the name given to the curve that a uniform chain adopts when allowed to hang freely under gravity (the name is derived from the Latin for chain, Catena). It looks rather like a parabola, but it has its own distinctive shape and can be defined mathematically by the equation

$$y = a\cosh\left(\frac{x}{a}\right) = a\frac{\left(e^{\frac{x}{a}} + e^{\frac{-x}{a}}\right)}{2}$$

The catenary is often used in architecture. The Gateway Arch in St. Louis, Missouri, United States is an example of such a structure.

Investigate how you might calculate the length of a catenary.

Research

Research how you can use spherical polar coordinates and integration to find the surface area of a sphere.

1 **a** Given $I_n = \int (\ln x)^n dx$, show that, for $n \geq 1$, $I_n = x(\ln x) - nI_{n-1}$ [4]

b Hence evaluate $\int_1^4 (\ln x)^3 dx$ [6]

2 **a** Given $I_n = \int \tanh^n x dx$, show that, for $n \geq 2$, $I_n = I_{n-2} - \dfrac{\tanh^{n-1} x}{n-1}$ [3]

b Hence find an expression for $\int \tanh^8 x dx$ [5]

3 A curve, C, has Cartesian equation $y = 3x^2$

a Show that the length of the arc from (0, 0) to (1, 3) is $\dfrac{1}{12}(\ln(6+\sqrt{37})+6\sqrt{37})$ [9]

The arc of the curve from (0, 0) to (1, 3) is rotated through 2π radians around the y-axis.

b Calculate the surface area of revolution. [6]

4 An arc of a curve is given parametrically by the equations $x = a\cos^3 t$, $y = a\sin^3 t$, for $0 \leq t \leq \dfrac{\pi}{2}$. The points A and B on the curve correspond to the values $t = 0$ and $t = \dfrac{\pi}{2}$ respectively.

a Find the length of the arc, AB, of the curve. [6]

b Find the area of the curved surface generated when this arc is rotated through 2π radians about the x-axis. [5]

5 Given $I_n = \int x^n \cos x dx$

a Show that $I_n = x^n \sin x + nx^{n-1} \cos x - n(n-1)I_{n-2}$ [3]

b Use the formula to find $\int x^3 \cos x dx$ [3]

c Use the formula to evaluate $\int_0^\pi x^6 \cos x dx$. Give your answer in terms of π [4]

6 The section of the curve $y = \dfrac{1}{3}\ln x$ between $x = 1$ and $x = 8$ is rotated through 2π radians around the y-axis.

Calculate the area of the surface produced. Give your answer to 3 significant figures. [7]

7 A curve is defined using polar coordinates as $r = 1 + 2\cos\theta$

a Sketch the curve for $0 \leq \theta \leq \pi$ [2]

b Show that the length of the arc from $\theta = 0$ to $\theta = \pi$ is given by the integral $1\int_0^\pi \sqrt{5+4\cos\theta}d\theta$ [3]

8 An arc, L, of a parabola is given parametrically by the equations $x = at^2$, $y = 2at$, for $0 \leq t \leq 2$
L is rotated through 2π radians about the x-axis.

   a Show that the area of the surface of revolution is given by $8\pi a^2 \int_0^2 t\sqrt{1+t^2}\,dt$ **[3]**

   b Find this surface area.   **[3]**

   c Show also that the length of L is given by $2a\int_0^2 \sqrt{1+t^2}\,dt$ **[3]**

   d Find this length.   **[8]**

9 The curve C is defined using polar coordinates as $r = 2\theta$

   Calculate the length of the arc of the curve from $r = 0$ to $r = 4$ **[7]**

10 a Given $I_n = \int_0^{\frac{\pi}{2}} \sin^n x\,dx$, show that, for $n \geq 2$, $nI_n = (n-1)I_{n-2}$ **[6]**

   The region R is bounded by the curve $y = \sin^4 x$ and the x-axis, between $x = 0$ and $x = \dfrac{\pi}{2}$

   b Find the area of R **[4]**

   c Find the volume generated when R is rotated through 2π radians about the x-axis.   **[4]**

11 The curve C is defined using polar coordinates as $r = \sin\theta$

   a Sketch C for $0 \leq \theta \leq 2\pi$ **[2]**

   b Hence use the formula for arc length, $s = \int_{\theta_1}^{\theta_2} \sqrt{r^2 + \left(\dfrac{dr}{d\theta}\right)^2}\,d\theta$, and the equation $r = \sin\theta$ to

   show that the circumference of the circle is π **[3]**

   c Show that the surface area of revolution when the section of C between $\theta = 0$ and $\theta = \dfrac{\pi}{6}$

   is rotated through 2π radians around the initial line is $\pi\left(\dfrac{\pi}{6} - \dfrac{\sqrt{3}}{4}\right)$ **[3]**

12 Use integration to calculate the surface area of the volume formed when the curve

with polar equation $r = 3\cos\theta$ for $0 \leq \theta \leq \dfrac{\pi}{2}$ is rotated through π radians around the polar axis. **[5]**

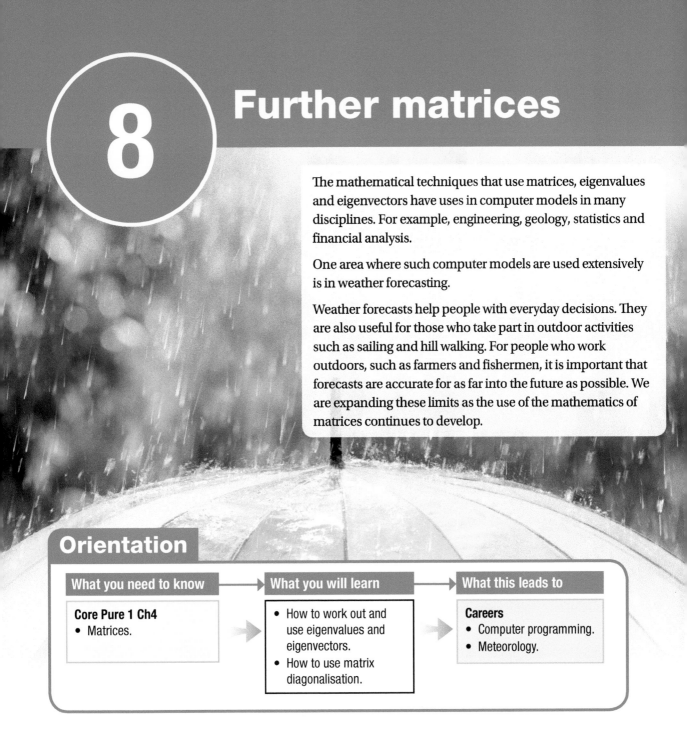

8 Further matrices

The mathematical techniques that use matrices, eigenvalues and eigenvectors have uses in computer models in many disciplines. For example, engineering, geology, statistics and financial analysis.

One area where such computer models are used extensively is in weather forecasting.

Weather forecasts help people with everyday decisions. They are also useful for those who take part in outdoor activities such as sailing and hill walking. For people who work outdoors, such as farmers and fishermen, it is important that forecasts are accurate for as far into the future as possible. We are expanding these limits as the use of the mathematics of matrices continues to develop.

Orientation

What you need to know	What you will learn	What this leads to
Core Pure 1 Ch4 • Matrices.	• How to work out and use eigenvalues and eigenvectors. • How to use matrix diagonalisation.	**Careers** • Computer programming. • Meteorology.

Fluency and skills

A vector whose direction is maintained under a transformation is known as an **eigenvector**. If the matrix used for the transformation is **A**, then, when the vector **x** is transformed using **A**, the result is a multiple of **x**

> **Key point**
>
> **Eigenvectors** of the square matrix **A** are non-zero vectors that satisfy the equation $\mathbf{Ax} = \lambda\mathbf{x}$
>
> λ is a scalar known as the **eigenvalue**.

You can rearrange the equation $\mathbf{Ax} = \lambda\mathbf{x}$ to give $\mathbf{Ax} - \lambda\mathbf{Ix} = 0$ since $\mathbf{x} = \mathbf{Ix}$

Then factorise to give $(\mathbf{A} - \lambda\mathbf{I})\mathbf{x} = 0$

Since **x** is a non-zero vector, it must be the case that the matrix $\mathbf{A} - \lambda\mathbf{I}$ is singular. Therefore $\det(\mathbf{A} - \lambda\mathbf{I}) = 0$

> You need to write $\lambda\mathbf{x}$ as $\lambda\mathbf{Ix}$, where **I** is an identity matrix with the same dimensions as **A** in order to be able to carry out the subtraction.

> **Key point**
>
> The equation $\det(\mathbf{A} - \lambda\mathbf{I}) = 0$ is the **characteristic equation** of **A** and is used to find the eigenvalues.

Example 1

Find the eigenvalues and corresponding eigenvectors of the matrix $\mathbf{A} = \begin{pmatrix} 3 & -1 \\ 4 & -2 \end{pmatrix}$

$$\mathbf{A} - \lambda\mathbf{I} = \begin{pmatrix} 3 & -1 \\ 4 & -2 \end{pmatrix} - \lambda \begin{pmatrix} 1 & 0 \\ 0 & 1 \end{pmatrix}$$

$$= \begin{pmatrix} 3-\lambda & -1 \\ 4 & -2-\lambda \end{pmatrix}$$

$$\det(\mathbf{A} - \lambda\mathbf{I}) = (3-\lambda)(-2-\lambda) - -4$$

$$\lambda^2 - \lambda - 2 = 0$$

$$(\lambda - 2)(\lambda + 1) = 0$$

$$\lambda = 2, -1$$

$$\begin{pmatrix} 3 & -1 \\ 4 & -2 \end{pmatrix}\begin{pmatrix} a \\ b \end{pmatrix} = 2\begin{pmatrix} a \\ b \end{pmatrix}$$

$$3a - b = 2a \Rightarrow a = b$$

$$4a - 2b = 2b \Rightarrow 4a = 4b$$

Solve the equation $\det(\mathbf{A} - \lambda\mathbf{I}) = 0$ to find the possible values of λ

These are the eigenvalues.

Use $\mathbf{Ax} = \lambda\mathbf{x}$ with $\mathbf{x} = \begin{pmatrix} a \\ b \end{pmatrix}$ and $\lambda = 2$ to find the possible vectors **x**

Both equations give $a = b$

(Continued on the next page)

So a possible eigenvector corresponding to the eigenvalue 2 is $\begin{pmatrix} 1 \\ 1 \end{pmatrix}$

$$\begin{pmatrix} 3 & -1 \\ 4 & -2 \end{pmatrix}\begin{pmatrix} a \\ b \end{pmatrix} = -1\begin{pmatrix} a \\ b \end{pmatrix}$$

$3a - b = -a \Rightarrow 4a = b$

$4a - 2b = -b \Rightarrow 4a = b$

So a possible eigenvector corresponding to the

eigenvalue -1 is $\begin{pmatrix} 1 \\ 4 \end{pmatrix}$

> Repeat process with $\lambda = -1$ to find the possible vectors **x**

> Both equations give
> $4a = b$

> Any non-zero multiples of these will also be eigenvectors.

Example 2

Find the eigenvalues and eigenvectors of $\begin{pmatrix} 1 & 2 \\ -3 & 1 \end{pmatrix}$

> Eigenvalues can be complex numbers.

$$\det\begin{pmatrix} 1-\lambda & 2 \\ -3 & 1-\lambda \end{pmatrix} = 0 \Rightarrow (1-\lambda)(1-\lambda) - -6 = 0$$

$\lambda^2 - 2\lambda + 7 = 0$

Solve the equation to give $\lambda = 1 \pm i\sqrt{6}$

$$\begin{pmatrix} 1 & 2 \\ -3 & 1 \end{pmatrix}\begin{pmatrix} a \\ b \end{pmatrix} = (1+i\sqrt{6})\begin{pmatrix} a \\ b \end{pmatrix}$$

$a + 2b = (1+i\sqrt{6})a \Rightarrow b = \dfrac{i\sqrt{6}}{2}a$

$-3a + b = (1+i\sqrt{6})b \Rightarrow b = \dfrac{i\sqrt{6}}{2}a$

So an eigenvector is $\begin{pmatrix} 1 \\ \dfrac{i\sqrt{6}}{2} \end{pmatrix}$

$$\begin{pmatrix} 1 & 2 \\ -3 & 1 \end{pmatrix}\begin{pmatrix} a \\ b \end{pmatrix} = (1-i\sqrt{6})\begin{pmatrix} a \\ b \end{pmatrix}$$

$a + 2b = (1-i\sqrt{6})a \Rightarrow b = -\dfrac{i\sqrt{6}}{2}a$

$-3a + b = (1-i\sqrt{6})b \Rightarrow b = -\dfrac{i\sqrt{6}}{2}a$

So another eigenvector is $\begin{pmatrix} 1 \\ -\dfrac{i\sqrt{6}}{2} \end{pmatrix}$

You can also find the **normalised eigenvectors** by dividing the eigenvector by its magnitude. Here are some examples.

$$\left\| \begin{pmatrix} 1 \\ -1 \\ 0 \end{pmatrix} \right\| = \sqrt{1^2 + 1^2 + 0^2} = \sqrt{2}, \text{ so a normalised eigenvector is } \begin{pmatrix} \dfrac{1}{\sqrt{2}} \\ -\dfrac{1}{\sqrt{2}} \\ 0 \end{pmatrix}$$

$$\left\| \begin{pmatrix} 5 \\ 1 \\ -2 \end{pmatrix} \right\| = \sqrt{5^2 + 1^2 + 2^2} = \sqrt{30}, \text{ so a normalised eigenvector is } \begin{pmatrix} \dfrac{5}{\sqrt{30}} \\ \dfrac{1}{\sqrt{30}} \\ -\dfrac{2}{\sqrt{30}} \end{pmatrix}$$

$$\left\| \begin{pmatrix} 2 \\ 1 \\ 0 \end{pmatrix} \right\| = \sqrt{2^2 + 1^2 + 0^2} = \sqrt{5}, \text{ so a normalised eigenvector is } \begin{pmatrix} \dfrac{2}{\sqrt{5}} \\ \dfrac{1}{\sqrt{5}} \\ 0 \end{pmatrix}$$

Key point

A **normalised vector** has a magnitude of 1. It is also known as a **unit** vector.

Example 3

Find the eigenvalues and normalised eigenvectors of $\mathbf{A} = \begin{pmatrix} 6 & -3 \\ -8 & 4 \end{pmatrix}$

$\det \begin{pmatrix} 6-\lambda & -3 \\ -8 & 4-\lambda \end{pmatrix} = 0 \Rightarrow (6-\lambda)(4-\lambda) - 24 = 0$ ← Use $\det(\mathbf{A} - \lambda\mathbf{I}) = 0$

$\lambda^2 - 10\lambda + 24 - 24 = 0$

$\lambda^2 - 10\lambda = 0$

$\lambda(\lambda - 10) = 0$

Therefore $\lambda = 0, 10$ are the eigenvalues ← An eigenvalue can be zero but an eigenvector is a non-zero vector.

$\begin{pmatrix} 6 & -3 \\ -8 & 4 \end{pmatrix} \begin{pmatrix} a \\ b \end{pmatrix} = 0 \begin{pmatrix} a \\ b \end{pmatrix}$

$6a - 3b = 0 \Rightarrow 2a = b$

(Continued on the next page)

So an eigenvector corresponding to the eigenvalue 0 is $\begin{pmatrix} 1 \\ 2 \end{pmatrix}$

The magnitude of this vector is $\sqrt{1^2 + 2^2} = \sqrt{5}$

Therefore a normalised eigenvector is $\begin{pmatrix} \dfrac{1}{\sqrt{5}} \\ \dfrac{2}{\sqrt{5}} \end{pmatrix}$ ●————— Divide by the magnitude.

$\begin{pmatrix} 6 & -3 \\ -8 & 4 \end{pmatrix} \begin{pmatrix} a \\ b \end{pmatrix} = 10 \begin{pmatrix} a \\ b \end{pmatrix}$

$6a - 3b = 10a \Rightarrow -3b = 4a$

So an eigenvector corresponding to the eigenvalue 10 is $\begin{pmatrix} 3 \\ -4 \end{pmatrix}$

The magnitude of this vector is $\sqrt{3^2 + 4^2} = 5$

Therefore a normalised eigenvector is $\begin{pmatrix} \dfrac{3}{5} \\ -\dfrac{4}{5} \end{pmatrix}$ ●————— This is a unit vector (has a magnitude of 1).

The same process can be used for any square matrix **A**; you will need to be able to find eigenvalues and eigenvectors of 2×2 and 3×3 matrices.

Example 4

Find the eigenvalues and eigenvectors of the matrix $\mathbf{T} = \begin{pmatrix} 2 & 2 & 1 \\ 1 & 1 & 2 \\ 0 & 0 & 2 \end{pmatrix}$

$\begin{vmatrix} 2-\lambda & 2 & 1 \\ 1 & 1-\lambda & 2 \\ 0 & 0 & 2-\lambda \end{vmatrix} = (2-\lambda)[(1-\lambda)(2-\lambda)-0] - 2[(2-\lambda)-0] + [0-0]$

$(2-\lambda)(\lambda^2 - 3\lambda + 2) - 2(2-\lambda) = 0$ ●————— Calculate the determinant and simplify.

$(2-\lambda)(\lambda^2 - 3\lambda + 2 - 2) = 0$

$(2-\lambda)(\lambda^2 - 3\lambda) = 0$ ————— Solve det(**A** − λ**I**) = 0 to find the eigenvalues.

$\lambda(2-\lambda)(\lambda - 3) = 0$ ●—————

(Continued on the next page)

$\lambda = 0, 2, 3$ are the eigenvalues

$$\begin{pmatrix} 2 & 2 & 1 \\ 1 & 1 & 2 \\ 0 & 0 & 2 \end{pmatrix} \begin{pmatrix} a \\ b \\ c \end{pmatrix} = 0 \begin{pmatrix} a \\ b \\ c \end{pmatrix}$$

Use $\mathbf{Ax} = \lambda\mathbf{x}$ with $\mathbf{x} = \begin{pmatrix} a \\ b \\ c \end{pmatrix}$ and $\lambda = 0$ to find the possible vectors $\mathbf{x}$

$2a + 2b + c = 0$

$a + b + 2c = 0$

$2c = 0 \Rightarrow c = 0$

$a + b = 0$ so $a = -b$

So a possible eigenvector corresponding to the eigenvalue 0 is $\begin{pmatrix} 1 \\ -1 \\ 0 \end{pmatrix}$

$$\begin{pmatrix} 2 & 2 & 1 \\ 1 & 1 & 2 \\ 0 & 0 & 2 \end{pmatrix} \begin{pmatrix} a \\ b \\ c \end{pmatrix} = 2 \begin{pmatrix} a \\ b \\ c \end{pmatrix}$$

$2a + 2b + c = 2a \Rightarrow c = -2b$

Repeat the process with $\lambda = 2$ to find a possible vector $\mathbf{x}$

$a + b + 2c = 2b \Rightarrow a + b + 2(-2b) = 2b \Rightarrow a = 5b$

$2c = 2c$

So a possible eigenvector corresponding to the eigenvalue 2 is $\begin{pmatrix} 5 \\ 1 \\ -2 \end{pmatrix}$

$$\begin{pmatrix} 2 & 2 & 1 \\ 1 & 1 & 2 \\ 0 & 0 & 2 \end{pmatrix} \begin{pmatrix} a \\ b \\ c \end{pmatrix} = 3 \begin{pmatrix} a \\ b \\ c \end{pmatrix}$$

Repeat the process with $\lambda = 3$ to find a possible vector $\mathbf{x}$

$2c = 3c \Rightarrow c = C$

$2a + 2b + c = 3a \Rightarrow a = 2b$

$a + b + 2c = 3b \Rightarrow a = 2b$

So a possible eigenvector corresponding to the eigenvalue 3 is $\begin{pmatrix} 2 \\ 1 \\ 0 \end{pmatrix}$

The eigenvectors are $\begin{pmatrix} 1 \\ -1 \\ 0 \end{pmatrix}$, $\begin{pmatrix} 5 \\ 1 \\ -2 \end{pmatrix}$ and $\begin{pmatrix} 2 \\ 1 \\ 0 \end{pmatrix}$

Example 5

The eigenvalues of the matrix $\mathbf{A} = \begin{pmatrix} 4 & -3 & 3 \\ 6 & -5 & 3 \\ 0 & 0 & -2 \end{pmatrix}$ are $-2, -2$ and 1

Find 3 non-parallel eigenvectors of $\mathbf{A}$

$\begin{pmatrix} 4 & -3 & 3 \\ 6 & -5 & 3 \\ 0 & 0 & -2 \end{pmatrix} \begin{pmatrix} a \\ b \\ c \end{pmatrix} = \begin{pmatrix} a \\ b \\ c \end{pmatrix}$

Use $\mathbf{Av} = \mathbf{v}$ to find the eigenvectors corresponding to the eigenvalue of 1

$-2c = c \Rightarrow z = 0$
$4a - 3b + 3c = a \Rightarrow 3a - 3b = 0$

Since $z = 0$

$\Rightarrow a = b$

Therefore an eigenvector corresponding to the eigenvalue

of 1 is $\begin{pmatrix} 1 \\ 1 \\ 0 \end{pmatrix}$

$\begin{pmatrix} 4 & -3 & 3 \\ 6 & -5 & 3 \\ 0 & 0 & -2 \end{pmatrix} \begin{pmatrix} a \\ b \\ c \end{pmatrix} = -2 \begin{pmatrix} a \\ b \\ c \end{pmatrix}$

Use $\mathbf{Av} = -2\mathbf{v}$ to find the eigenvectors corresponding to the eigenvalue of -2

$4a - 3b + 3c = -2a \Rightarrow 6a - 3b + 3c = 0$

$\Rightarrow 2a - b + c = 0$

This is the same as the first equation.

$6a - 5b + 3c = -2b \Rightarrow 6a - 3b + 3c = 0$

$-2c = -2c$

This just tells you that c can be any value.

If $a = 0$, then $b = c$, so an eigenvector corresponding to the

eigenvalue of -2 is $\begin{pmatrix} 0 \\ 1 \\ 1 \end{pmatrix}$

If $c = 0$, then $2a = b$, so another eigenvector corresponding

to the eigenvalue of -2 is $\begin{pmatrix} 1 \\ 2 \\ 0 \end{pmatrix}$

These eigenvectors are non-parallel.

Key point

The **Cayley–Hamilton theorem** states that a matrix satisfies its own **characteristic equation**.

To prove this for any 2×2 matrix, consider $\mathbf{A} = \begin{pmatrix} a & b \\ c & d \end{pmatrix}$

The characteristic equation is $\det(\mathbf{A} - \lambda\mathbf{I}) = 0$ which leads to $(a-\lambda)(d-\lambda) - bc = 0$

Expanding the brackets gives $\lambda^2 - (a+d)\lambda + (ad - bc) = 0$

Now replace λ by matrix $\mathbf{A}$

$$\begin{pmatrix} a & b \\ c & d \end{pmatrix}^2 - (a+d)\begin{pmatrix} a & b \\ c & d \end{pmatrix} + (ad-bc)\begin{pmatrix} 1 & 0 \\ 0 & 1 \end{pmatrix}$$

$$= \begin{pmatrix} a^2+bc & ab+bd \\ ac+cd & bc+d^2 \end{pmatrix} - \begin{pmatrix} a^2+ad & ab+bd \\ ac+cd & ad+d^2 \end{pmatrix} + \begin{pmatrix} ad-bc & 0 \\ 0 & ad-bc \end{pmatrix}$$

$$= \begin{pmatrix} a^2+bc-a^2-ad+ad-bc & ab+bd-ab-bd \\ ac+cd-ac-cd & bc+d^2-ad-d^2+ad-bc \end{pmatrix}$$

$$= \begin{pmatrix} 0 & 0 \\ 0 & 0 \end{pmatrix} \text{ as required}$$

> Notice that this term is multiplied by the identity matrix, $\mathbf{I}$ Otherwise you would be trying to add a constant to a matrix, which isn't possible.

Example 6

Verify the Cayley–Hamilton theorem for the matrix $\mathbf{A} = \begin{pmatrix} 1 & 0 \\ 2 & 3 \end{pmatrix}$

$\det\begin{pmatrix} 1-\lambda & 0 \\ 2 & 3-\lambda \end{pmatrix} = 0 \Rightarrow (1-\lambda)(3-\lambda) - 0 = 0$

Which becomes $\lambda^2 - 4\lambda + 3 = 0$

$$\begin{pmatrix} 1 & 0 \\ 2 & 3 \end{pmatrix}^2 - 4\begin{pmatrix} 1 & 0 \\ 2 & 3 \end{pmatrix} + 3\begin{pmatrix} 1 & 0 \\ 0 & 1 \end{pmatrix} = \begin{pmatrix} 1 & 0 \\ 8 & 9 \end{pmatrix} - \begin{pmatrix} 4 & 0 \\ 8 & 12 \end{pmatrix} + \begin{pmatrix} 3 & 0 \\ 0 & 3 \end{pmatrix}$$

$$= \begin{pmatrix} 1-4+3 & 0-0+0 \\ 8-8+0 & 9-12+3 \end{pmatrix}$$

$$= \begin{pmatrix} 0 & 0 \\ 0 & 0 \end{pmatrix} \text{ as required}$$

> Replace λ with the matrix $\mathbf{A}$
>
> You need to replace 3 by 3$\mathbf{I}$, where $\mathbf{I}$ is the 2×2 identity matrix.

Example 7

$$\mathbf{M} = \begin{pmatrix} 1 & 2 & 0 \\ 3 & 0 & -1 \\ 0 & 0 & -2 \end{pmatrix}$$

a Show that the characteristic equation of $\mathbf{M}$ is $-\lambda^3 - \lambda^2 + 8\lambda + 12 = 0$

b Show that $\mathbf{M}$ satisfies its own characteristic equation.

(Continued on the next page)

a $\det\begin{pmatrix} 1-\lambda & 2 & 0 \\ 3 & -\lambda & -1 \\ 0 & 0 & -2-\lambda \end{pmatrix}=0$

Use $\det(\mathbf{M}-\lambda\mathbf{I})=0$

$$\Rightarrow (1-\lambda)[(-\lambda)(-2-\lambda)+0]-2[3(-2-\lambda)-0]+0=0$$

$$\lambda(1-\lambda)(2+\lambda)+6(2+\lambda)=0$$

$$2\lambda+\lambda^2-2\lambda^2-\lambda^3+12+6\lambda=0$$

$$-\lambda^3-\lambda^2+8\lambda+12=0 \text{ as required}$$

b $-\mathbf{M}^3-\mathbf{M}^2+8\mathbf{M}+12\mathbf{I}=-\begin{pmatrix} 1 & 2 & 0 \\ 3 & 0 & -1 \\ 0 & 0 & -2 \end{pmatrix}^3-\begin{pmatrix} 1 & 2 & 0 \\ 3 & 0 & -1 \\ 0 & 0 & -2 \end{pmatrix}^2$

Substitute M into the LHS of the characteristic equation.

$$+8\begin{pmatrix} 1 & 2 & 0 \\ 3 & 0 & -1 \\ 0 & 0 & -2 \end{pmatrix}+12\begin{pmatrix} 1 & 0 & 0 \\ 0 & 1 & 0 \\ 0 & 0 & 1 \end{pmatrix}$$

$$=-\begin{pmatrix} 13 & 14 & 2 \\ 21 & 6 & -10 \\ 0 & 0 & -8 \end{pmatrix}-\begin{pmatrix} 7 & 2 & -2 \\ 3 & 6 & 2 \\ 0 & 0 & 4 \end{pmatrix}$$

Work out $\mathbf{M}^3$ and $\mathbf{M}^2$

$$+\begin{pmatrix} 8 & 16 & 0 \\ 24 & 0 & -8 \\ 0 & 0 & -16 \end{pmatrix}+\begin{pmatrix} 12 & 0 & 0 \\ 0 & 12 & 0 \\ 0 & 0 & 12 \end{pmatrix}$$

$$=\begin{pmatrix} -13-7+8+12 & -14-2+16 & -2+2 \\ -21-3+24 & -6-6+12 & 10-2-8 \\ 0 & 0 & 8-4-16+12 \end{pmatrix}$$

$$=\begin{pmatrix} 0 & 0 & 0 \\ 0 & 0 & 0 \\ 0 & 0 & 0 \end{pmatrix} \text{so } \mathbf{M} \text{ satisfies its own characteristic equation.}$$

Exercise 8.1A Fluency and skills

1 Find the eigenvalues and eigenvectors for each of these matrices.

a $\begin{pmatrix} 2 & 3 \\ 0 & -4 \end{pmatrix}$ **b** $\begin{pmatrix} 3 & -1 \\ 4 & -2 \end{pmatrix}$

2 Find the eigenvalues and eigenvectors for each of these matrices.

a $\begin{pmatrix} 1 & 0 & -5 \\ 4 & 5 & 1 \\ 0 & 0 & -3 \end{pmatrix}$ **b** $\begin{pmatrix} 1 & 3 & 0 \\ 2 & 0 & 1 \\ 0 & 0 & 2 \end{pmatrix}$

3 a Find the eigenvalues and normalised eigenvectors for each of these matrices.

i $\begin{pmatrix} 3 & 0 \\ 3 & 7 \end{pmatrix}$ **ii** $\begin{pmatrix} 4 & -5 \\ -1 & 0 \end{pmatrix}$

iii $\begin{pmatrix} 5 & -3 & 0 \\ 0 & 2 & 0 \\ 0 & -5 & -4 \end{pmatrix}$ **iv** $\begin{pmatrix} -7 & 0 & 0 \\ 5 & 4 & 1 \\ 4 & 0 & 9 \end{pmatrix}$

b Demonstrate that each of the matrices in part **a** satisfies its own characteristic equation.

4 Find the eigenvalues and eigenvectors for each of these matrices.

a $\begin{pmatrix} 0 & 1 \\ -1 & 0 \end{pmatrix}$ **b** $\begin{pmatrix} 3 & 2 \\ -4 & -1 \end{pmatrix}$

c $\begin{pmatrix} 3 & 0 & 0 \\ 0 & 2 & 1 \\ 1 & -2 & 4 \end{pmatrix}$ **d** $\begin{pmatrix} 1 & -1 & 0 \\ 1 & 0 & 0 \\ 0 & 0 & 1 \end{pmatrix}$

5 Given that $\mathbf{A} = \begin{pmatrix} 1 & 3 & -1 \\ -2 & 3 & 2 \\ 1 & 0 & 2 \end{pmatrix}$, show that 3 is the only real eigenvalue of $\mathbf{A}$ and find the normalised eigenvector corresponding to it.

6 Given that $\mathbf{A} = \begin{pmatrix} -2 & 6 & -3 \\ 3 & 2 & 6 \\ 2 & 6 & -3 \end{pmatrix}$

a Show that −7 is an eigenvalue of $\mathbf{A}$ and find the other two eigenvalues.

b Find the eigenvector corresponding to the eigenvalue −7

7 Verify the Cayley–Hamilton theorem for each of these matrices.

a $\begin{pmatrix} 1 & 4 \\ 2 & -3 \end{pmatrix}$ **b** $\begin{pmatrix} 5 & 7 \\ -4 & 1 \end{pmatrix}$

c $\begin{pmatrix} 4 & 0 & 1 \\ 6 & 2 & 0 \\ 0 & 1 & 0 \end{pmatrix}$ **d** $\begin{pmatrix} 1 & 0 & 0 \\ 2 & 0 & 0 \\ 0 & 1 & 0 \end{pmatrix}$

8 The matrix $\mathbf{T} = \begin{pmatrix} 9 & -5 & -10 \\ 25 & -21 & -10 \\ 0 & 0 & -16 \end{pmatrix}$ has a repeated eigenvalue of −16

a Find the other eigenvalue of $\mathbf{T}$

b Find two non-parallel eigenvectors corresponding to the repeated eigenvalue of −16

9 Find

a The eigenvalues,

b Three non-parallel eigenvectors of the matrix $\begin{pmatrix} -10 & 0 & 5 \\ 0 & 10 & 0 \\ 20 & 0 & 5 \end{pmatrix}$

Reasoning and problem-solving

The Cayley–Hamilton theorem can be used to find $\mathbf{A}^n$ or $\mathbf{A}^{-1}$ for a given matrix $\mathbf{A}$

Strategy

To raise a matrix to a power of $\mathbf{A}$

(1) Find the characteristic equation.

(2) Apply the Cayley–Hamilton (C–H) theorem.

(3) Rearrange the characteristic equation.

(4) Multiply both sides of the characteristic equation by a power of $\mathbf{A}$

Example 8

Given that $\mathbf{A} = \begin{pmatrix} 1 & 3 \\ 2 & -2 \end{pmatrix}$, use the Cayley-Hamilton theorem to find each of these matrices.

a $\mathbf{A}^2$

b $\mathbf{A}^3$

c $\mathbf{A}^{-1}$

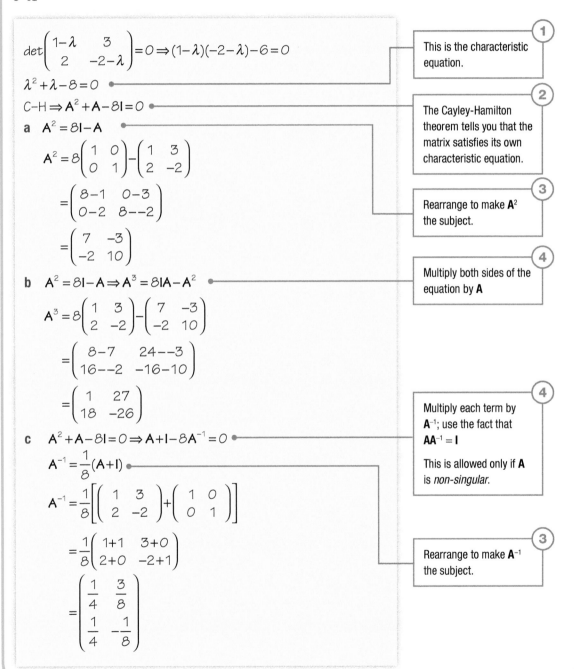

$det\begin{pmatrix} 1-\lambda & 3 \\ 2 & -2-\lambda \end{pmatrix} = 0 \Rightarrow (1-\lambda)(-2-\lambda)-6=0$

(1) This is the characteristic equation.

$\lambda^2 + \lambda - 8 = 0$

$C-H \Rightarrow A^2 + A - 8I = 0$

(2) The Cayley-Hamilton theorem tells you that the matrix satisfies its own characteristic equation.

a $A^2 = 8I - A$

$A^2 = 8\begin{pmatrix} 1 & 0 \\ 0 & 1 \end{pmatrix} - \begin{pmatrix} 1 & 3 \\ 2 & -2 \end{pmatrix}$

(3) Rearrange to make $\mathbf{A}^2$ the subject.

$= \begin{pmatrix} 8-1 & 0-3 \\ 0-2 & 8--2 \end{pmatrix}$

$= \begin{pmatrix} 7 & -3 \\ -2 & 10 \end{pmatrix}$

b $A^2 = 8I - A \Rightarrow A^3 = 8IA - A^2$

(4) Multiply both sides of the equation by $\mathbf{A}$

$A^3 = 8\begin{pmatrix} 1 & 3 \\ 2 & -2 \end{pmatrix} - \begin{pmatrix} 7 & -3 \\ -2 & 10 \end{pmatrix}$

$= \begin{pmatrix} 8-7 & 24--3 \\ 16--2 & -16-10 \end{pmatrix}$

$= \begin{pmatrix} 1 & 27 \\ 18 & -26 \end{pmatrix}$

c $A^2 + A - 8I = 0 \Rightarrow A + I - 8A^{-1} = 0$

(4) Multiply each term by $\mathbf{A}^{-1}$; use the fact that $\mathbf{AA}^{-1} = \mathbf{I}$

This is allowed only if $\mathbf{A}$ is *non-singular*.

$A^{-1} = \frac{1}{8}(A+I)$

$A^{-1} = \frac{1}{8}\left[\begin{pmatrix} 1 & 3 \\ 2 & -2 \end{pmatrix} + \begin{pmatrix} 1 & 0 \\ 0 & 1 \end{pmatrix} \right]$

(3) Rearrange to make $\mathbf{A}^{-1}$ the subject.

$= \frac{1}{8}\begin{pmatrix} 1+1 & 3+0 \\ 2+0 & -2+1 \end{pmatrix}$

$= \begin{pmatrix} \frac{1}{4} & \frac{3}{8} \\ \frac{1}{4} & -\frac{1}{8} \end{pmatrix}$

Example 9

$$\mathbf{M} = \begin{pmatrix} 20 & -16 & -8 \\ 14 & -10 & -1 \\ -8 & 28 & 6 \end{pmatrix}$$

Given that the characteristic polynomial of **M** is $-\lambda^3 + 16\lambda^2 - 48\lambda - 1920$, use the Cayley–Hamilton theorem to find the matrix $\mathbf{M}^{-1}$

$$-\mathbf{M}^3 + 16\mathbf{M}^2 - 48\mathbf{M} - 1920\mathbf{I} = 0$$

Since the Cayley–Hamilton theorem tells you that M satisfies its own characteristic equation.

$$\Rightarrow -\mathbf{M}^3\mathbf{M}^{-1} + 16\mathbf{M}^2\mathbf{M}^{-1} - 48\mathbf{M}\mathbf{M}^{-1} - 1920\mathbf{I}\mathbf{M}^{-1} = 0$$

$$\Rightarrow -\mathbf{M}^2 + 16\mathbf{M} - 48\mathbf{I} - 1920\mathbf{M}^{-1} = 0$$

$$\Rightarrow 1920\mathbf{M}^{-1} = -\mathbf{M}^2 + 16\mathbf{M} - 48\mathbf{I}$$

Multiply each term by **M**$^{-1}$

$$= -\begin{pmatrix} 20 & -16 & -8 \\ 14 & -10 & -1 \\ -8 & 28 & 6 \end{pmatrix}^2 + 16\begin{pmatrix} 20 & -16 & -8 \\ 14 & -10 & -1 \\ -8 & 28 & 6 \end{pmatrix}$$

$$-48\begin{pmatrix} 1 & 0 & 0 \\ 0 & 1 & 0 \\ 0 & 0 & 1 \end{pmatrix}$$

$$= -\begin{pmatrix} 240 & -384 & -192 \\ 148 & -152 & -108 \\ 184 & 16 & 72 \end{pmatrix} + \begin{pmatrix} 320 & -256 & -128 \\ 224 & -160 & -16 \\ -128 & 448 & 96 \end{pmatrix}$$

$$-\begin{pmatrix} 48 & 0 & 0 \\ 0 & 48 & 0 \\ 0 & 0 & 48 \end{pmatrix}$$

$$= \begin{pmatrix} 32 & 128 & 64 \\ 76 & -56 & 92 \\ -312 & 432 & -24 \end{pmatrix}$$

$$\Rightarrow \mathbf{M}^{-1} = \frac{1}{1920}\begin{pmatrix} 32 & 128 & 64 \\ 76 & -56 & 92 \\ -312 & 432 & -24 \end{pmatrix} = \frac{1}{480}\begin{pmatrix} 8 & 32 & 16 \\ 19 & -14 & 23 \\ -78 & 108 & -6 \end{pmatrix}$$

Example 10

The characteristic equation of a matrix, **M**, is $\lambda^2 - 3\lambda + 4 = 0$

Find the values of a and b such that $\mathbf{M}^4 = a\mathbf{M}^2 + b\mathbf{M}$

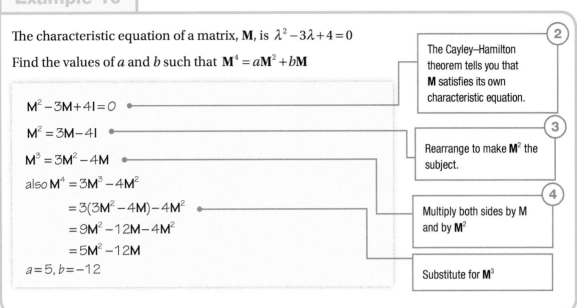

$M^2 - 3M + 4I = 0$ •————————————————— The Cayley–Hamilton theorem tells you that **M** satisfies its own characteristic equation. ②

$M^2 = 3M - 4I$ •————————————————— Rearrange to make $\mathbf{M}^2$ the subject. ③

$M^3 = 3M^2 - 4M$ •

also $M^4 = 3M^3 - 4M^2$

$\quad\quad = 3(3M^2 - 4M) - 4M^2$ •————————— Multiply both sides by M and by $\mathbf{M}^2$ ④

$\quad\quad = 9M^2 - 12M - 4M^2$

$\quad\quad = 5M^2 - 12M$

$a = 5, b = -12$ ————————————————————— Substitute for $\mathbf{M}^3$

Exercise 8.1B Reasoning and problem-solving

1 Given that $\mathbf{A} = \begin{pmatrix} -6 & -5 \\ 4 & 7 \end{pmatrix}$

    a Work out the characteristic equation of $\mathbf{A}$

    b Use the Cayley–Hamilton theorem to find each of these matrices.

        i $\mathbf{A}^2$ **ii** $\mathbf{A}^3$ **iii** $\mathbf{A}^{-1}$

2 Given that $\mathbf{B} = \begin{pmatrix} 1 & 9 \\ 2 & -3 \end{pmatrix}$, use the Cayley–Hamilton theorem to find the inverse of $\mathbf{B}$

3 Given that $\mathbf{M} = \begin{pmatrix} k & 1 \\ 2 & 0 \end{pmatrix}$

    a Find the characteristic equation of $\mathbf{M}$ in terms of k

    b Hence find $\mathbf{M}^3$ and $\mathbf{M}^{-1}$ in terms of k

4 $\mathbf{M} = \begin{pmatrix} a & 0 & 1 \\ -1 & 2 & 3 \\ -1 & 0 & -2 \end{pmatrix}$

    a Show that $\mathbf{M}^2 = \begin{pmatrix} a^2-1 & 0 & a-2 \\ -a-5 & 4 & -1 \\ 2-a & 0 & 3 \end{pmatrix}$

Given that $a = 2$

b Show that the characteristic equation of **M** is $\lambda^3 - 2\lambda^2 - 3\lambda + 6 = 0$

c Use the Cayley–Hamilton theorem to show that $\mathbf{M}^3 = \begin{pmatrix} 6 & 0 & 3 \\ -17 & 8 & 7 \\ -3 & 0 & -6 \end{pmatrix}$

d Hence find

    i $\mathbf{M}^4$ **ii** $\mathbf{M}^{-1}$

5 Use the Cayley–Hamilton theorem to find the inverse of $\mathbf{A} = \begin{pmatrix} 3 & 4 & 1 \\ 0 & 2 & 1 \\ 0 & 0 & -6 \end{pmatrix}$

6 The characteristic equation of the non-singular matrix **A** is $\lambda^3 - 3\lambda^2 + 5 = 0$

    a Show that $\mathbf{A}^4 = 9\mathbf{A}^2 - 5\mathbf{A} - 15\mathbf{I}$

    b Find an expression for the inverse of **A** in terms of **A** and $\mathbf{A}^2$

7 Let $\mathbf{M} = \begin{pmatrix} 1 & 3 & -2 \\ 2 & 1 & 1 \\ 0 & 3 & -3 \end{pmatrix}$

Use the Cayley–Hamilton theorem to show that $\mathbf{M}^4 = a\mathbf{M}^2 + b\mathbf{M}$, where a and b are integers to be found.

8 Let $\mathbf{M} = \begin{pmatrix} 2 & -1 & 0 \\ 4 & -1 & -2 \\ 5 & 8 & 4 \end{pmatrix}$

Use the Cayley–Hamilton theorem to show that $\mathbf{M}^4 = a\mathbf{M}^2 + b\mathbf{M} + c\mathbf{I}$, where a, b and c are integers to be found.

9 A matrix **A** has characteristic equation $\lambda^2 - 7\lambda = 0$

Use the Cayley–Hamilton theorem to prove by induction that $\mathbf{A}^n = 7^{n-1}\mathbf{A}$, $n \in \mathbb{N}, n \geq 2$

Matrix diagonalisation

Fluency and skills

A square matrix is **diagonal** if all its elements except those on the leading diagonal are zero.

You can convert a square matrix into diagonal form, which can be useful when dealing with powers of matrices.

Key point

A matrix, **M**, can be **diagonalised** by finding **P** and **D** such that $\mathbf{D} = \mathbf{P}^{-1}\mathbf{MP}$. It can be shown that:

- **D** is a diagonal matrix with the eigenvalues along the leading diagonal
- **P** is a matrix where the columns are the eigenvectors.

The eigenvectors in the columns of **P** must occur in the same order as their corresponding eigenvalues in **D**

Example 1

Diagonalise the matrix $\mathbf{A} = \begin{pmatrix} 36 & 54 \\ 216 & 36 \end{pmatrix}$ by finding matrices **P** and **D** such that $\mathbf{D} = \mathbf{P}^{-1}\mathbf{MP}$

$\det\begin{pmatrix} 36-\lambda & 54 \\ 216 & 36-\lambda \end{pmatrix} = 0$ | Solve $\det(\mathbf{A} - \lambda\mathbf{I}) = 0$

$(36-\lambda)(36-\lambda) - 11664 = 0$

$(36-\lambda)^2 = 11664$

$36 - \lambda = \pm 108$

$\lambda = -72, 144$ | These are the eigenvalues.

So $\mathbf{D} = \begin{pmatrix} -72 & 0 \\ 0 & 144 \end{pmatrix}$

$\begin{pmatrix} 36 & 54 \\ 216 & 36 \end{pmatrix}\begin{pmatrix} a \\ b \end{pmatrix} = -72\begin{pmatrix} a \\ b \end{pmatrix}$ | Find corresponding eigenvectors.

$36a + 54b = -72a \Rightarrow 108a = 54b$

$\Rightarrow 2a = b$

(Continued on the next page)

So an eigenvector corresponding to the eigenvalue -72 is $\begin{pmatrix} 1 \\ 2 \end{pmatrix}$

$\begin{pmatrix} 36 & 54 \\ 216 & 36 \end{pmatrix} \begin{pmatrix} a \\ b \end{pmatrix} = 144 \begin{pmatrix} a \\ b \end{pmatrix}$

$36a + 54b = 144a \Rightarrow 108a = 108b$

$\Rightarrow a = b$

So an eigenvector corresponding to the eigenvalue 144 is $\begin{pmatrix} 1 \\ 1 \end{pmatrix}$

Therefore $\mathbf{P} = \begin{pmatrix} 1 & 1 \\ 2 & 1 \end{pmatrix}$ •————

> Ensure that the order of the eigenvectors in **P** is the same as the order of the corresponding eigenvalues in **D**

Example 2

Diagonalise the matrix $\mathbf{M} = \begin{pmatrix} 2 & 0 & 0 \\ 0 & 1 & -2 \\ 0 & -2 & 4 \end{pmatrix}$ by finding matrices **P** and **D** such that $\mathbf{D} = \mathbf{P}^{-1}\mathbf{MP}$

$\det \begin{pmatrix} 2-\lambda & 0 & 0 \\ 0 & 1-\lambda & -2 \\ 0 & -2 & 4-\lambda \end{pmatrix} = (2-\lambda)[(1-\lambda)(4-\lambda)-4] = 0$

$(2-\lambda)(\lambda^2 - 5\lambda + 4 - 4) = 0$

$\lambda(2-\lambda)(\lambda-5) = 0 \Rightarrow \lambda = 0, 2, 5$ •————

> Use the characteristic equation to find the eigenvalues.

$\begin{pmatrix} 2 & 0 & 0 \\ 0 & 1 & -2 \\ 0 & -2 & 4 \end{pmatrix} \begin{pmatrix} a \\ b \\ c \end{pmatrix} = \lambda \begin{pmatrix} a \\ b \\ c \end{pmatrix}$ •————

> Use $\mathbf{Mx} = \lambda\mathbf{x}$ to find the eigenvectors.

When $\lambda = 0$

$2a = 0 \Rightarrow a = 0$

$b - 2c = 0 \Rightarrow b = 2c$

$-2b + 4c = 0 \Rightarrow b = 2c$

So an eigenvector is $\begin{pmatrix} 0 \\ 2 \\ 1 \end{pmatrix}$

When $\lambda = 2$

$2a = 2a$

$b - 2c = 2b \Rightarrow b = -2c$

$-2b + 4c = 2c \Rightarrow b = c$

Therefore $b = c = 0$

(Continued on the next page)

So an eigenvector is $\begin{pmatrix} 1 \\ 0 \\ 0 \end{pmatrix}$

$$\begin{pmatrix} 2 & 0 & 0 \\ 0 & 1 & -2 \\ 0 & -2 & 4 \end{pmatrix} \begin{pmatrix} a \\ b \\ c \end{pmatrix} = \lambda \begin{pmatrix} a \\ b \\ c \end{pmatrix}$$

When $\lambda = 5$

$2a = 5a \Rightarrow a = 0$

$b - 2c = 5b \Rightarrow -2b = c$

$-2b + 4c = 5c \Rightarrow c = -2b$

So an eigenvector is $\begin{pmatrix} 0 \\ 1 \\ -2 \end{pmatrix}$

Therefore $\mathbf{D} = \begin{pmatrix} 0 & 0 & 0 \\ 0 & 2 & 0 \\ 0 & 0 & 5 \end{pmatrix}$ and $\mathbf{P} = \begin{pmatrix} 0 & 1 & 0 \\ 2 & 0 & 1 \\ 1 & 0 & -2 \end{pmatrix}$

> Ensure that you put the columns of **P** in the correct order.

> You could use your calculator to check that $\mathbf{D} = \mathbf{P}^{-1}\mathbf{MP}$

Key point

Two eigenvectors, $\mathbf{x}_1$ and $\mathbf{x}_2$, are **orthogonal** (perpendicular) if $\mathbf{x}_1 \cdot \mathbf{x}_1 = 0$ (This is the scalar product.)

Key point

A matrix, **M**, is symmetric if $\mathbf{M} = \mathbf{M}^{\mathrm{T}}$

For example, $\mathbf{M} = \begin{pmatrix} -5 & 12 \\ 12 & 2 \end{pmatrix}$ is a symmetric matrix since

$\mathbf{M}^{\mathrm{T}} = \begin{pmatrix} -5 & 12 \\ 12 & 2 \end{pmatrix} = \mathbf{M}$

The eigenvalues of **M** are $\lambda = -14, 11$

With corresponding normalised eigenvectors $\mathbf{x} = \begin{pmatrix} -\dfrac{4}{5} \\ \dfrac{3}{5} \end{pmatrix}, \begin{pmatrix} \dfrac{3}{5} \\ \dfrac{4}{5} \end{pmatrix}$

> The eigenvectors of any symmetric matrix will always be orthogonal. If you have a 3×3 matrix, then every possible pair of eigenvectors is orthogonal.

These vectors are orthogonal since $\begin{pmatrix} -\dfrac{4}{5} \\ \dfrac{3}{5} \end{pmatrix} \cdot \begin{pmatrix} \dfrac{3}{5} \\ \dfrac{4}{5} \end{pmatrix} = -\dfrac{12}{25} + \dfrac{12}{25} = 0$

The matrix formed by these eigenvectors is also orthogonal:

$\mathbf{P} = \begin{pmatrix} -\dfrac{4}{5} & \dfrac{3}{5} \\ \dfrac{3}{5} & \dfrac{4}{5} \end{pmatrix}$

> The matrix formed from orthogonal, normalised eigenvectors will itself always be orthogonal.

A square matrix, **P**, is **orthogonal** if $\mathbf{PP}^T = \mathbf{I}$

This implies that $\mathbf{P}^T = \mathbf{P}^{-1}$ for an orthogonal matrix.

M can be diagonalised by $\mathbf{D} = \mathbf{P}^{-1}\mathbf{MP}$, so, if **M** is symmetric, this can be written as $\mathbf{D} = \mathbf{P}^T\mathbf{MP}$ since **P** is orthogonal so $\mathbf{P}^{-1} = \mathbf{P}^T$

> In general, it is considerably easier to find the transpose of a matrix than to find its inverse.

Key point

A *symmetric* matrix, **M**, can be diagonalised by finding **P** and **D** such that $\mathbf{D} = \mathbf{P}^T\mathbf{MP}$. It can be shown that:

- **D** is a diagonal matrix with the eigenvalues along the leading diagonal,
- **P** is a matrix where the columns are the normalised eigenvalues.

The normalised eigenvectors in the columns of **P** will occur in the same order as their corresponding eigenvalues in **D**

Example 3

> Notice that **M** is symmetric which means that $\mathbf{P}^{-1} = \mathbf{P}^T$

The matrix $\mathbf{M} = \begin{pmatrix} 3 & -2 \\ -2 & 0 \end{pmatrix}$ has eigenvectors $\begin{pmatrix} -2 \\ 1 \end{pmatrix}$ and $\begin{pmatrix} 1 \\ 2 \end{pmatrix}$

a Verify that the eigenvectors are orthogonal.

b Find orthogonal matrix **P** and diagonal matrix **D** such that $\mathbf{P}^T\mathbf{AP} = \mathbf{D}$

a $\begin{pmatrix} -2 \\ 1 \end{pmatrix} \cdot \begin{pmatrix} 1 \\ 2 \end{pmatrix} = -2 + 2$

> Calculate the scalar product.

$= 0$, therefore they are orthogonal

b $\begin{pmatrix} 3 & -2 \\ -2 & 0 \end{pmatrix}\begin{pmatrix} -2 \\ 1 \end{pmatrix} = \lambda_1\begin{pmatrix} -2 \\ 1 \end{pmatrix}$

> Use an eigenvector to find an eigenvalue.

$-8 = -2\lambda_1 \Rightarrow \lambda_1 = 4$

$\begin{pmatrix} 3 & -2 \\ -2 & 0 \end{pmatrix}\begin{pmatrix} 1 \\ 2 \end{pmatrix} = \lambda_2\begin{pmatrix} 1 \\ 2 \end{pmatrix}$

> Repeat with the other eigenvector.

$\lambda_2 = -1$

Therefore the diagonal matrix is $\mathbf{D} = \begin{pmatrix} 4 & 0 \\ 0 & -1 \end{pmatrix}$

The magnitude of both $\begin{pmatrix} -2 \\ 1 \end{pmatrix}$ and $\begin{pmatrix} 1 \\ 2 \end{pmatrix}$ is $\sqrt{2^2 + 1^2} = \sqrt{5}$

(Continued on the next page)

So the normalised eigenvectors are $\begin{pmatrix} -\dfrac{2}{\sqrt{5}} \\ \dfrac{1}{\sqrt{5}} \end{pmatrix}$ and $\begin{pmatrix} \dfrac{1}{\sqrt{5}} \\ \dfrac{2}{\sqrt{5}} \end{pmatrix}$

> Divide by the magnitude to normalise.

Therefore, the orthogonal matrix is $\mathbf{P} = \begin{pmatrix} -\dfrac{2}{\sqrt{5}} & \dfrac{1}{\sqrt{5}} \\ \dfrac{1}{\sqrt{5}} & \dfrac{2}{\sqrt{5}} \end{pmatrix}$

> Ensure that the eigenvectors are in the same order as the corresponding eigenvalues in **D**

Example 4

The matrix $\mathbf{A} = \begin{pmatrix} 1 & 2 & 0 \\ 2 & 4 & 0 \\ 0 & 0 & -6 \end{pmatrix}$ has eigenvalues $\lambda = 0, 5$ and -6

a Verify that the normalised eigenvectors are all orthogonal.

b Find orthogonal matrix **P** and diagonal matrix **D** such that $\mathbf{P}^{\mathrm{T}}\mathbf{AP} = \mathbf{D}$

a $\begin{pmatrix} 1 & 2 & 0 \\ 2 & 4 & 0 \\ 0 & 0 & -6 \end{pmatrix}\begin{pmatrix} a \\ b \\ c \end{pmatrix} = \lambda \begin{pmatrix} a \\ b \\ c \end{pmatrix}$

When $\lambda = 0$

$-6c = 0 \Rightarrow c = 0$

$a + 2b = 0 \Rightarrow a = -2b$

$2a + 4b = b \Rightarrow a = -2b$

The eigenvector is $\begin{pmatrix} -2 \\ 1 \\ 0 \end{pmatrix}$, so the normalised eigenvector is $\begin{pmatrix} -\dfrac{2}{\sqrt{5}} \\ \dfrac{1}{\sqrt{5}} \\ 0 \end{pmatrix}$

> Divide by the magnitude which is $\sqrt{2^2 + 1^2 + 0^2} = \sqrt{5}$

Using a similar process, the other normalised eigenvectors are

$\begin{pmatrix} \dfrac{1}{\sqrt{5}} \\ \dfrac{2}{\sqrt{5}} \\ 0 \end{pmatrix}$ and $\begin{pmatrix} 0 \\ 0 \\ 1 \end{pmatrix}$

$\begin{pmatrix} -\dfrac{2}{\sqrt{5}} \\ \dfrac{1}{\sqrt{5}} \\ 0 \end{pmatrix} \cdot \begin{pmatrix} \dfrac{1}{\sqrt{5}} \\ \dfrac{2}{\sqrt{5}} \\ 0 \end{pmatrix} = -\dfrac{2}{5} + \dfrac{2}{5} + 0 = 0$ so orthogonal

(Continued on the next page)

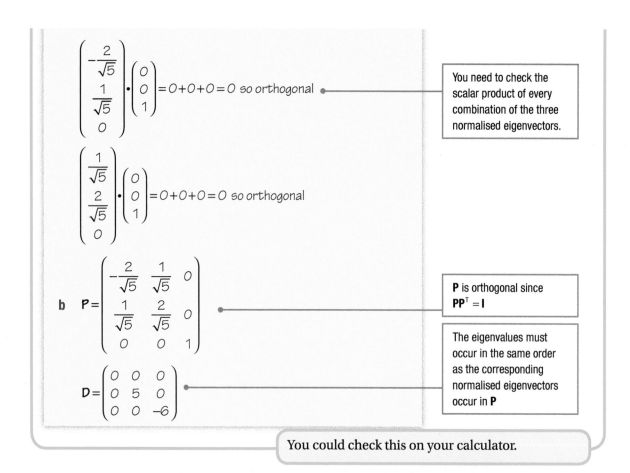

$$\begin{pmatrix} -\dfrac{2}{\sqrt{5}} \\ \dfrac{1}{\sqrt{5}} \\ 0 \end{pmatrix} \cdot \begin{pmatrix} 0 \\ 0 \\ 1 \end{pmatrix} = 0+0+0 = 0 \text{ so orthogonal}$$

You need to check the scalar product of every combination of the three normalised eigenvectors.

$$\begin{pmatrix} \dfrac{1}{\sqrt{5}} \\ \dfrac{2}{\sqrt{5}} \\ 0 \end{pmatrix} \cdot \begin{pmatrix} 0 \\ 0 \\ 1 \end{pmatrix} = 0+0+0 = 0 \text{ so orthogonal}$$

b $\quad P = \begin{pmatrix} -\dfrac{2}{\sqrt{5}} & \dfrac{1}{\sqrt{5}} & 0 \\ \dfrac{1}{\sqrt{5}} & \dfrac{2}{\sqrt{5}} & 0 \\ 0 & 0 & 1 \end{pmatrix}$

P is orthogonal since $\mathbf{PP}^\mathrm{T} = \mathbf{I}$

$$D = \begin{pmatrix} 0 & 0 & 0 \\ 0 & 5 & 0 \\ 0 & 0 & -6 \end{pmatrix}$$

The eigenvalues must occur in the same order as the corresponding normalised eigenvectors occur in **P**

You could check this on your calculator.

Exercise 8.2A Fluency and skills

1 Diagonalise each of these matrices by finding matrix **P** such that $\mathbf{P}^{-1}\mathbf{AP}$ is a diagonal matrix.

a $\quad \mathbf{A} = \begin{pmatrix} 1 & 4 \\ -2 & -5 \end{pmatrix}$ b $\quad \mathbf{A} = \begin{pmatrix} 2 & 6 \\ 1 & -3 \end{pmatrix}$

c $\quad \mathbf{A} = \begin{pmatrix} -4 & 0 & 0 \\ 5 & 2 & 6 \\ 1 & 6 & -3 \end{pmatrix}$

d $\quad \mathbf{A} = \begin{pmatrix} 7 & 0 & 0 \\ 2 & 8 & 0 \\ -2 & 1 & -5 \end{pmatrix}$

2 Verify that each of these pairs of vectors is orthogonal.

a $\quad \begin{pmatrix} 3 \\ 4 \end{pmatrix}$ and $\begin{pmatrix} 4 \\ -3 \end{pmatrix}$ b $\quad \begin{pmatrix} 2 \\ -3 \end{pmatrix}$ and $\begin{pmatrix} -12 \\ -8 \end{pmatrix}$

c $\quad \begin{pmatrix} 3 \\ -5 \\ 1 \end{pmatrix}$ and $\begin{pmatrix} 5 \\ 3 \\ 0 \end{pmatrix}$ d $\quad \begin{pmatrix} 2 \\ 3 \\ -1 \end{pmatrix}$ and $\begin{pmatrix} 5 \\ -4 \\ -2 \end{pmatrix}$

3 Given that $\mathbf{A} = \begin{pmatrix} -\dfrac{5}{13} & 0 & -\dfrac{12}{13} \\ 0 & -1 & 0 \\ -\dfrac{12}{13} & 0 & \dfrac{5}{13} \end{pmatrix}$, verify that

A is orthogonal by

a Verifying that the vectors that form the columns of **A** are orthogonal,

b Verifying that $\mathbf{AA}^\mathrm{T} = \mathbf{I}$

4 Diagonalise each of these symmetric matrices by finding an orthogonal matrix **P** such that $\mathbf{P}^\mathrm{T}\mathbf{MP}$ is a diagonal matrix.

a $\quad \mathbf{M} = \begin{pmatrix} 2 & 0 \\ 0 & 7 \end{pmatrix}$ b $\quad \mathbf{M} = \begin{pmatrix} 3 & 4 \\ 4 & -3 \end{pmatrix}$

c $\quad \mathbf{M} = \begin{pmatrix} 7 & -1 & 0 \\ -1 & 7 & 0 \\ 0 & 0 & -7 \end{pmatrix}$

Reasoning and problem-solving

You can use the diagonalised form of a matrix to calculate powers of the matrix more easily.

If $\mathbf{A} = \mathbf{PDP}^{-1}$ then $\mathbf{A}^n = (\mathbf{PDP}^{-1})^n$

$\qquad\qquad\qquad = (\mathbf{PDP}^{-1})(\mathbf{PDP}^{-1})(\mathbf{PDP}^{-1})\ldots(\mathbf{PDP}^{-1})$

$\qquad\qquad\qquad = (\mathbf{PD})(\mathbf{P}^{-1}\mathbf{P})\mathbf{D}(\mathbf{P}^{-1}\mathbf{P})\mathbf{D}\ldots(\mathbf{P}^{-1}\mathbf{P})(\mathbf{DP}^{-1})$

$\qquad\qquad\qquad = (\mathbf{PD})\mathbf{DD}\ldots\mathbf{D}(\mathbf{DP}^{-1})$

$\qquad\qquad\qquad = \mathbf{PD}^n\mathbf{P}^{-1}$

> Since matrix multiplication is associative.

> Since $\mathbf{P}^{-1}\mathbf{P} = \mathbf{I}$

Key point

If $\mathbf{A} = \mathbf{PDP}^{-1}$, then $\mathbf{A}^n = \mathbf{PD}^n\mathbf{P}^{-1}$

Alternatively, if $\mathbf{A}$ is a symmetric matrix, you can use the following.

Key point

If $\mathbf{A} = \mathbf{PDP}^{\mathrm{T}}$, then $\mathbf{A}^n = \mathbf{PD}^n\mathbf{P}^{\mathrm{T}}$

You can use these to solve problems involving $\mathbf{A}^n$, since if $\mathbf{D}$ is 2×2, then $\mathbf{D}^n = \begin{pmatrix} a & 0 \\ 0 & b \end{pmatrix}^n = \begin{pmatrix} a^n & 0 \\ 0 & b^n \end{pmatrix}$ and if $\mathbf{D}$ is 3×3, then

$$\mathbf{D}^n = \begin{pmatrix} a & 0 & 0 \\ 0 & b & 0 \\ 0 & 0 & c \end{pmatrix}^n = \begin{pmatrix} a^n & 0 & 0 \\ 0 & b^n & 0 \\ 0 & 0 & c^n \end{pmatrix}$$

You can use proof by induction to prove this result.

Strategy

To calculate powers of a square matrix, $\mathbf{A}$

① Diagonalise the matrix using $\mathbf{A} = \mathbf{PDP}^{-1}$, or $\mathbf{A} = \mathbf{PDP}^{\mathrm{T}}$ if $\mathbf{A}$ is symmetric.

② Use $\mathbf{A}^n = \mathbf{PD}^n\mathbf{P}^{-1}$, or $\mathbf{A} = \mathbf{PD}^n\mathbf{P}^{\mathrm{T}}$ if $\mathbf{A}$ is symmetric.

③ Use the fact that $\begin{pmatrix} a & 0 \\ 0 & b \end{pmatrix}^n = \begin{pmatrix} a^n & 0 \\ 0 & b^n \end{pmatrix}$ or $\begin{pmatrix} a & 0 & 0 \\ 0 & b & 0 \\ 0 & 0 & c \end{pmatrix}^n = \begin{pmatrix} a^n & 0 & 0 \\ 0 & b^n & 0 \\ 0 & 0 & c^n \end{pmatrix}$

Example 5

Given that $\mathbf{A} = \begin{pmatrix} 3 & -1 \\ 0 & 5 \end{pmatrix}$, show that $\mathbf{A}^n = \begin{pmatrix} 3^n & \dfrac{3^n}{2} - \dfrac{5^n}{2} \\ 0 & 5^n \end{pmatrix}$

$det\begin{pmatrix} 3-\lambda & -1 \\ 0 & 5-\lambda \end{pmatrix} = 0 \Rightarrow (3-\lambda)(5-\lambda) = 0$

The eigenvalues are $\lambda = 3$ and 5

> Find the eigenvalues using the characteristic equation.

$\begin{pmatrix} 3 & -1 \\ 0 & 5 \end{pmatrix}\begin{pmatrix} a \\ b \end{pmatrix} = 3\begin{pmatrix} a \\ b \end{pmatrix}$

$5b = 3b \Rightarrow b = 0$

$3a - b = 3a$

So an eigenvector is $\begin{pmatrix} 1 \\ 0 \end{pmatrix}$

> This is already a normalised eigenvector.

$\begin{pmatrix} 3 & -1 \\ 0 & 5 \end{pmatrix}\begin{pmatrix} a \\ b \end{pmatrix} = 5\begin{pmatrix} a \\ b \end{pmatrix}$

$5b = 5b$

$3a - b = 5a \Rightarrow b = -2a$

So an eigenvector is $\begin{pmatrix} 1 \\ -2 \end{pmatrix}$

So a normalised eigenvector is $\begin{pmatrix} \dfrac{1}{\sqrt{5}} \\ -\dfrac{2}{\sqrt{5}} \end{pmatrix}$

> Divide the eigenvector by its magnitude to find the normalised eigenvector.

So $\mathbf{A} = \begin{pmatrix} 1 & \dfrac{1}{\sqrt{5}} \\ 0 & -\dfrac{2}{\sqrt{5}} \end{pmatrix}\begin{pmatrix} 3 & 0 \\ 0 & 5 \end{pmatrix}\begin{pmatrix} 1 & \dfrac{1}{2} \\ 0 & -\dfrac{\sqrt{5}}{2} \end{pmatrix}$

> **(1)** Find $\mathbf{P}^{-1}$ then write in the form $\mathbf{A} = \mathbf{PDP}^{-1}$

$\mathbf{A}^n = \begin{pmatrix} 1 & \dfrac{1}{\sqrt{5}} \\ 0 & -\dfrac{2}{\sqrt{5}} \end{pmatrix}\begin{pmatrix} 3 & 0 \\ 0 & 5 \end{pmatrix}^n\begin{pmatrix} 1 & \dfrac{1}{2} \\ 0 & -\dfrac{\sqrt{5}}{2} \end{pmatrix}$

> **(2)** Use $\mathbf{A}^n = \mathbf{PD}^n\mathbf{P}^{-1}$

$= \begin{pmatrix} 1 & \dfrac{1}{\sqrt{5}} \\ 0 & -\dfrac{2}{\sqrt{5}} \end{pmatrix}\begin{pmatrix} 3^n & 0 \\ 0 & 5^n \end{pmatrix}\begin{pmatrix} 1 & \dfrac{1}{2} \\ 0 & -\dfrac{\sqrt{5}}{2} \end{pmatrix}$

> **(3)** Simplify $\mathbf{D}^n$ then multiply the matrices together.

$= \begin{pmatrix} 3^n & \dfrac{5^n}{\sqrt{5}} \\ 0 & -\dfrac{2(5^n)}{\sqrt{5}} \end{pmatrix}\begin{pmatrix} 1 & \dfrac{1}{2} \\ 0 & -\dfrac{\sqrt{5}}{2} \end{pmatrix}$

$= \begin{pmatrix} 3^n & \dfrac{3^n}{2} - \dfrac{5^n}{2} \\ 0 & 5^n \end{pmatrix}$ as required

1 Given that $\mathbf{A} = \begin{pmatrix} 1 & 0 \\ 3 & 2 \end{pmatrix}$

    a Work out $\mathbf{A}^6$

    b Find the matrix $\mathbf{A}^n$ in its simplest form.

2 Given that $\mathbf{T} = \begin{pmatrix} 1 & -2 \\ -2 & 4 \end{pmatrix}$

    a Work out $\mathbf{T}^5$

    b Show that $\mathbf{T}^n = 5^{n-1} \begin{pmatrix} 1 & -2 \\ -2 & 4 \end{pmatrix}$

3 Given that $\mathbf{M} = \begin{pmatrix} 5 & 2 \\ 2 & 5 \end{pmatrix}$

    a State matrices $\mathbf{U}$ and $\mathbf{D}$ such that $\mathbf{M} = \mathbf{U}\mathbf{D}\mathbf{U}^{\mathrm{T}}$

    b Work out the eigenvalues of $\mathbf{M}^3$

    c Write down the eigenvectors of $\mathbf{M}^3$

4 The matrix $\mathbf{B}$ can be written as

$$\mathbf{B} = \begin{pmatrix} 1 & 2 \\ -3 & 1 \end{pmatrix} \begin{pmatrix} 7 & 0 \\ 0 & -7 \end{pmatrix} \begin{pmatrix} \dfrac{1}{7} & -\dfrac{2}{7} \\ \dfrac{3}{7} & \dfrac{1}{7} \end{pmatrix}$$

State the eigenvalues and eigenvectors of $\mathbf{B}^2$

5 The matrix $\mathbf{R}$ can be written as

$$\mathbf{R} = \begin{pmatrix} 1 & 2 & 1 \\ 0 & -3 & 1 \\ 1 & 0 & 2 \end{pmatrix} \begin{pmatrix} 3 & 0 & 0 \\ 0 & 2 & 0 \\ 0 & 0 & -4 \end{pmatrix} \begin{pmatrix} 6 & 4 & -5 \\ -1 & -1 & 1 \\ -3 & -2 & 3 \end{pmatrix}$$

State the eigenvalues and the normalised eigenvectors of $\mathbf{R}^4$

6 Given that $\mathbf{A} = \begin{pmatrix} 5 & -1 & 0 \\ 2 & 2 & 0 \\ 0 & 0 & 1 \end{pmatrix}$

    a Work out $\mathbf{A}^3$

    b Find the matrix $\mathbf{A}^n$ in its simplest form.

7 Prove by induction that

$$\begin{pmatrix} a & 0 & 0 \\ 0 & b & 0 \\ 0 & 0 & c \end{pmatrix}^n = \begin{pmatrix} a^n & 0 & 0 \\ 0 & b^n & 0 \\ 0 & 0 & c^n \end{pmatrix}$$

for all positive integers n

8 **a** Find the eigenvalues and corresponding normalised eigenvectors

of $\mathbf{M} = \begin{pmatrix} 1 & 0 & \sqrt{3} \\ 0 & 3 & 0 \\ \sqrt{3} & 0 & -1 \end{pmatrix}$

    b Hence find $\mathbf{M}^6$

9 Given that $\mathbf{A} = \begin{pmatrix} -2 & -4 \\ 1 & 3 \end{pmatrix}$

    a Show that, when n is even,

$$\mathbf{A}^n = \frac{1}{3} \begin{pmatrix} 4 - 2^n & 4 - 4(2^n) \\ 2^n - 1 & 4(2^n) - 1 \end{pmatrix}$$

    b Work out the matrix $\mathbf{A}^n$ when n is odd.

Chapter summary

- Eigenvectors of the square matrix **A** are non-zero vectors that satisfy the equation $\mathbf{Ax} = \lambda\mathbf{x}$
- λ is a scalar known as the eigenvalue.
- The characteristic equation $\det(\mathbf{A} - \lambda\mathbf{I}) = 0$ can be used to find the eigenvalues.
- A normalised vector has a magnitude of 1. It is also known as a unit vector.
- The Cayley–Hamilton theorem states that a matrix satisfies its own characteristic equation.
- A square matrix is diagonal if all its elements except those on the leading diagonal are zero.
- A matrix, **M**, can be **diagonalised** by finding **P** and **D** such that $\mathbf{D} = \mathbf{P}^{-1}\mathbf{MP}$
    - **D** is a diagonal matrix with the eigenvalues along the leading diagonal.
    - **P** is a matrix where the columns are the eigenvalues.
    - The eigenvectors in the columns of **P** must occur in the same order as their corresponding eigenvalues in **D**
- Two eigenvectors, $\mathbf{x}_1$ and $\mathbf{x}_2$, are orthogonal if $\mathbf{x}_1 \cdot \mathbf{x}_1 = 0$
- A matrix, **M**, is symmetric if $\mathbf{M} = \mathbf{M}^{\mathrm{T}}$
- A square matrix, **P**, is orthogonal if $\mathbf{PP}^{\mathrm{T}} = \mathbf{I}$; this implies that $\mathbf{P}^{\mathrm{T}} = \mathbf{P}^{-1}$ for an orthogonal matrix.
- If $\mathbf{A} = \mathbf{PDP}^{-1}$, then $\mathbf{A}^n = \mathbf{PD}^n\mathbf{P}^{-1}$
- For a symmetric matrix, **A**, if $\mathbf{A} = \mathbf{PDP}^{\mathrm{T}}$, then $\mathbf{A}^n = \mathbf{PD}^n\mathbf{P}^{\mathrm{T}}$

Check and review

You should now be able to...	Review Questions
✔ Find the eigenvalues and eigenvectors of a 2×2 matrix and a 3×3 matrix.	1, 2, 3
✔ Use the Cayley–Hamilton theorem to find powers of a matrix.	4, 5
✔ Diagonalise a square matrix.	6, 7
✔ Use diagonal form to raise a matrix to a power.	8

1 Find the eigenvalues and corresponding eigenvectors of

  a $\begin{pmatrix} -3 & 5 \\ 4 & -2 \end{pmatrix}$ b $\begin{pmatrix} -15 & 12 \\ 6 & -21 \end{pmatrix}$

2 Find the eigenvalues and corresponding eigenvectors of

  a $\begin{pmatrix} 2 & 0 & 0 \\ 2 & 3 & 2 \\ 7 & -4 & -3 \end{pmatrix}$ b $\begin{pmatrix} 4 & 2 & 9 \\ 0 & 9 & 0 \\ 2 & 1 & 7 \end{pmatrix}$

3   Given that $\mathbf{M} = \begin{pmatrix} -1 & 0 & 2 \\ -1 & 2 & 0 \\ -4 & 0 & 3 \end{pmatrix}$

a   Show that $\lambda = 2$ is the only real eigenvalue of $\mathbf{M}$

b   Find the eigenvalue corresponding to $\lambda = 2$

4   $\mathbf{B} = \begin{pmatrix} -6 & 2 \\ 4 & -1 \end{pmatrix}$

Use the Cayley–Hamilton theorem to find

a $\mathbf{B}^2$

b $\mathbf{B}^3$

c $\mathbf{B}^{-1}$

5   $\mathbf{A} = \begin{pmatrix} 1 & 1 & 0 \\ 4 & 2 & 1 \\ -1 & 0 & -2 \end{pmatrix}$

a   Find $\mathbf{A}^2$

b   Show that the characteristic equation is $-\lambda^3 + \lambda^2 + 8\lambda + 3 = 0$

c   Use the Cayley–Hamilton theorem to find

   i $\mathbf{A}^3$

   ii   The inverse of $\mathbf{A}$

6   $\mathbf{A} = \begin{pmatrix} -3 & -2 & 0 \\ 0 & 2 & 0 \\ 3 & 1 & 0 \end{pmatrix}$

State a matrix $\mathbf{P}$ and a diagonal matrix $\mathbf{D}$ such that $\mathbf{D} = \mathbf{P}^{-1}\mathbf{AP}$

7   $\mathbf{A} = \begin{pmatrix} -5 & 0 & 0 \\ 0 & 1 & -1 \\ 0 & -1 & 1 \end{pmatrix}$

State an orthogonal matrix $\mathbf{P}$ and a diagonal matrix $\mathbf{D}$ such that $\mathbf{D} = \mathbf{P}^{\mathrm{T}}\mathbf{AP}$

8   $\mathbf{M} = \begin{pmatrix} 2 & 2 & 0 \\ 1 & 1 & 0 \\ 0 & 2 & 1 \end{pmatrix}$

Show that $\mathbf{M}^n = \begin{pmatrix} 2\left(3^{n-1}\right) & 2\left(3^{n-1}\right) & 0 \\ 3^{n-1} & 3^{n-1} & 0 \\ 3^{n-1} - \dfrac{2}{3} & 3^{n-1} + \dfrac{1}{3} & 1 \end{pmatrix}$

Did you know?

Internet search engines use algorithms that rank the importance of pages according to an eigenvector of a weighted link matrix.

Google

Google Search   I'm Feeling Lucky

Research

There are several alternative methods for solving systems of linear equations. Find out about:
- Cramer's rule
- Cholesky decomposition
- Quantum algorithm for linear systems of equations.

Research

Find the eigenvalues and the eigenvectors of the matrix $A = \begin{bmatrix} 2 & 1 \\ 1 & 2 \end{bmatrix}$.

Now plot the four points (0,0), (1,0), (0, 1) and (1,1) and draw in the three vectors as shown below. Transform each of the four points using matrix A. Draw in the new vectors created by the transformed points.

For each of the vectors, consider the following questions.
- Which vectors have had their direction maintained and why?
- Which vectors have been enlarged, by how much, and why?
- How do these observations relate to the eigenvalues?
- How do these observations relate to the eigenvectors?

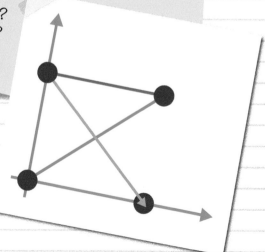

1 a Find the eigenvalues and corresponding eigenvectors of the matrix

   $A = \begin{pmatrix} 2 & -3 \\ -8 & 4 \end{pmatrix}$ **[5]**

 b Hence state the equations of two lines which are invariant under a transformation described by **A** **[2]**

2 $A = \begin{pmatrix} 6 & 2 \\ -1 & 4 \end{pmatrix}$

 a Find the eigenvalues and corresponding eigenvectors of **A** **[5]**

 b Verify that **A** satisfies its own characteristic equation. **[3]**

3 $M = \begin{pmatrix} 0 & -3 \\ -1 & 2 \end{pmatrix}$

 a Convert the matrix **M** into diagonal form by finding matrices **D** and **P**

   such that $D = P^{-1}MP$ **[7]**

 b Use your answer to part **a** to show that $M^3 = \begin{pmatrix} 6 & -21 \\ -7 & 20 \end{pmatrix}$ **[3]**

4 Prove that $D = P^{-1}MP \Rightarrow M^4 = PD^4P^{-1}$ **[5]**

5 Given that $M = \begin{pmatrix} 2 & 1 \\ -1 & 1 \end{pmatrix}$

 a Show that **M** has complex eigenvalues. **[3]**

 b Find the eigenvectors of **M** **[3]**

 c Verify the Cayley–Hamilton theorem for the matrix **M** **[4]**

6 Given that $A = \begin{pmatrix} 2 & 0 & 1 \\ 0 & 1 & 0 \\ 1 & 0 & 2 \end{pmatrix}^n$, prove that $A^n = \frac{1}{2}\begin{pmatrix} 3^n+1 & 0 & 3^n-1 \\ 0 & 2 & 0 \\ 3^n-1 & 0 & 3^n+1 \end{pmatrix}$ for all $n \in \mathbb{N}$ **[5]**

7 $T = \begin{pmatrix} 1 & 2 & 0 \\ 0 & 0 & 3 \\ 2 & 0 & 1 \end{pmatrix}$

 a Show that $\lambda = 3$ is the only real eigenvalue of **T** **[6]**

 b Find the unit eigenvector corresponding to $\lambda = 3$ **[5]**

8 The characteristic equation of a matrix **M** is $\lambda^2 + 5\lambda + 6 = 0$

 a Use the Cayley–Hamilton theorem to show that $M^3 = 19M + 30I$ **[4]**

 b Hence find an expression for M^4 in terms of **M** **[3]**

9 Given that $\mathbf{M} = \begin{pmatrix} 0 & 0 & 2 \\ -2 & 1 & 0 \\ 2 & 0 & 0 \end{pmatrix}$

    a Find matrix $\mathbf{P}$ and diagonal matrix $\mathbf{D}$ such that $\mathbf{M} = \mathbf{PDP}^{-1}$ **[8]**

    b Hence find $\mathbf{M}^4$. You must show how you used your answer to part **a**.   **[3]**

10 $\mathbf{A} = \begin{pmatrix} 1 & a \\ 2 & -4 \end{pmatrix}$

Given that matrix $\mathbf{A}$ is non-singular, use the Cayley–Hamilton theorem to find the inverse of $\mathbf{A}$. You must show your working clearly.   **[4]**

11 $\mathbf{A} = \begin{pmatrix} 3 & -1 & 0 \\ 2 & 1 & 4 \\ 3 & 0 & -2 \end{pmatrix}$

    a Show that the characteristic equation of $\mathbf{A}$ can be written as $\lambda^3 - 2\lambda^2 - 3\lambda + 22 = 0$ **[3]**

    b Use the Cayley–Hamilton theorem to show that $\mathbf{A}^4 = 7\mathbf{A}^2 + c\mathbf{A} + d\mathbf{I}$, where c and d are constants to be found.   **[6]**

12 Given that $\mathbf{M} = \begin{pmatrix} 1 & -2 & 3 \\ 0 & 1 & -1 \\ 1 & -2 & 1 \end{pmatrix}$

    a Show that $\mathbf{M}$ is non-singular.   **[2]**

    b **i** Show that $\mathbf{M}^{-1} = a\mathbf{M}^2 + b\mathbf{M} + c\mathbf{I}$, where a, b and c are constants to be found.

       ii Explain how you used the fact that $\mathbf{M}$ is non-singular.   **[6]**

13 Matrix $\mathbf{A}$ can be written as $\mathbf{PDP}^{T}$, where $\mathbf{P} = \begin{pmatrix} a & b \\ b & -a \end{pmatrix}$ and $\mathbf{D} = \begin{pmatrix} k & 0 \\ 0 & 0 \end{pmatrix}$

Show that $\mathbf{A}^n = k^n \begin{pmatrix} a^2 & ab \\ ab & b^2 \end{pmatrix}$ **[4]**

14 The eigenvectors of a symmetric matrix, $\mathbf{S}$, are $v_1 = \begin{pmatrix} 1 \\ 0 \\ 0 \end{pmatrix}$, $v_2 = \begin{pmatrix} 0 \\ -1 \\ 1 \end{pmatrix}$ and $v_3 = \begin{pmatrix} 0 \\ 1 \\ 1 \end{pmatrix}$

    a Verify that the normalised eigenvectors are all orthogonal.   **[4]**

Given that the corresponding eigenvalues of $\mathbf{S}$ are $\lambda_1 = 2, \lambda_2 = -1, \lambda_3 = 1$,

    b Find the matrix $\mathbf{S}$ **[1]**

9 Number theory

Modular arithmetic is central to our use of bar codes. It is also used in other coding systems and cryptography (creating secure communication, for example, for internet banking transactions).

Bar codes are used in shops to keep track of what is being sold and how much each item should cost the customer. Every purchase is tracked. This helps to ensure that stock levels are kept to just the right levels and so that pricing can be altered without having to change the information on every single item. This is particularly important if the shopkeeper wants to lower or raise prices.

Orientation

What you need to know	What you will learn	What this leads to
KS4 • Sets. • Tests for divisibility.	• How to use the Euclidean algorithm. • How to use modular arithmetic. • How to use congruence equations. **A Level** • How to use combinatorics (choosing distinct items from a set).	**Careers** • Crytography.

Division and the Euclidean algorithm

Fluency and skills

The study of integers and their properties is known as number theory. One such property you can study is whether or not an integer is divisible by another integer.

The integer a is divisible by the integer b if there exists an integer q such that $a = qb$

If a is divisible by b you can write $b|a$ which is read as 'b divides a'

You may already be familiar with tests for divisibility by 2, 3, 5 and 10. The Key point lists the tests that you need to know. The proofs are covered later in this chapter.

Key point

- N is divisible by 2 if the units digit is divisible by 2
- N is divisible by 3 if the sum of the digits is divisible by 3
- N is divisible by 4 if the number created by the tens and units digits is divisible by 4
- N is divisible by 5 if the units digit is divisible by 5
- N is divisible by 6 if it is divisible by 2 and 3
- N is divisible by 9 if the sum of the digits is divisible by 9
- N is divisible by 10 if the units digit is 0
- N is divisible by 11 if the alternating sum of the digits is divisible by 11

An 'alternating sum' is a series where the signs alternate between positive and negative.

Example 1

Explain why 57 258 is divisible by 6

57 258 is divisible by 2 since the units digit is 8 and $8 = 4 \times 2$, so is divisible by 2

57 258 is divisible by 3 since the sum of the digits is 27 and $27 = 3 \times 9$, so is divisible by 3

Therefore 57 258 is divisible by 6

Use the divisibility tests to show that it is divisible by both 2 and 3

You can write $6 | 57\,258$

Example 2

Explain why 37 194 817 is divisible by 11

The alternating sum of the digits of 37 194 817 is

$3 - 7 + 1 - 9 + 4 - 8 + 1 - 7 = -22$

$-22 = -2 \times 11$ so is divisible by 11

Hence 37 194 817 is divisible by 11

Negative integers can be shown to be divisible in the same way as positive integers.

You can write $11 | 37\,194\,817$

When an integer does not divide another integer exactly, you may be interested instead in the remainder from the division.

The **division theorem** states that for any integers a and b with $b \neq 0$ there are unique integers q and r such that $a = qb + r$ where $0 \leq r < b$ The integer q is called the **quotient** and r is called the **remainder**.

You can use the division theorem to find the highest common factor (written hcf) of two numbers. A process for doing this is called the **Euclidean algorithm** and is as follows.

Another name for the **highest common factor** is the **greatest common divisor**. The highest common factor of two integers, a and b is written $hcf(a, b)$

Key point

Euclidean algorithm

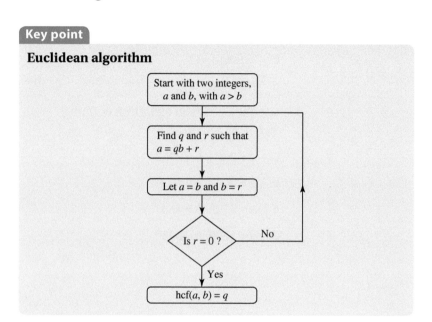

Start with two integers, a and b, with $a > b$

Find q and r such that $a = qb + r$

Let $a = b$ and $b = r$

Is $r = 0$? — No

Yes

$hcf(a, b) = q$

Example 3

Use the Euclidean algorithm to find the highest common factor of 266 and 378

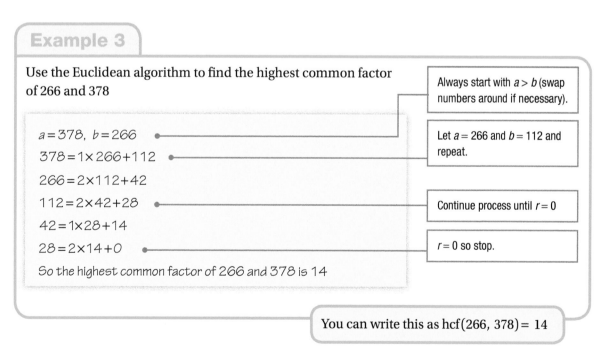

$a = 378, \ b = 266$

$378 = 1 \times 266 + 112$

$266 = 2 \times 112 + 42$

$112 = 2 \times 42 + 28$

$42 = 1 \times 28 + 14$

$28 = 2 \times 14 + 0$

So the highest common factor of 266 and 378 is 14

Always start with $a > b$ (swap numbers around if necessary).

Let $a = 266$ and $b = 112$ and repeat.

Continue process until $r = 0$

$r = 0$ so stop.

You can write this as $hcf(266, 378) = 14$

1   Use the rules of divisibility to show that

   a $2 \mid 37894$

   b $3 \mid 16815$

   c $3 \mid 998784$

   d $5 \mid 673225$

   e $5 \mid 18950$

   f $10 \mid 786010$

2   Use the rules of divisibility to show that

   a $4 \mid 238764$

   b $4 \mid 17508$

   c $6 \mid 543522$

   d $6 \mid 4926036$

   e $9 \mid 786015$

   f $9 \mid 1397367$

   g $11 \mid 519372711$

   h $11 \mid 693088$

3   Use the Euclidean algorithm to find the highest common factor of each pair of numbers.

   a   85 and 221

   b   144 and 120

   c   216 and 342

   d   1092 and 378

4   Use the Euclidean algorithm to find $\text{hcf}(a, b)$ when

   a $a = 2673, b = 2727$

   b $a = 2077, b = 1829$

   c $a = 4199, b = 456$

   d $a = 1260, b = 5460$

Reasoning and problem-solving

Consider using the Euclidean algorithm to find the highest common factor of 15 and 40

$40 = 2 \times 15 + 10$

$15 = 1 \times 10 + 5$

$10 = 2 \times 5 + 0$

So $\text{hcf}(15, 40) = 5$

Now rearrange $15 = 1 \times 10 + 5$ to give $5 = 15 - 1 \times 10$ and rearrange $40 = 2 \times 15 + 10$ to give $10 = 40 - 2 \times 15$

Then substitute to give $5 = 15 - 1 \times 10$

$$= 15 - 1 \times (40 - 2 \times 15)$$

Expand the brackets: $5 = 15 - 1 \times 40 + 2 \times 15$

Simplify: $5 = 3 \times 15 - 1 \times 40$

This result can be generalised for all integers, a and b, and is called **Bézout's identity**.

Key point

Bézout's identity

For all non-zero integers a and b where $\text{hcf}(a, b) = c$, there exist integers x and y such that $ax + by = c$

Strategy

To find integers x and y such that $ax + by = c$ where $\text{hcf}(a, b) = c$

(1) Use the Euclidean algorithm to find the highest common factor of a and b

(2) Work backwards, using the algorithm, to substitute into your sum for c

(3) Simplify by collecting multiples together.

Example 4

Use the Euclidean algorithm with back substitution to find the integers x and y such that $133x + 189y = 7$

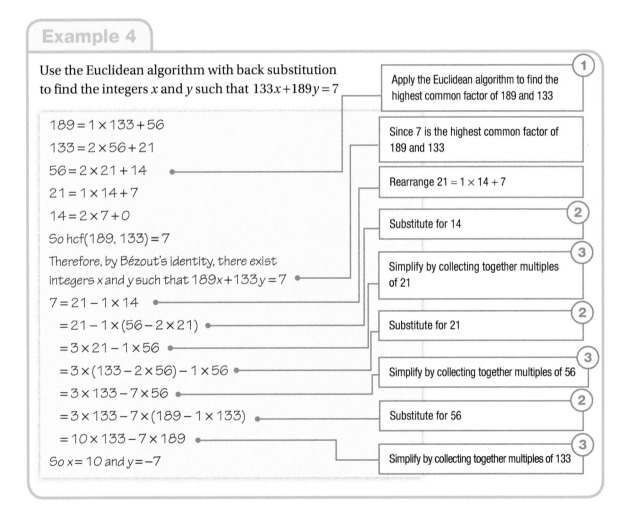

$189 = 1 \times 133 + 56$

$133 = 2 \times 56 + 21$

$56 = 2 \times 21 + 14$

$21 = 1 \times 14 + 7$

$14 = 2 \times 7 + 0$

So $\text{hcf}(189, 133) = 7$

Therefore, by Bézout's identity, there exist integers x and y such that $189x + 133y = 7$

$7 = 21 - 1 \times 14$

$\quad = 21 - 1 \times (56 - 2 \times 21)$

$\quad = 3 \times 21 - 1 \times 56$

$\quad = 3 \times (133 - 2 \times 56) - 1 \times 56$

$\quad = 3 \times 133 - 7 \times 56$

$\quad = 3 \times 133 - 7 \times (189 - 1 \times 133)$

$\quad = 10 \times 133 - 7 \times 189$

So $x = 10$ and $y = -7$

(1) Apply the Euclidean algorithm to find the highest common factor of 189 and 133

Since 7 is the highest common factor of 189 and 133

Rearrange $21 = 1 \times 14 + 7$

(2) Substitute for 14

(3) Simplify by collecting together multiples of 21

(2) Substitute for 21

(3) Simplify by collecting together multiples of 56

(2) Substitute for 56

(3) Simplify by collecting together multiples of 133

Two integers, a and b are **relatively prime** (also known as **coprime**) if $\mathrm{hcf}(a, b) = 1$

Therefore a special case of Bézout's identity is

> **Key point**
>
> For relatively prime integers a and b, there exist integers x and y such that $ax + by = 1$

In fact, you can go a step further and state

> **Key point**
>
> The equation $ax + by = c$ with $a, b, c \in \mathbb{Z}$ has integer solutions if and only if $\mathrm{hcf}(a, b) | c$

Example 5

a Explain how you know that the equation $289x + 799y = 51$ has integer solutions.

b Find a possible pair of solutions.

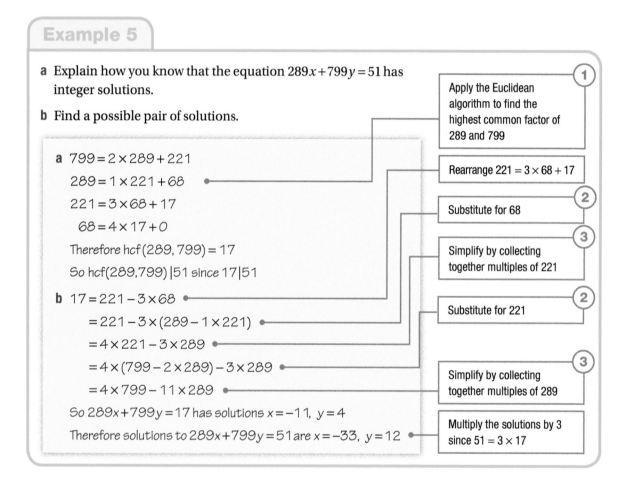

a $799 = 2 \times 289 + 221$

   $289 = 1 \times 221 + 68$ ●

   $221 = 3 \times 68 + 17$

   $68 = 4 \times 17 + 0$

   Therefore $\mathrm{hcf}(289, 799) = 17$

   So $\mathrm{hcf}(289, 799) | 51$ since $17 | 51$

b $17 = 221 - 3 \times 68$ ●

   $\quad = 221 - 3 \times (289 - 1 \times 221)$ ●

   $\quad = 4 \times 221 - 3 \times 289$ ●

   $\quad = 4 \times (799 - 2 \times 289) - 3 \times 289$ ●

   $\quad = 4 \times 799 - 11 \times 289$ ●

   So $289x + 799y = 17$ has solutions $x = -11,\ y = 4$

   Therefore solutions to $289x + 799y = 51$ are $x = -33,\ y = 12$ ●

Apply the Euclidean algorithm to find the highest common factor of 289 and 799

Rearrange $221 = 3 \times 68 + 17$

② Substitute for 68

③ Simplify by collecting together multiples of 221

② Substitute for 221

③ Simplify by collecting together multiples of 289

Multiply the solutions by 3 since $51 = 3 \times 17$

1 **a** Use the Euclidean algorithm to show that the highest common factor of 912 and 336 is 48

    b Hence write 48 in the form $912a + 336b$, where a and b are integers to be found.

2 **a** Use the Euclidean algorithm to show that the highest common factor of 405 and 864 is 27

    b Hence write 27 in the form $405a + 432b$, where a and b are integers to be found.

3 Use the Euclidean algorithm to find integers x and y such that

    a $95x + 115y = 5$

    b $180x + 264y = 12$

    c $216x + 184y = 8$

    d $224x + 288y = 32$

    e $1189x + 1107y = 41$

4 For each equation, explain whether or not integer solutions exist.

    a $92x + 69y = 23$

    b $65x + 39y = 26$

    c $238x + 88y = 11$

    d $152x + 95y = 114$

5 **a** Explain how you know that the equation $234a + 91b = 52$ has integer solutions.

    b Hence find integers a and b such that $234a + 91b = 52$

6 **a** Explain how you know that the equation $648a + 1593b = 216$ has integer solutions.

    b Hence find integers a and b such that $648a + 1593b = 216$

7 If $c = \mathrm{hcf}(a, b)$ then prove that the integers $\dfrac{a}{c}$ and $\dfrac{b}{c}$ are coprime.

8 The integers a, b and c are such that $a \mid bc$ and $\mathrm{hcf}(a, b) = 1$. Prove that $a \mid c$

Fluency and skills

When you are using the 12-hour clock, five hours after 11:00 is 4:00 and three hours before 1:00 is 10:00. This is an example of **modular arithmetic**, the modulus in this case being 12

So you could write $11 + 5 \equiv 4 \ (\text{mod } 12)$ and $1 - 2 \equiv 11 \ (\text{mod } 12)$

Every time you reach 12 you start again from 0; 12 is said to be **congruent** to 0 in mod 12

Any modulus can be used for modular arithmetic: for example, using modulus 5, whenever you reach a multiple of 5 you start again from 0. Therefore 5 is congruent to 0, 6 is congruent to 1 and so on.

0	1	2	3	4
5	6	7	8	9
10	11	12	13	14
15	16	17	18	19

> You have previously used $\equiv$ to mean 'is identical to' but it can also be used to mean 'is congruent to', as in this example.

So, for example, $3 + 4 \equiv 2 \ (\text{mod } 5)$ and $4 \times 4 \equiv 1 \ (\text{mod } 5)$

Another way of thinking about this is that $a \ (\text{mod } n)$ is the remainder when a is divided by n

Key point

Definition of congruence modulo n

For all integers a, b and n,

$a \equiv b \ (\text{mod } n)$ if and only if $n \mid (a - b)$

Modular arithmetic has various properties which you will prove later in this section.

Key point

Properties of modular arithmetic

For all integers a, b, c and n

$a \equiv a \ (\text{mod } n)$	(reflexive property)
If $a \equiv b \ (\text{mod } n)$ then $b \equiv a \ (\text{mod } n)$	(symmetric property)
If $a \equiv b \ (\text{mod } n)$ and $b \equiv c \ (\text{mod } n)$ then $a \equiv c \ (\text{mod } n)$	(transitive property)

You can use rules to add, subtract and multiply with modular arithmetic.

If $a \equiv b \ (\text{mod } n)$, then a can be written as $a = b + kn$, where k is an integer. Similarly, if $c \equiv d \ (\text{mod } n)$, then $c = d + mn$, where m is an integer.

So $a + c = (b + kn) + (d + mn)$

$\qquad = (b + d) + (k + m)n$

Therefore the solution can be written as $b + d \ (\text{mod } n)$ since $k + m$ is an integer.

For integers a, b, c, d and positive integer n, if $a \equiv b$ (mod n) and $c \equiv d$ (mod n), then:

- $a+c \equiv b+d$ (mod n)
- $a-c \equiv b-d$ (mod n)
- $ac \equiv bd$ (mod n)

These rules can be used to simplify calculations.

Example 1

Use the rules of modular arithmetic to calculate

a $53+14$ (mod 10)　　**b** 53×14 (mod 10)　　**c** $1572-7624$ (mod 5)　　**d** 1572×7624 (mod 5)

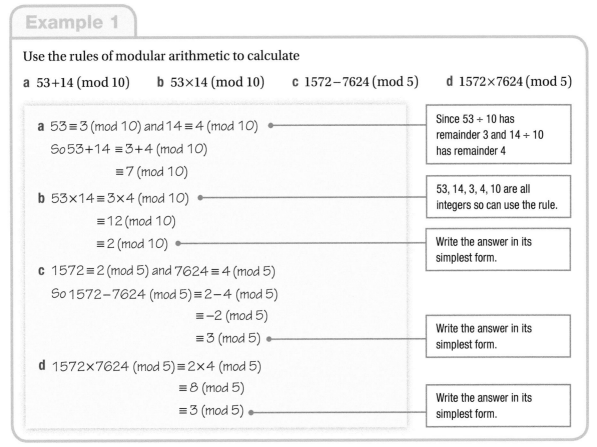

a $53 \equiv 3$ (mod 10) and $14 \equiv 4$ (mod 10)

　So $53+14 \equiv 3+4$ (mod 10)

　　　　$\equiv 7$ (mod 10)

> Since $53 \div 10$ has remainder 3 and $14 \div 10$ has remainder 4

b $53 \times 14 \equiv 3 \times 4$ (mod 10)

　　　$\equiv 12$ (mod 10)

　　　$\equiv 2$ (mod 10)

> 53, 14, 3, 4, 10 are all integers so can use the rule.

> Write the answer in its simplest form.

c $1572 \equiv 2$ (mod 5) and $7624 \equiv 4$ (mod 5)

　So $1572-7624$ (mod 5) $\equiv 2-4$ (mod 5)

　　　　　　$\equiv -2$ (mod 5)

　　　　　　$\equiv 3$ (mod 5)

> Write the answer in its simplest form.

d 1572×7624 (mod 5) $\equiv 2 \times 4$ (mod 5)

　　　　　$\equiv 8$ (mod 5)

　　　　　$\equiv 3$ (mod 5)

> Write the answer in its simplest form.

Unlike addition, subtraction and multiplication in modular arithmetic, there is no equivalent rule for division. You can see that in this example.

$24 \equiv 3$ (mod 7) and $12 \equiv 5$ (mod 7)

but $24 \div 12$ (mod 7) $\neq 3 \div 5$ (mod 7)

In general, division is not well defined.

However, we do have a rule for integer powers, since they represent repeated multiplication.

If $a \equiv b$ (mod n), where a, b, n are integers, then, since $a^2 = a \times a$ and $b^2 = b \times b$, you can use the multiplication rule to see that $a^2 \equiv b^2$ (mod n)

You can use the multiplication rule again to see that

$a^3 \equiv b^3$ (mod n) since $a^3 = a^2 \times a$ and $b^3 = b^2 \times b$

This could be continued indefinitely, and leads to this general rule.

If $a \equiv b$ (mod n) for a, b, $n \in \mathbb{Z}$, then $a^k \equiv b^k$ (mod n) for $k \in \mathbb{Z}^+$

Example 2

Use the power rule of modular arithmetic to work out the value of

a $7^{24} \pmod 8$

b $7^{35} \pmod 8$

a $7 \equiv -1 \pmod 8$

$\quad 7^{24} \equiv (-1)^{24} \pmod 8$ ——— Using the power rule of modular arithmetic.

$\quad\quad \equiv 1 \pmod 8$ ——— Since (-1) to any even power is 1

b $7^{35} \equiv (-1)^{35} \pmod 8$

$\quad\quad \equiv -1 \pmod 8$ ——— Since (-1) to any odd power is -1

$\quad\quad \equiv 7 \pmod 8$

Example 3

Work out the final digit of the number 12^{20} without using a calculator. Show your method.

$12 \equiv 2 \pmod{10}$ ——— Finding the final digit of a number is the same as writing it modulus 10

$12^{20} \equiv 2^{20} \pmod{10}$

$\quad\quad \equiv (2^4)^5 \pmod{10}$ ——— Using the power rule of modular arithmetic.

$\quad\quad \equiv 16^5 \pmod{10}$

$\quad\quad \equiv 6^5 \pmod{10}$ ——— Using index law: $(a^m)^n = a^{mn}$

$\quad\quad \equiv 6 \pmod{10}$ ——— Since 6 to any power must have a final digit of 6

So the final digit of 12^{20} is 6

Exercise 9.2A Fluency and skills

1 Write each number in the form $a \pmod n$, where $0 \leq a < n$, using the modulus given.

   a $7 \pmod 3$ **b** $12 \pmod 7$

   c $19 \pmod 4$ **d** $27 \pmod 9$

   e $25 \pmod 6$ **f** $-5 \pmod 8$

   g $-55 \pmod{11}$ **h** $48 \pmod{13}$

2 Use modular arithmetic to work out these calculations. Show your method clearly. Write each answer in the form $a \pmod n$, where $0 \leq a < n$, using the modulus given.

   a $21 + 19 \pmod 3$ **b** $4 + 25 \pmod 7$

   c $68 - 34 \pmod 4$ **d** $79 - 94 \pmod 9$

   e $5 \times 14 \pmod 6$ **f** $25 \times 37 \pmod 8$

   g $82 \times -16 \pmod{11}$ **h** $29 \times 75 \pmod{13}$

Number theory Modular arithmetic

3 Use the exponential rule of modular arithmetic to simplify these powers. Give your answers in the form $a \pmod n$ where $0 \leq a < n$, using the modulus given.

    a $37\,951^{37} \pmod{10}$ **b** $1736^{26} \pmod 5$

    c $982^9 \pmod 5$ **d** $3219^{48} \pmod 3$

    e $3268^{84} \pmod 3$ **f** $12\,653^{11} \pmod 6$

4 Use the power rule of modular arithmetic to work out these calculations. Show your method clearly. Write each answer in the form $a \pmod n$, where $0 \leq a < n$, using the modulus given.

    a $5^{133} \pmod 4$ **b** $4^{67} \pmod 2$

    c $7^{92} \pmod 4$ **d** $14^{39} \pmod 3$

    e $54^{13} \pmod{11}$ **f** $73^6 \pmod 5$

5 Demonstrate how modular arithmetic can be used to find the final digits of these numbers without using a calculator.

    a 14^{27} **b** 15^{12}

    c 12^{36} **d** 39^{28}

    e 153^{32} **f** 1322^{30}

Reasoning and problem-solving

The rules for divisibility of 2, 3, 4, 5, 6, 9, 10 and 11 are given in the previous section.

Modular arithmetic can be used to prove these rules and derive others. This approach uses the fact that any natural number, N, can be partitioned into multiples of powers of 10. For example,
$6249 = 6 \times 1000 + 2 \times 100 + 4 \times 10 + 9$

$$= 6 \times 10^3 + 2 \times 10^2 + 4 \times 10 + 9$$

So, in general, you can write $N = 10^n a_n + 10^{n-1} a_{n-1} + \ldots + 10^2 a_2 + 10 a_1 + a_0$, where $a_0, a_1, a_2, \ldots, a_n$ are integers between 0 and 9

Strategy 1

To prove a divisibility rule

1. Write $N = 10^n a_n + 10^{n-1} a_{n-1} + \ldots + 10^2 a_2 + 10 a_1 + a_0$

2. Take the required modulus of the expression.

3. Use known facts about the divisibility of some part of the expression for N

Example 4

Prove that a natural number, N, is divisible by 5 if the unit digit is 5 or 0

The proof of the divisibility rules for 2 and 10 are very similar to this proof.

For any natural number N,
$N = 10^n a_n + 10^{n-1} a_{n-1} + \ldots + 10^2 a_2 + 10 a_1 + a_0$ ← Write in the general form. ①

$N \equiv (10^n a_n + 10^{n-1} a_{n-1} + \ldots + 10^2 a_2 + 10 a_1) \pmod 5 + a_0 \pmod 5$ ← Take $\pmod 5$ ②

    $\equiv 0 + a_0 \pmod 5$ ← ③

    $\equiv a_0 \pmod 5$

Therefore $N \equiv 0 \pmod 5$ if the units digit, a_0, equals 0 or 5

Since $10^n a_n + 10^{n-1} a_{n-1} + \ldots + 10^2 a_2 + 10 a_1$ is divisible by 10 and hence divisible by 5

Example 5

Prove that a natural number, N, is divisible by 4 if the number created by the tens and unit digits is divisible by 4

For any natural number N,
$$N = 10^n a_n + 10^{n-1} a_{n-1} + \ldots + 10^2 a_2 + 10 a_1 + a_0$$

$$N \equiv (10^n a_n + 10^{n-1} a_{n-1} + \ldots + 10^2 a_2)(\mathrm{mod}\ 4) + (10 a_1 + a_0)(\mathrm{mod}\ 4)$$

$$\equiv 0 + 10 a_1 + a_0\ (\mathrm{mod}\ 4)$$

$$\equiv 10 a_1 + a_0\ (\mathrm{mod}\ 4)$$

$$N \equiv 0\ (\mathrm{mod}\ 4)\ \text{if}\ 10 a_1 + a_0\ \text{is divisible by 4}$$

① Write in the general form.

② Take (mod 4)

③ Since $10^n a_n + 10^{n-1} a_{n-1} + \ldots + 10^2 a_2$ is divisible by 100 and hence divisible by 4

In other words, when the number created by the tens and units digits is divisible by 4

Example 6

Prove that a natural number, N, is divisible by 9 if the sum of the digits is divisible by 9

The proof of the divisibility rule for 3 is very similar to this proof.

For any natural number N,
$$N = 10^n a_n + 10^{n-1} a_{n-1} + \ldots + 10^2 a_2 + 10 a_1 + a_0$$

$$10 a_1 \equiv 1 \times a_1\ (\mathrm{mod}\ 9)$$

$$\equiv a_1\ (\mathrm{mod}\ 9)$$

$$10 \equiv 1\ (\mathrm{mod}\ 9) \Rightarrow 10^n \equiv 1\ (\mathrm{mod}\ 9)\ \text{for all natural numbers}\ n$$

Therefore
$$10^2 a_2 \equiv a_2\ (\mathrm{mod}\ 9),\ 10^3 a_3 \equiv a_3\ (\mathrm{mod}\ 9),\ \ldots,\ 10^n a_n \equiv a_n\ (\mathrm{mod}\ 9)$$

$$N \equiv 10^n a_n\ (\mathrm{mod}\ 9) + \ldots + 10^2 a_2\ (\mathrm{mod}\ 9) + 10 a_1\ (\mathrm{mod}\ 9) + a_0\ (\mathrm{mod}\ 9)$$

$$\equiv a_n + a_{n-1} + \ldots + a_1 + a_0\ (\mathrm{mod}\ 9)$$

$$N \equiv 0\ (\mathrm{mod}\ 9)\ \text{if}\ a_n + a_{n-1} + \ldots + a_1 + a_0\ \text{is divisible by 9}$$

① Write in the general form.

Using the multiplication rule of modular arithmetic.

② Take (mod 9)

In other words, when the sum of the digits is divisible by 9

You can prove the properties of modular arithmetic using the definition.

Example 7

Prove that $a \equiv b\ (\mathrm{mod}\ n) \Rightarrow b \equiv a\ (\mathrm{mod}\ n)$ for all $a, b, n \in \mathbb{Z}$

$$a \equiv b\ (\mathrm{mod}\ n) \Rightarrow n \mid (a - b)$$

$$\Rightarrow n \mid (-1)(a - b)$$

$$\Rightarrow n \mid (b - a)$$

$$\text{Therefore}\ b \equiv a\ (\mathrm{mod}\ n)$$

Using the definition of congruence modulo n since if n divides $a - b$ it will also divide any integer multiple of $a - b$

You have proved the symmetry of modular congruence.

You can find the remainder when a large number is divided by a prime number using **Fermat's little theorem** which states that, for p a prime number, then $a^p \equiv a \pmod{p}$ for all integers a

If p is a prime number and a is an integer which is not a multiple of p then $a^{p-1} \equiv 1 \pmod{p}$

This can be stated using modular arithmetic:

> **Key point**
>
> **Fermat's little theorem**
>
> If p is a prime number, then $a^p \equiv a \pmod{p}$ for all integers a

By writing $a^p - a$ as $a(a^{p-1} - 1)$ you can see that either a is a multiple of p or $a^{p-1} - 1$ must be a multiple of p

This is a very useful result and can also be stated using modular arithmetic:

> **Key point**
>
> **Fermat's little theorem**
>
> If p is a prime number and a is an integer such that a and p are coprime, then $a^{p-1} \equiv 1 \pmod{p}$

This result can be used to find the remainder when dividing by a prime number, p. In modular arithmetic this remainder is known as the **least positive residue** modulo p

Strategy 2

To find the least positive residue modulus p using Fermat's little theorem

1. Write the power in terms of $p - 1$
2. Use index laws.
3. Use Fermat's little theorem.

Example 8

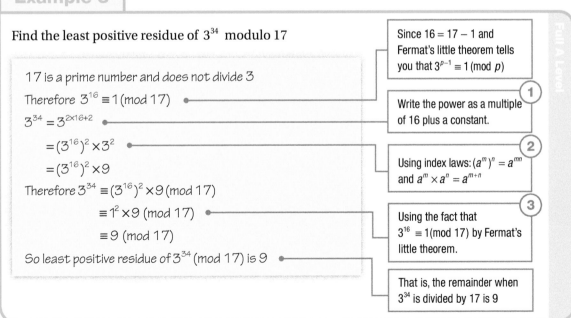

Find the least positive residue of 3^{34} modulo 17

> Since $16 = 17 - 1$ and Fermat's little theorem tells you that $3^{p-1} \equiv 1 \pmod{p}$

17 is a prime number and does not divide 3

Therefore $3^{16} \equiv 1 \pmod{17}$

$3^{34} = 3^{2 \times 16 + 2}$

> 1. Write the power as a multiple of 16 plus a constant.

$= (3^{16})^2 \times 3^2$

$= (3^{16})^2 \times 9$

> 2. Using index laws: $(a^m)^n = a^{mn}$ and $a^m \times a^n = a^{m+n}$

Therefore $3^{34} \equiv (3^{16})^2 \times 9 \pmod{17}$

$\equiv 1^2 \times 9 \pmod{17}$

$\equiv 9 \pmod{17}$

> 3. Using the fact that $3^{16} \equiv 1 \pmod{17}$ by Fermat's little theorem.

So least positive residue of $3^{34} \pmod{17}$ is 9

> That is, the remainder when 3^{34} is divided by 17 is 9

Exercise 9.2B Reasoning and problem-solving

1 Use modular arithmetic to prove that a natural number is divisible by 10 if the units digit is zero.

2 Use modular arithmetic to prove that a natural number is divisible by 2 if the units digit is divisible by 2

3 Use modular arithmetic to prove that a natural number is divisible by 3 if the sum of the digits is divisible by 3

4 Use modular arithmetic to find the last two digits of 1709^{12}

5 a Prove that if k is divisible by 4 then the last digit of 2^k is 6

   b Hence find the last digit of 2^{1001}

6 Prove that a natural number is divisible by 11 if the alternating sum of the digits is divisible by 11

7 Prove the reflexive property of modulo arithmetic.

8 Prove that if

   $a \equiv b \pmod{n}$ and $b \equiv c \pmod{n}$,

   then $a \equiv c \pmod{n}$ for all $a, b, c, n \in \mathbb{Z}$

9 Prove that if

   $a \equiv b \pmod{n}$ and $c \equiv d \pmod{n}$,

   then $a - c \equiv b - d \pmod{n}$ for all

   $a, b, c, d, n \in \mathbb{Z}$

10 Use Fermat's little theorem to find the remainder when

   a 2^{59} is divided by 29

   b 3^{67} is divided by 23

   c 17^{18} is divided by 3

   d 31^{67} is divided by 7

11 Use Fermat's little theorem to find the least residue of

   a 5^{32} modulus 11

   b 27^{109} modulus 13

   c 19^{802} modulus 401

   d 47^{2585} modulus 137

12 What is the remainder when 25^{22} is divided by 23? Explain how Fermat's little theorem can be used to give the solution.

13 Explain how Fermat's little theorem can be used to find the remainder from

   a $59^{17} \div 17$

   b $63^{19} \div 19$

   c $129^{37} \div 37$

   d $2445^{163} \div 163$

14 What is the remainder when

   a $3^{16} + 2^{32}$ is divided by 17

   b $5^{30} - 6^{70}$ is divided by 11?

15 Prove by induction that $a^p \equiv a \pmod{p}$ for all positive integers a and p

Fluency and skills

Full A Level

You can find the integer solutions to congruence equations of the form $ax \equiv b \pmod{n}$, where a, b and n are integers. For small values of n, the easiest approach is simply to consider the possible values of x such that $0 \leq x < n$

Example 1

Find the integer solutions to $3x \equiv 4 \pmod 5$

If $x = 0$, then $3x = 0$ but $0 \equiv 0 \pmod 5$

If $x = 1$, then $3x = 3$ but $3 \equiv 3 \pmod 5$

If $x = 2$, then $3x = 6$ but $6 \equiv 1 \pmod 5$

If $x = 3$, then $3x = 9$ and $9 \equiv 4 \pmod 5$ ⟶ Check every value of x between 0 and 4

If $x = 4$, then $3x = 12$ but $12 \equiv 2 \pmod 5$

The only value of x in the interval $0 \leq x < 5$ that satisfies the congruence equation is $x = 3$ ⟶ So $x = 3$ is a solution.

However, any value which is 3 (mod 5) will also satisfy the equation, so the solution is $x \equiv 3 \pmod 5$

For larger values of n, it is not efficient to check every possible solution for $0 \leq x < n$ so you need a different approach.

For example, if you wanted to solve the equation $7x \equiv 1 \pmod{135}$, then you wouldn't want to have to check 135 values for x

Instead, you can use the fact that if $7x \equiv 1 \pmod{135}$ then $7x$ must be 1 more than some multiple of 135, which you can write as $7x = 1 - 135k$ for some integer k

This can be rearranged to give $7x + 135k = 1$

The highest common factor of 7 and 135 is 1, so here you have Bézout's identity which you know can be solved using back substitution into Euclid's algorithm.

Example 2

Find the integer solutions to $7x \equiv 1 \pmod{135}$

$7x \equiv 1 \pmod{135} \Rightarrow 7x = 1 - 135k$ for some integer k

$7x + 135k = 1$ ⟶ Rearrange.

(Continued on the next page)

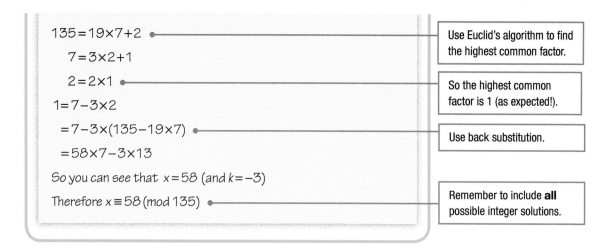

$135 = 19 \times 7 + 2$ — Use Euclid's algorithm to find the highest common factor.

$7 = 3 \times 2 + 1$

$2 = 2 \times 1$ — So the highest common factor is 1 (as expected!).

$1 = 7 - 3 \times 2$

$= 7 - 3 \times (135 - 19 \times 7)$ — Use back substitution.

$= 58 \times 7 - 3 \times 13$

So you can see that $x = 58$ (and $k = -3$)

Therefore $x \equiv 58 \,(\mathrm{mod}\ 135)$ — Remember to include **all** possible integer solutions.

Since $17 \times 58 \equiv 1 \,(\mathrm{mod}\ 135)$, you have found that 58 is the **multiplicative inverse** of 17 $(\mathrm{mod}\ 135)$

Key point

If $ax \equiv 1 \,(\mathrm{mod}\ n)$, then x is the multiplicative inverse of a $(\mathrm{mod}\ n)$ and can be found using Bézout's identity.

Suppose the previous example was changed to $7y \equiv 2 \,(\mathrm{mod}\ 135)$

The multiplication rules of modular arithmetic tells you that since $7x \equiv 1 \,(\mathrm{mod}\ 135)$ and $2 \equiv 2 \,(\mathrm{mod}\ 135)$, then $2 \times 7x \equiv 2 \,(\mathrm{mod}\ 135)$, i.e. $y = 2x$. So, since $x \equiv 58 \,(\mathrm{mod}\ 135)$, $y \equiv 116 \,(\mathrm{mod}\ 135)$

Example 3

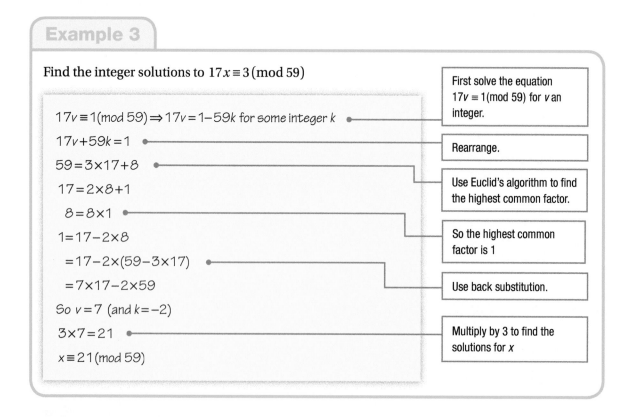

Find the integer solutions to $17x \equiv 3 \,(\mathrm{mod}\ 59)$

$17v \equiv 1 \,(\mathrm{mod}\ 59) \Rightarrow 17v = 1 - 59k$ for some integer k — First solve the equation $17v \equiv 1 \,(\mathrm{mod}\ 59)$ for v an integer.

$17v + 59k = 1$ — Rearrange.

$59 = 3 \times 17 + 8$ — Use Euclid's algorithm to find the highest common factor.

$17 = 2 \times 8 + 1$

$8 = 8 \times 1$

$1 = 17 - 2 \times 8$ — So the highest common factor is 1

$= 17 - 2 \times (59 - 3 \times 17)$

$= 7 \times 17 - 2 \times 59$ — Use back substitution.

So $v = 7$ (and $k = -2$)

$3 \times 7 = 21$ — Multiply by 3 to find the solutions for x

$x \equiv 21 \,(\mathrm{mod}\ 59)$

In the examples so far you have been able to solve $ax \equiv b \pmod{n}$ since $\text{hcf}(a, n) | b$

Consider the congruence equation $2x \equiv 3 \pmod{12}$. In order to solve this equation you would need to have an integer k such that $2x = 3 + 12k$. Clearly no such integer exists since $12k$ will be a multiple of 2 for every integer x so $3 + 12k$ will not be a multiple of 2. However, $2x$ is a multiple of 2 for all integers x so there are no solutions to the equation.

Key point

$ax \equiv b \pmod{n}$ has integer solutions x if and only if $\text{hcf}(a, n) | b$

Exercise 9.3A Fluency and skills

1 Find the integer solutions to each of these congruence equations.

  a $2x \equiv 1 \pmod{3}$

  b $3x \equiv 1 \pmod{4}$

  c $7x \equiv 4 \pmod{5}$

  d $6x \equiv 2 \pmod{4}$

  e $2x \equiv 3 \pmod{7}$

  f $5x \equiv 3 \pmod{8}$

2 Use Bézout's identity to find the multiplicative inverse of

  a $7 \pmod{11}$

  b $5 \pmod{23}$

  c $9 \pmod{13}$

  d $13 \pmod{28}$

  e $37 \pmod{82}$

  f $45 \pmod{163}$

3 Use Bézout's identity to find the integer solutions to each of these congruence equations.

  a $5x \equiv 1 \pmod{37}$

  b $3x \equiv 1 \pmod{157}$

  c $7x \equiv 1 \pmod{24}$

  d $18x \equiv 1 \pmod{263}$

  e $29x \equiv 1 \pmod{139}$

  f $124x \equiv 1 \pmod{397}$

4 Use Bézout's identity to find the integer solutions to each of these congruence equations.

  a $4x \equiv 2 \pmod{27}$

  b $5x \equiv 3 \pmod{82}$

  c $2x \equiv 38 \pmod{85}$

  d $13x \equiv 2 \pmod{126}$

  e $4x \equiv 3 \pmod{225}$

  f $17x \equiv 2 \pmod{379}$

5 Explain why these congruence equations do not have any integer solutions.

  a $5x \equiv 1 \pmod{25}$

  b $14x \equiv 1 \pmod{133}$

  c $9x \equiv 2 \pmod{27}$

  d $8x \equiv 3 \pmod{128}$

  e $21x \equiv 3 \pmod{168}$

  f $48x \equiv 8 \pmod{192}$

You can also solve congruence equations of the form $ax + k \equiv b \pmod{n}$ by first subtracting k from each side.

Strategy

To solve a congruence equation

(1) Write in the form $ax \equiv b \pmod{n}$, where hcf(a, b, n) = 1

(2) Find the multiplicative inverse of $a \pmod{n}$

(3) Multiply by b then write the solutions in a simplified form.

(4) Write in the original modulus, making sure that you include all solutions.

Example 4

Solve the congruence equation $7x + 15 \equiv 10 \pmod{12}$

$7x \equiv -5 \pmod{12}$ **(1)** Subtract 15 from both sides of the equation.

$7x \equiv 7 \pmod{12}$

$12 = 1 \times 7 + 5$

$7 = 1 \times 5 + 2$

$5 = 2 \times 2 + 1$ Use Euclid's algorithm to find the highest common factor of 7 and 12

$2 = 2 \times 1$

So hcf(7, 12) = 1

Find v, k such that $1 = 7v + 12k$

$1 = 5 - 2 \times 2$

$\quad = 5 - 2(7 - 5)$

$\quad = 3 \times 5 - 2 \times 7$ Write 1 in terms of 12 and 7 using Bézout's identity.

$\quad = 3(12 - 7) - 2 \times 7$

$\quad = 3 \times 12 - 5 \times 7$

So $v = -5$, $k = 3$

Hence the multiplicative inverse of 7 (mod 12) is -5 (mod 12)

which can be written 7 (mod 12)   **(2)** 7 (mod 12) is self-inverse since $7 \times 7 \equiv 1 \pmod{12}$

$10 \times 7 = 70$ so $x \equiv 70 \pmod{12}$

which can be written $x \equiv 10 \pmod{12}$ **(3)** Since $70 \equiv 10 \pmod{12}$

Sometimes a congruence equation can be simplified before you solve it. For example, $8x \equiv 2 \pmod{10}$ can be written as $8x = 2+10k$ for some integer k, but this simplifies to $4x = 1+5k$, so the congruence equation becomes $4x \equiv 1 \pmod 5$, which is simpler to solve. However, you should give your solutions in terms of the original modulus.

The solution to $4x \equiv 1 \pmod 5$ is $x \equiv 4 \pmod 5$ which can be written as $x \equiv 4 \pmod{10}$. However, this will only describe half of the possible solutions: you also have $x \equiv 9 \pmod{10}$ since $9 \equiv 4 \pmod 5$

Key point

The congruence equation $ax \equiv b \pmod m$, where $\operatorname{hcf}(a, m) | b$ has N solutions $\pmod m$, where $N = \operatorname{hcf}(a, m)$

Example 5

Find the integer solutions to $6x \equiv 9 \pmod{21}$

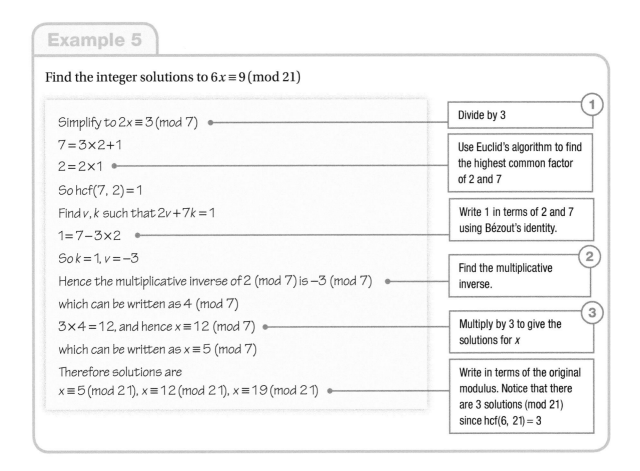

Simplify to $2x \equiv 3 \pmod 7$ — ① Divide by 3

$7 = 3 \times 2 + 1$

$2 = 2 \times 1$ — Use Euclid's algorithm to find the highest common factor of 2 and 7

So $\operatorname{hcf}(7, 2) = 1$

Find v, k such that $2v + 7k = 1$ — Write 1 in terms of 2 and 7 using Bézout's identity.

$1 = 7 - 3 \times 2$

So $k = 1, v = -3$

Hence the multiplicative inverse of $2 \pmod 7$ is $-3 \pmod 7$ — ② Find the multiplicative inverse.

which can be written as $4 \pmod 7$

$3 \times 4 = 12$, and hence $x \equiv 12 \pmod 7$ — ③ Multiply by 3 to give the solutions for x

which can be written as $x \equiv 5 \pmod 7$

Therefore solutions are $x \equiv 5 \pmod{21}$, $x \equiv 12 \pmod{21}$, $x \equiv 19 \pmod{21}$ — Write in terms of the original modulus. Notice that there are 3 solutions $\pmod{21}$ since $\operatorname{hcf}(6, 21) = 3$

1   Use Bézout's identity to find the integer solutions to each of these congruence equations.
Give your answers using the modulus specified in the question.

a $12x \equiv 108 \,(\text{mod } 126)$

b $6x \equiv 15 \,(\text{mod } 165)$

c $8x \equiv 12 \,(\text{mod } 462)$

d $45x \equiv 30 \,(\text{mod } 285)$

2   Explain how many integer solutions (mod 51) there are to the congruence equation
$12x \equiv 27 \,(\text{mod } 51)$

3   Explain how many integer solutions (mod 98) there are to the congruence equation
$42x \equiv 21 \,(\text{mod } 98)$

4   Explain how many integer solutions (mod 209) there are to the congruence equation
$33x \equiv 22 \,(\text{mod } 209)$

5   Solve each of these congruence equations, giving your answers using the modulus specified in
the question.

a $3x + 8 \equiv 2 \,(\text{mod } 5)$

b $7x - 7 \equiv 3 \,(\text{mod } 4)$

c $5x + 8 \equiv 9 \,(\text{mod } 12)$

d $4x - 13 \equiv 4 \,(\text{mod } 15)$

e $8x + 35 \equiv 27 \,(\text{mod } 68)$

f $125x - 62 \equiv 48 \,(\text{mod } 90)$

Combinatorics

Fluency and skills

Suppose you wished to chose two distinct items from a set of 5; call them A, B, C, D and E. You could list all the possibilities in a systematic way:

A and B

A and C   B and C

A and D   B and D   C and D

A and E   B and E   C and E   D and E

So there are 10 possible pairs of distinct items that could be selected. Notice how each pair is only included once since the order in which they are selected is not important. These are known as the **combinations**.

Key point

A **combination** is an *unordered* arrangement of objects from a set.

If you were to consider *ordered* arrangements of two items from the set of 5, then each combination would be counted twice, for example A and B could have been either A then B or B then A. So in the example above there would be $10 \times 2 = 20$ **permutations**.

Key point

A **permutation** is an *ordered* arrangement of objects from a set.

If you wished to choose four distinct items from the same set of 5, then the list of combinations would be

A and B and C and D   A and B and D and E   B and C and D and E

A and B and C and E   A and C and D and E

So there are 5 combinations.

Consider the first of these combinations. They could be arranged in 24 ways:

ABCD	BACD	CABD	DABC
ABDC	BADC	CADB	DACB
ACBD	BCAD	CBAD	DBAC
ACDB	BCDA	CBDA	DBCA
ADBC	BDAC	CDAB	DCAB
ADCB	BDCA	CDBA	DCBA

Each of the other combinations will also have 24 ways of being arranged, so in total there are $5 \times 24 = 120$ permutations.

Clearly, as the numbers get bigger it will be inefficient to write out all the combinations and permutations.

There are $^nC_r = \dfrac{n!}{r!(n-r)!}$ ways of choosing r distinct items from a set of n items.

Key point

The number of combinations when choosing r distinct items from a set of n distinct items is $^nC_r = \dfrac{n!}{r!(n-r)!}$

You have just seen that there are 24 ways to arrange 4 distinct items. This is because there are 4 possible positions for the first item, then 3 for the next, then 2, then 1. In other words, there are $4! = 4 \times 3 \times 2 \times 1$ ways to arrange 4 distinct items.

So you could multiply the value of ^nC_r by 4! to find the number of permutations, ^nP_r

Suppose you wish to choose r distinct items from a list of n distinct items. There will be $r!$ ways to arrange each combination so the number of permutations is $\dfrac{n!}{r!(n-r)!} \times r! = \dfrac{n!}{(n-r)!}$

Key point

The number of permutations when choosing r distinct items from a set of n distinct items is $^nP_r = \dfrac{n!}{(n-r)!}$

Example 1

A code for a lock is a typical example of when order does matter: you will need to find the number of permutations.

The code for a lock is 6 distinct digits taken from the numbers 0–9

a How many possible codes are there?

b How many different arrangements of each possible set of digits are there?

c How many possible codes are there if the 6 digits do not need to be distinct?

a In this case, $n = 10$ and $r = 6$

$^{10}P_6 = \dfrac{10!}{(10-6)!}$

$= \dfrac{10!}{4!}$

$= 151\,200$

So there are $151\,200$ permutations.

> The number of permutations is given by $^nP_r = \dfrac{n!}{(n-r)!}$

b Each set of digits can be arranged in $6! = 720$ ways

c If the digits are not distinct, then each of the digits can be any of the numbers 0–9

So there are 10 possibilities for the first digit, 10 for the second and so on

$10 \times 10 \times 10 \times 10 \times 10 \times 10 = 10^6 = 1\,000\,000$

So there are $1\,000\,000$ permutations.

Suppose that, instead of a free choice of six values from 0–9, four values are chosen from the digits 0–5 followed by two values from the digits 6–9

The number of permutations when choosing four values from a set of 6 (0, 1, 2, 3, 4, 5) is $^6P_4 = \dfrac{6!}{(6-4)!}$

$$= 360$$

The number of permutations when choosing two values from a set of 4 (6, 7, 8, 9) is $^4P_2 = \dfrac{4!}{(4-2)!}$

$$= 12$$

Therefore, the total number of possibilities is $360 \times 12 = 4320$
This is known as the **multiplication principle** of counting.

Calculator

Try it on your calculator

Permutations and combinations can be found using your calculator.

Activity
Find out how to work out $^{15}C_4$ and $^{15}P_4$ on *your* calculator.

> **Key point**
>
> **The multiplication principle of counting**
>
> If there are p ways to do one thing and q ways to do another, then there are $p \times q$ ways of doing both things.

You may notice that this is similar to the intersection rule of probability:

$P(A \cap B) = P(A) \times P(B)$ when A and B are independent. There is also the **addition principle** of counting which is similar to the union rule of probability:

$P(A \cup B) = P(A) + P(B)$ when A and B are mutually exclusive.

> **Key point**
>
> **The addition principle of counting**
>
> If there are p ways to do one thing and q ways to do another and it is not possible to do both together, then there are $p + q$ ways of doing either thing.

Example 2

The letters of the alphabet are arranged into the vowels and the consonants. 4 distinct letters are to be selected at random. How many combinations are there if you select

a 2 vowels and 2 consonants,

b 4 vowels or 4 consonants?

a The number of combinations of 2 vowels is $^5C_2 = 10$ ● — Since there are 5 vowels (a, e, i, o, u).

The number of combinations of 2 consonants is $^{21}C_2 = 210$

So the number of combinations of 2 vowels and 2 consonants is $10 \times 210 = 2100$ ●

b The number of combinations of 4 vowels is $^5C_4 = 5$

Using the multiplication principle.

The number of combinations of 4 consonants is $^{21}C_4 = 5985$

So the number of combinations of 4 vowels or 4 consonants is $5 + 5985 = 5990$ ●

Using the addition principle.

1 How many ways are there of arranging 5 distinct items?

2 How many ways are there of arranging 12 distinct items?

3 A group of 5 pupils is to be selected from a class of 30. How many possible groups are there?

4 A starter, main course and dessert must be chosen from a list of 7 starters, 9 main courses and 3 desserts. How many possible combinations are there?

5 7 distinct tapas dishes are to be selected from a menu containing 8 with meat, 3 with fish and 9 vegetarian. How many combinations are there if

   a The 7 tapas are selected at random from the whole menu,

   b 3 meat tapas are selected, 2 fish and 2 vegetarian,

   c 4 tapas containing meat or fish and 3 vegetarian tapas are selected,

   d 5 vegetarian tapas are selected and then the remaining 2 are selected from any part of the menu,

   e Either the 7 dishes all contain meat or fish or are all vegetarian?

6 If **7** meals are to be selected from a list of 17, how many possible combinations are there?

7 How many different 4-digit numbers can be made from the digits 1–9 if

   a No digits are repeated,

   b Digits can be repeated any number of times?

8 How many permutations are there when 6 letters are chosen from the first 12 letters of the alphabet if

   a No letters are repeated,

   b Letters can be repeated any number of times?

9 A code consists of 7 digits. Find the number of possible codes in each of these scenarios.

   a The digits are all selected from the numbers 1–9 and the digits are

      i All distinct,

      ii Not necessarily distinct.

   b The digits are all distinct and 4 digits are taken from the numbers 1–5 and then the rest are taken from the numbers 6–9

   c Two digits are taken from the numbers 1–5 and then the rest are taken from the numbers 1–9 and the digits are

      i All distinct,

      ii Not necessarily distinct.

10 A class contains 12 boys and 15 girls. A group of 8 pupils is to be selected from the class. How many possible groups are there if

   a The group can contain any number of boys and girls that add to a total of 8

   b The group contains 4 boys and 4 girls,

   c The group contains either 8 boys or 8 girls,

   d The group contains 5 girls plus 3 more pupils of either gender?

Reasoning and problem-solving

A **set** is a collection of objects known as **elements**. The order of the elements is not relevant. A part of a set is called a **subset**. Consider the set $\{1, 2, 3\}$. The subsets of this are:

$\varnothing$ which is the **empty set** (i.e. has no elements)

$\{1\}, \{2\}, \{3\}$ which are subsets of size 1

$\{1, 2\}, \{1, 3\}, \{2, 3\}$ which are subsets of size 2

$\{1, 2, 3\}$ which is the set itself, but also a subset of size 3

So there are 8 subsets of the set $\{1, 2, 3\}$. The first 7 of these are known as **proper subsets** but the final example (which is the set itself) is not a proper subset.

> If set B is a proper subset of set A, you can write $B \subset A$: for example, $\{1\} \subset \{1, 2, 3\}$. If set B is a subset of set A (i.e. it could possibly be the set itself), then you can write $B \subseteq A$

You can use the techniques of combinatorics to find the number of subsets of a set.

Strategy

To find the number of subset of a set

(1) Use $^{n}C_{r}$ to find the number of sets of size r for $r = 0, 1, 2, 3, \ldots, n - 1$

(2) Add to find the total number of proper subsets.

(3) Add on one set of size n if you require all subsets (not just the proper subsets).

Example 3

How many subsets are there of a set with 6 elements?

There are 6 subsets of size 1

There are $^{6}C_{2} = 15$ subsets of size 2

There are $^{6}C_{3} = 20$ subsets of size 3

There are $^{6}C_{4} = 15$ subsets of size 4

There are $^{6}C_{5} = 6$ subsets of size 5

So there are $1 + 6 + 15 + 20 + 15 + 6 = 63$ proper subsets.

There is 1 subset of size 6 (the set itself).

So there are $63 + 1 = 64$ subsets.

Use $^{6}C_{r}$ to find the number of sets of size r for $r = 1, 2, 3, \ldots, 5$

Add up the subsets of size 0 (the empty set), 1, 2, 3, 4 and 5 to find the number of proper subsets.

Add one for the set itself.

Notice that $2^{6} = 64$

You can use induction to prove this result.

Let $n = 0$. A set of size 0 has one subset: itself (the empty set).

$2^0 = 1$, therefore the statement is true for $n = 0$

Assume that the statement is true for $n = k$, i.e. assume that a set of size k has 2^k subsets.

Now add another element into the set so that it is of size $k + 1$. The subsets of this new set can be split into two types: those that contain the new element and those that don't.

There are 2^k subsets that do not contain the new element since these are the subsets of the set of size k. By adding the new element into each of these subsets you get 2^k more sets that do include the new element.

So the total number of subsets for a set of size k is $2 \times 2^k = 2^{k+1}$, as required.

> For example, subsets of the set $\{1, 2, 3\}$ can be split into those containing 3 and those not containing 3
>
> | Not containing 3 | Containing 3 |
> |---|---|
> | Ø | $\{3\}$ |
> | $\{1\}, \{2\}$ | $\{1, 3\}, \{2, 3\}$ |
> | $\{1, 2\}$ | $\{1, 2, 3\}$ |
>
> So there are $2^2 = 4$ subsets for the set $\{1, 2\}$ and $2^3 = 8$ subsets for the set $\{1, 2, 3\}$

Exercise 9.4B Reasoning and problem-solving

1 How many subsets of size 5 are there for a set of size 12?

2 How many subsets of size 8 are there for a set of size 18?

3 By enumerating the subsets of different sizes, show that a set of size 5 has 32 subsets.

4 By enumerating the subsets of different sizes, show that a set of size 7 has 128 subsets.

5 How many subsets will a set of size 17 have?

6 How many subsets will a set of size 24 have?

7 How many proper subsets will a set of size 19 have?

8 How many proper subsets will a set of size 21 have?

9 How many more subsets will a set of size 13 have compared with a set of size 15?

10 How many proper subsets with more than 2 elements will a set of size 9 have?

11 How many subsets with more than 3 elements will a set of size 19 have?

12 Show that there are 2^n more subsets for a set of size $n + 1$ compared with a set of size n

13 Show that there are $2^n(2^n - 1)$ more subsets for a set of size $2n$ compared with a set of size n

14 How many more subsets are there for a set of size $n + 3$ compared with a set of size n? Give your answer in the form $A(2^n)$, where A is a constant to be found.

15 How many more ways are there of arranging $n + 1$ items compared with n items?

16 How many more ways are there of arranging $n + 2$ items compared with n items?

17 Prove that $^{k+1}C_r = {}^kC_r + {}^kC_{r-1}$ for all positive integers r and k

18 How many more combinations are there if you select 1 item from each of two sets of size n as opposed to 2 distinct items from either of the sets of size n

Chapter summary

- N is divisible by 2 if the units digit is divisible by 2
- N is divisible by 3 if the sum of the digits is divisible by 3
- N is divisible by 4 if the number created by the tens and units digits is divisible by 4
- N is divisible by 5 if the units digit is divisible by 5
- N is divisible by 6 if it is divisible by 2 and 3
- N is divisible by 9 if the sum of the digits is divisible by 9
- N is divisible by 10 if the units digit is 0
- N is divisible by 11 if the alternating sum of the digits is divisible by 11
- **Euclidean algorithm**

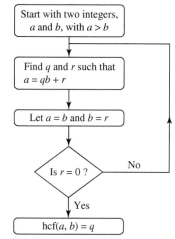

Start with two integers,
a and b, with $a > b$

Find q and r such that
$a = qb + r$

Let $a = b$ and $b = r$

Is $r = 0$? → No

Yes

$\text{hcf}(a, b) = q$

- For all non-zero integers a and b where $\text{hcf}(a, b) = c$, there exist integers x and y such that $ax + by = c$
- For relatively prime integers a and b, there exist integers x and y such that $ax + by = 1$
- The equation $ax + by = c$ with $a, b, c \in \mathbb{Z}$ has integer solutions if and only if $\text{hcf}(a, b) | c$
- For all integers a, b, c, and n
  - $a \equiv b \pmod{n}$ if and only if $n | (a - b)$
  - $a \equiv a \pmod{n}$
  - If $a \equiv b \pmod{n}$ then $b \equiv a \pmod{n}$
  - If $a \equiv b \pmod{n}$ and $b \equiv c \pmod{n}$ then $a \equiv c \pmod{n}$
  - If $a \equiv b \pmod{n}$ and $c \equiv d \pmod{n}$ then
    $a + c = b + d \pmod{n}$
    $a - c = b - d \pmod{n}$
    $ac = bd \pmod{n}$ as long as a, b, c, d, are integers and n is a positive integer
  - If $a \equiv b \pmod{n}$ for $a, b, n \in \mathbb{Z}$, then $a^k \equiv b^k \pmod{n}$ for $k \in \mathbb{Z}^+$

- If $ax \equiv 1 \pmod{n}$, then x is the multiplicative inverse of $a \pmod{n}$ and can be found using Bézout's identity.
  - $ax \equiv b \pmod{n}$ has integer solutions, x, if and only if $\mathrm{hcf}(a, n)|b$ **Full A Level**
  - The congruence equation $ax \equiv b \pmod{m}$, where $\mathrm{hcf}(a, m)|b$, has N solutions $\pmod{m}$, where $N = \mathrm{hcf}(a, m)$
  - If p is a prime number, then $a^p = a \pmod{p}$ for all integers a
  - If p is a prime number and a is an integer which is not a multiple of p then $a^{p-1} = 1 \pmod{p}$
  - The theorem can be used to find the least positive residue modulus p
- A combination is an unordered arrangement of objects from a set. The number of combinations of r elements from a set of size n is given by ${}^nC_r = \dfrac{n!}{r!(n-r)!}$
- A permutation is an ordered arrangement of objects from a set. The number of permutations of r elements from a set of size n is given by ${}^nP_r = \dfrac{n!}{(n-r)!}$
- The multiplication principle of counting:
  - If there are p ways to do one thing and q ways to do another, then there are $p \times q$ ways of doing both things.
- The addition principle of counting:
  - If there are p ways to do one thing and q ways to do another and it is not possible to do both together, then there are $p + q$ ways of doing either thing.
- A collection of some or all of the elements of a set is a subset.
- A finite set of size n has 2^n subsets for all integers $n \geq 0$

Check and review

You should now be able to...	Review Questions
✔ Apply Euclid's algorithm to find the highest common factor of two numbers.	1
✔ Use back substitution to identify Bézout's identity for two numbers.	2
✔ Know and apply divisibility tests for 2, 3, 4, 5, 6, 9, 10 and 11	3
✔ Apply addition and subtraction laws for congruences.	4
✔ Apply multiplication and power laws for congruences.	5
✔ Solve congruence equations. **Full A Level**	6, 7
✔ Know and apply Fermat's little theorem. **Full A Level**	8, 9
✔ Calculate the number of combinations or permutations.	10, 11
✔ Know and use the multiplication principle of counting.	12
✔ Know and use the addition principle of counting.	13
✔ Be able to find the number of subsets of a set of a given size.	14

1 Use Euclid's algorithm to find the highest common factor of 1562 and 561

2 Use back substitution into Euclid's algorithm to find the Bézout identity for 551 and 1159

3 Use divisibility tests to show that the number 1980 is divisible by

   a 2   b 3   c 4   d 5

   e 6   f 9   g 10   h 11

4 Use the laws of modular arithmetic to calculate the value of

   a $27\,683 + 78\,239 \pmod 5$

   b $864 - 403 \pmod 4$

   Give your answers in their simplest form.

5 Use the laws of modular arithmetic to calculate the value of

   a $66\,331 \times 302 \pmod 3$

   b $3782^{15} \pmod{10}$

6 Find the integer solutions to $17x \equiv 1 \pmod{72}$

7 Find the integer solutions to $39x \equiv 26 \pmod{65}$. Write your answers in modulus 65

8 Use Fermat's little theorem to find the remainder when 3^{57} is divided by 19

9 Use Fermat's little theorem to find the least positive residue of $15^{98} \pmod{13}$

10 Calculate the number of possible combinations when 8 distinct houses are chosen from a street containing 25 houses.

11 The code for a safe is 5 digits long and can use any of the digits 0–6. How many possible codes are there if

   a The code consists of 4 distinct digits,

   b Repetition of digits is allowed?

12 An exercise routine consists of one warm-up exercise from a list of 5, followed by three cardiovascular exercises from a list of 7, then four strength exercises from a list of 9 and finally two cool-down exercises from a list of 6

   Calculate the number of different possible routines given that the order of exercises within each type does not matter.

13 A person selects either 3 different vegetables or 4 different fruits from a selection of 10 vegetables and 8 fruits. How many possible combinations are there?

14 a How many subsets will a set containing 14 elements have?

   b How many of these subsets will contain exactly 5 elements?

   c How many of these subsets will contain fewer than 2 elements?

Did you know?

The Russian-British mathematician, Leonid Mirsky, described the wide-ranging nature of combinatorics as 'a range of linked studies which have something in common and yet diverge widely in their objectives, their methods, and the degree of coherence they have attained'.

Research

Combinatorics can be seen in campanology - the study of bells. Find out about the Hamiltonian cycles (which you may have looked at in Decision maths) that were studied in some Cayley graphs.

Research

Find out about the Diffie-Hellman key exchange. It was one of the first methods designed to set up SSL connections to encrypt web traffic. It was a major development in cryptography, as the two parties communicating do not need prior knowledge of each other to jointly establish a secret over an open channel. Before the development of methods such as Diffie-Hellman, cryptographic keys had to be transferred in a physical form. One of the most well-known examples of a physical list of keys is the German Enigma machine.

1 **a** Without performing any division, explain why 2892 is divisible by 6 **[2]**

b Use the Euclidean algorithm to find the highest common factor of 2892 and 348

Show each step of the algorithm. **[3]**

2 **a** Without performing any division, show that 6182 is divisible by 11 **[2]**

b Use the Euclidean algorithm to determine whether 6182 and 1911 are coprime. **[4]**

3 Use the Euclidean algorithm to find integers a and b such that $37a + 33b = 1$ **[4]**

4 The greatest common divisor of 490 and 182 is d

a Using back substitution, find integer values, x and y, satisfying the Bezout's identity

$490x + 182y = d$ **[5]**

b Write down two more pairs of integer values that satisfy the same identity. **[1]**

5 Use modular arithmetic to calculate

a $73 + 94 \pmod 7$ **[2]**

b $81 \times 66 \pmod{13}$ **[2]**

c $76^{82} \pmod{11}$ **[2]**

6 Use Fermat's little theorem to show that $2^{45} + 1 \equiv 0 \pmod{11}$ **[3]**

7 Use Fermat's little theorem to find the least positive residue of $23^{97} \pmod{13}$ **[3]**

8 **a** Find the integer solutions to the congruence equation $7x + 11 \equiv 10 \pmod{12}$ **[6]**

b Explain why there are no integer solutions to the congruence equation $6x \equiv 1 \pmod{30}$ **[1]**

Full A Level

9 A five-digit code for a safe can use the numbers from 0 to 9

    a How many different codes are possible if the digits do not need to be distinct?   **[1]**

    Given that the digits *do* have to be distinct,

    b How many possible codes are there?   **[2]**

    It is decided that the code must start with an odd digit.

    c How many possible codes are there now?   **[2]**

    d What is the probability that the code is an even number?   **[3]**

10 A hockey coach has to select a team of 11 players consisting of one goalkeeper, one sweeper, three defenders, three midfielders and three forwards.

    Her squad contains three goalkeepers, two sweepers, five defenders, eight midfielders and seven forwards.

    How many possible teams are there if

    a The defenders, midfielders and forwards can play anywhere in their 'line',   **[2]**

    b The defenders, midfielders and forwards are selected in 'left', 'centre' and 'right' positions?   **[2]**

11 A set contains 15 distinct elements.

    a How many proper subsets are there?   **[2]**

    b How many of these subsets will contain exactly 6 elements?   **[2]**

    c How many of these subsets will have more than 12 elements?   **[2]**

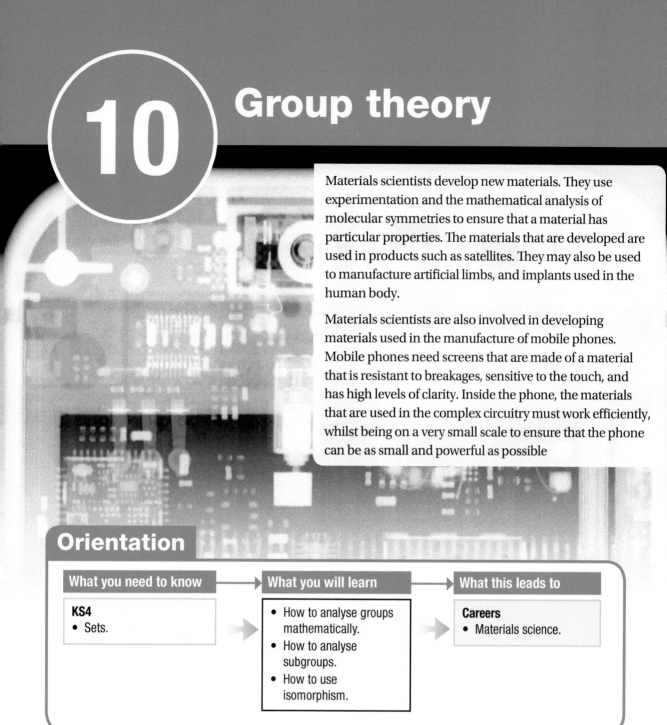

10 Group theory

Materials scientists develop new materials. They use experimentation and the mathematical analysis of molecular symmetries to ensure that a material has particular properties. The materials that are developed are used in products such as satellites. They may also be used to manufacture artificial limbs, and implants used in the human body.

Materials scientists are also involved in developing materials used in the manufacture of mobile phones. Mobile phones need screens that are made of a material that is resistant to breakages, sensitive to the touch, and has high levels of clarity. Inside the phone, the materials that are used in the complex circuitry must work efficiently, whilst being on a very small scale to ensure that the phone can be as small and powerful as possible

Orientation

What you need to know	What you will learn	What this leads to
KS4 • Sets.	• How to analyse groups mathematically. • How to analyse subgroups. • How to use isomorphism.	**Careers** • Materials science.

Fluency and skills

A group is a collection of mathematical objects that can be combined subject to a set of basic rules, or axioms.

An example of a group is the set of permutations of the numbers 1, 2 and 3

You can list these permutations: (1 2 3), (1 3 2), (2 1 3), (2 3 1), (3 1 2) and (3 2 1). You can also write the permutations using notation which indicates how the original order of the numbers changes under each permutation.

$$e = \begin{pmatrix} 1 & 2 & 3 \\ 1 & 2 & 3 \end{pmatrix}, a = \begin{pmatrix} 1 & 2 & 3 \\ 1 & 3 & 2 \end{pmatrix}, b = \begin{pmatrix} 1 & 2 & 3 \\ 2 & 1 & 3 \end{pmatrix}, c = \begin{pmatrix} 1 & 2 & 3 \\ 2 & 3 & 1 \end{pmatrix}, d = \begin{pmatrix} 1 & 2 & 3 \\ 3 & 1 & 2 \end{pmatrix}, f = \begin{pmatrix} 1 & 2 & 3 \\ 3 & 2 & 1 \end{pmatrix}$$

The six permutations are called **elements**. The first of these permutations leaves the order of the numbers unchanged. This element is known as the **identity**, e

In order to be a group, the set of elements must contain an identity element.

A second condition for the set of objects to be a group is that any combination of the elements is contained within the original set. This condition is known as **closure**.

If you apply permutation b and then permutation c then under the permutation cb, 1 maps to 2 maps to 3, 2 maps to 1 maps to 2 and 3 maps to 3 maps to 1

Overall, the result is permutation f

All of the possible combinations of two permutations can be shown in a **Cayley table**.

		First permutation					
	followed by	e	a	b	c	d	f
Second permutation	e	e	a	b	c	d	f
	a	a	e	d	f	b	c
	b	b	c	e	a	f	d
	c	c	b	f	d	e	a
	d	d	f	a	e	c	b
	f	f	d	c	b	a	e

You can see from the Cayley table that for any combination of two permutations, the result is one of the original set of permutations.

In addition to this, you can see that every element has another element which, when combined, leads to the identity element e

For example, $aa = e$ and $cd = e$

These elements are known as **inverse** elements. Since a, b, e and f combine with themselves to produce the identity element they are known as **self-inverse**, while d is the inverse of c and vice versa.

The final condition for a set of elements to be a group is known as **associativity**. Three elements are associative if $a(bc) = (ab)c$, that is, bc followed by a gives the same result as c followed by ab

From the table above, you can see that $a(bc) = aa$ and $(ab)c = dc$ and both aa and dc give e

Hence a, b and c are associative. This can be shown for any other combination of the elements in the same way.

Since this final condition is met, you can say that the set of permutations of the numbers 1, 2 and 3 forms a **group**.

Key point

The conditions under which a set of mathematical objects form a group under a given binary operation are known as the **axioms**. These are **closure**, the existence of an **identity element**, **associativity** and the existence of an **inverse** element for each member of the set.

A binary operation is an operation that combines two elements of a set according to a given rule.

Using formal notation, a group can be defined as follows.

Key point

A group $(S, \circ)$ is a non-empty set S with a binary operation $\circ$ such that:

- $\circ$ is closed in S
- $\circ$ is associative
- there is an identity element, e, such that $x \circ e = e \circ x = x$ for all x
- each element has an inverse, x^{-1}, such that $x \circ x^{-1} = x^{-1} \circ x = e$

The most difficult axiom to test for is associativity. However, there are certain binary operations that are known to be associative. For example, modular multiplication and addition are associative, as is matrix multiplication. Also, any binary operation that can be interpreted as the composition of mappings is associative. You can use these facts without proof.

Example 1

a Draw a Cayley table for the binary operation addition modulo 4 ($+_4$) on the set $S = \{0, 1, 2, 3\}$

b Is the set closed under $+_4$?

c State the element that is the identity element.

d For each element, state its inverse.

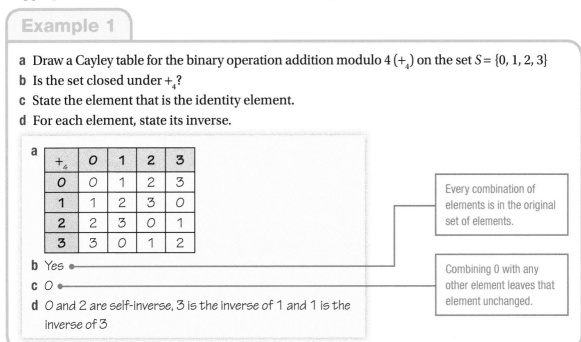

a

$+_4$	0	1	2	3
0	0	1	2	3
1	1	2	3	0
2	2	3	0	1
3	3	0	1	2

Every combination of elements is in the original set of elements.

b Yes

c 0

d 0 and 2 are self-inverse, 3 is the inverse of 1 and 1 is the inverse of 3

Combining 0 with any other element leaves that element unchanged.

There are several terms that you need to know.

The **order** of a group is equal to the number of elements in the group.

The **period** (or order) of a particular element, x, of a group is the smallest non-negative integer n such that $x^n = e$, where e is the identity.

In the permutations example above, the order of the group is 6 since there are 6 different permutations.

Element a has period 2 since $a^2 = e$ and element c has period 3 since $c^3 = c(cc) = cd = e$

An **abelian** group is a group with the additional property of **commutativity** between the elements of the group.

Commutativity is the property that, for all elements of a group, $xy = yx$ under the given binary operation.

In the permutations example, $ba \neq ab$, therefore this group is not an abelian group.

In Example 1, $1 + 3 = 3 + 1$ and so on, so this group *is* an abelian group.

Abelian groups are characterised by a line of symmetry down the leading diagonal.

Exercise 10.1A Fluency and skills

1 a Draw a Cayley table for the binary operation multiplication modulo 5 ($\times_5$) on the set $S = \{0, 1, 2, 3, 4\}$

  b Is the set closed under $\times_5$?

  c State the element that is the identity element.

  d For each element, write down its inverse.

  e State, with a reason, whether or not S forms a group.

2 a Draw a Cayley table for the binary operation addition modulo 6 ($+_6$) on the set $S = \{0, 1, 2, 3, 4, 5\}$

  b Is the set closed under $+_6$?

  c State the element that is the identity element.

  d Show that S forms a group under $+_6$

  e Is the group formed an abelian group? Give a reason for your answer.

3 The binary operation $x \bullet y$ is defined as $|x - y|$

  a Draw a Cayley table for the binary operation when applied to the set $S = \{0, 1, 2, 3\}$

  b Is the set closed for $x \bullet y$?

  c Identify the identity element.

  d Fahima says that the set S forms a group under $x \bullet y$. Is Fahima correct? Give a reason for your answer.

4 Show that the set of matrices, S, of the form $\begin{pmatrix} 1 & p \\ 0 & 1 \end{pmatrix}$, $p \in \mathbb{Z}$, forms an abelian group under the operation of matrix multiplication.

5 Prove that the set of natural numbers, $\mathbb{N}$, does not form a group under the operation of subtraction.

6 The set S, defined as $S = \{1, 2, 3, 4, 5, 6\}$, forms a group G under the binary operation $\times_7$

   a State the order of the group G

   b Determine the period of the element 6 in the group G

7 **a** Show that the set $S = \{\mathbb{Z}\}$ forms a group under the binary operation $\bullet$ where $x \bullet y = x + y - 2$

   b Explain why the set $T = \{\mathbb{Z}^+\}$ does not form a group under the same binary operation.

Reasoning and problem-solving

The set of all symmetries of a regular polygon also forms a group.

These groups are called **dihedral groups** (denoted by $\boldsymbol{D_n}$ where n is the number of sides in the regular n-gon).

A **cyclic group** is formed if, for example, only rotational symmetries are considered. Cyclic groups are characterised by having at least one **generator** element $\langle g \rangle$ that generates all of the other elements of the group.

Strategy

To show that a given set forms a group under a given binary operation

(1) Write down the elements of the set.

(2) Produce a Cayley table to show the combinations of each element under the given binary operation.

(3) Check that the binary operation meets the axioms necessary to be a group.

Example 2

a Show that the set of all symmetries of an equilateral triangle forms a group.

b Write down the cyclic group, C_3, represented by the set of rotational symmetries of an equilateral triangle and state an element that can be used as a generator.

a

r_0 = rotation of 0° about the origin (i.e. the triangle is in its initial orientation)

r_1 = rotation of 120° anticlockwise about the origin

r_2 = rotation of 240° anticlockwise about the origin

(1) Define the point of intersection of the lines of symmetry as the origin and then list the symmetries in turn.

(Continued on the next page)

141

m_1 = reflection in the mirror line through A

m_2 = reflection in the mirror line through B

m_3 = reflection in the mirror line through C

	r_0	r_1	r_2	m_1	m_2	m_3
r_0	r_0	r_1	r_2	m_1	m_2	m_3
r_1	r_1	r_2	r_0	m_2	m_3	m_1
r_2	r_2	r_0	r_1	m_3	m_1	m_2
m_1	m_1	m_3	m_2	r_0	r_2	r_1
m_2	m_2	m_1	m_3	r_1	r_0	r_2
m_3	m_3	m_2	m_1	r_2	r_1	r_0

> ② Draw up a Cayley table to show the combinations of the different symmetries.

Axioms

Identity: r_0 is the identity element.

Inverses: r_0, m_1, m_2 and m_3 are self-inverse; r_1 is the inverse of r_2 and vice versa.

Closure: Every combination of symmetries is in the original set of symmetries.

> ③ Check that the binary operation representing the combination of two symmetries satisfies the axioms.

Associativity: Since the binary operation is a composition of mappings, the operation is associative.

Hence the set of symmetries of an equilateral triangle forms a group (this is the dihedral group D_3)

b

	r_0	r_1	r_2
r_0	r_0	r_1	r_2
r_1	r_1	r_2	r_0
r_2	r_2	r_0	r_1

> This is the Cayley table for the rotational symmetries.

The group C_3 is therefore $\{r_0, r_1, r_2\}$

The group can be generated by successively applying symmetry r_1

$r_1{}^1 = r_1$

$r_1{}^2 = r_2$

$r_1{}^3 = r_0$

Hence r_1 is a generator of the group which can be denoted by $\langle r_1 \rangle$

> r_2 is also a generator of the group since $r_2{}^2 = r_1$ and $r_2{}^3 = r_0$
> Either r_1 or r_2 are suitable answers.

1 a Show that the set of all symmetries of a square forms a group and state the order of the group.

b Write down the cyclic group, C_4, represented by the set of rotational symmetries of a square and state two different elements that are generators.

2 Jeremiah defines the cyclic group represented by the set of rotational symmetries of a regular hexagon as $C_6 = \{r_0, r_1, r_2, r_3, r_4, r_5\}$

a Using a Cayley table, or otherwise, find all of the generators of Jeremiah's group.

He claims that the group C_6 is abelian.

b Is Jeremiah correct?

3 a Give a geometric interpretation of the dihedral group D_5

b Explain why the order of D_5 is 10

Philomena claims that the order of any dihedral group, D_n, is equal to $2n$

c Explain why Philomena is correct.

4 The group G is defined as $G = (\langle 5 \rangle, \times_7)$

a Find the set of all elements contained within G

b Is G an abelian group?

5 The group R is defined as $R = (\langle 3 \rangle, +_7)$

a Draw a Cayley table for R

b Write down the order of the group.

Joanna claims that 3 is not the unique generator of the group.

c Assess Joanna's claim.

6 The group G is defined as

$$G = \left(\left\langle \begin{pmatrix} 0 & 1 \\ -1 & 0 \end{pmatrix} \right\rangle, \text{matrix multiplication} \right)$$

a Find all of the elements of G and state its order.

b Give a geometrical interpretation of G

7 A cyclic group G under the binary operation • has this Cayley table

•	a	b	c	d
a	a	b	c	d
b	b	a	d	c
c	c	d	b	a
d	d	c	a	b

a Write down the identity element.

b Find a generator of G

8 The set of symmetries of a circle forms an infinite group, O_2

a Write down the identity element.

b State why the associativity property holds for this group.

c Write down the inverse of

i A rotation through 32.1°

ii A reflection in a line of symmetry inclined at $\theta°$

The table shows the effects of combining two symmetries, 'rot' (a rotation) and 'ref' (a reflection).

	rot	**ref**
rot	?	ref
ref	ref	rot

d What is represented by '?'

Give a reason for your answer.

e Use this table to explain why the set of symmetries of a circle has the closure property.

[Note: The group O_2 is known as the **orthogonal** group and the subscript '2' tells you that you are dealing with a two-dimensional object.]

Fluency and skills

Key point

A **subgroup** of a group G is any subset H of G such that H itself is also a group under the same binary operation as G

The **trivial subgroup** consisting of just the identity element is a subgroup of the (parent) group.

The group itself is also a subgroup of the group.

Key point

A **non-trivial subgroup** is any subgroup that is not the trivial subgroup.

A **proper subgroup** is any subgroup that is not the group itself.

You need to be able to show that a stated group H is a subgroup of another stated group G. You do this by checking four conditions:

- That H is non-empty
- That the identity element in G exists in H
- That H is closed under the binary operation for G
- That the inverse of each element of H belongs to H

Example 1

$\mathbb{R} \backslash \{0\}$ denotes the set of real numbers excluding zero.

a Show that $H = (\mathbb{Q}, +)$ is a subgroup of $G = (\mathbb{R}, +)$

b Show that the set $J = \{x \in \mathbb{R} : x \geq 1\}$ is not a subgroup of $K = (\mathbb{R} \backslash \{0\}, \times)$

a H is non-empty since there exist an infinite number of elements in H

The identity element of G under the binary operation addition is O and $O \in \mathbb{Q}$

H is closed since if $x, y \in \mathbb{Q}$, then $x + y \in \mathbb{Q}$

The inverse of an element x is x^{-1}, which is $-x$ under the binary operation of addition, and if $x \in \mathbb{Q}$, then $-x \in \mathbb{Q}$

Hence H is a subgroup of G

b J is non-empty since there exist an infinite number of elements in J

The identity element of K under the binary operation multiplication is 1, and 1 is in J

(Continued on the next page)

J is closed since if *x* and *y* are in *J*, their product *xy* is in *J*

The inverse of an element *x* is x^{-1}, which is $\dfrac{1}{x}$ under the binary operation of multiplication, but if $x > 1$, $x^{-1} < 1$, so *J* does not contain the inverse of *x*

Hence *J* is not a subgroup of *K*

> If you can show that any given condition is false, you do not have to check all of the conditions, since a single counter-example is enough.

You also need to be able to find subgroups for a given group.

Example 2

A group *G* is formed by the set $S = \{a, b, c, d\}$ under the binary operation •

A Cayley table is drawn to show the outcome for each pair of elements under •

•	*a*	*b*	*c*	*d*
a	*a*	*b*	*c*	*d*
b	*b*	*a*	*d*	*c*
c	*c*	*d*	*b*	*a*
d	*d*	*c*	*a*	*b*

Find all the non-trivial subgroups of *G*

Since *a* is the identity element, the group {*a*} is not a non-trivial subgroup, so this should not be included.

Since subgroups are groups under the same binary operation as the original group, all subgroups must contain the identity element *a*

Hence the options are {*a*, *b*}, {*a*, *c*}, {*a*, *d*}, {*a*, *b*, *c*}, {*a*, *b*, *d*}, {*a*, *c*, *d*} and {*a*, *b*, *c*, *d*}

Checking each one:

{*a*, *b*} is non-empty, closed and, since *a* and *b* are self-inverse, {*a*, *b*} is a subgroup of *G*

{*a*, *c*} is non-empty but, since $c^2 = b$, it is not closed.

{*a*, *d*} is non-empty but, since $d^2 = b$, it is not closed.

{*a*, *b*, *c*} is non-empty but, since $bc = d$, it is not closed.

{*a*, *b*, *d*} is non-empty but, since $bd = c$, it is not closed.

{*a*, *c*, *d*} is non-empty but, since $cd = b$, it is not closed.

{*a*, *b*, *c*, *d*} is the group itself so is, by definition, a non-trivial subgroup of *G*

Hence the non-trivial subgroups of *G* are {*a*, *b*} and {*a*, *b*, *c*, *d*}

1 Show that the group $H=(\mathbb{Z},+)$ is a subgroup of $G=(\mathbb{R},+)$

2 Show that the group of rotations of an equilateral triangle is a subgroup of the group of all symmetries of an equilateral triangle.

3 A group $G=(\{1, 2, 3, 4\}, \times_5)$. Find all the proper subgroups of G

4 A group $H=(\{0, 1, 2, 3\}, +_4)$. Find all the non-trivial subgroups of H

5 **a** Show that the group C_4 contains only one proper subgroup other than the trivial subgroup.

  b Explain how group H in question **4** and C_4 are related.

6 The Klein group $V=(\{a, b, c, d\}, \bullet)$ has this Cayley table

$\bullet$	a	b	c	d
a	a	b	c	d
b	b	a	d	c
c	c	d	a	b
d	d	c	b	a

Find all the proper subgroups of V

7 M is the set of all non-singular matrices such that $M=\left\{\begin{pmatrix} a & b \\ c & d \end{pmatrix} : a,b,c,d \in \mathbb{R}, ad-bc \neq 0\right\}$

Given that M forms a group under the binary operation of matrix multiplication, show that the set $N=\left\{\begin{pmatrix} 1 & 0 \\ 0 & 1 \end{pmatrix}\begin{pmatrix} -1 & 0 \\ 0 & -1 \end{pmatrix}\right\}$ is a subgroup of M

Reasoning and problem-solving

So far you have been identifying subgroups by checking all possible combinations of elements. If the number of elements is large, however, this becomes an arduous task. Imagine the group of all symmetries of a regular octagon. This would have order 16 and you would have to check a substantial number of cases.

Lagrange's theorem allows you to reduce the number of cases significantly.

Key point

Lagrange's theorem states that for any finite group G, the order of every subgroup of G divides the order of G

Also by Lagrange's theorem, the period of any element in the group G is a factor of the order of G

The consequence of this is that, for the example of the symmetries of the regular octagon, you would only need to look for subgroups of order 1 (the trivial subgroup containing just the identity which is always a subgroup), order 16 (the group itself), order 2, order 4 and order 8. For a group of order 16, this is still quite a few, but significantly fewer than if you had to check for groups of order 3, 5, 7, etc. as well.

To find all the possible subgroups of a particular group

(1) Use Lagrange's theorem to find the order of the possible subgroups.

(2) Use a systematic process to identify the possibilities.

(3) Check each possibility against the conditions for being a subgroup.

Example 3

The group $G = (\{0, 1, 2, 3, 4, 5\}, +_6)$

a State the order of G

b Write down the order of possible subgroups of G. Justify your answer.

c Use your answer to part **b** to find all the proper subgroups of G

a There are six elements in G so the order is 6

b 1, 2, 3 and 6 are factors of 6 so these are the orders of possible subgroups. ●————————————————

> **(1)** Use Lagrange's theorem.

c List all the possibilities:

$\{0\}$ – this is the trivial subgroup.

$\{0, 1, 2, 3, 4, 5, 6\}$ – this is the group itself so is *not* a proper subgroup.

Other possibilities: $\{0, 1\}, \{0, 2\}, \{0, 3\}, \{0, 4\}, \{0, 5\}, \{0, 1, 2\}, \{0, 1, 3\}, \{0, 1, 4\}, \{0, 1, 5\}, \{0, 2, 3\}, \{0, 2, 4\}, \{0, 2, 5\}, \{0, 3, 4\}, \{0, 3, 5\}$ and $\{0, 4, 5\}$ ●————————

> **(2)** List the possibilities.

For the two-element options, the element other than the identity must be self-inverse.

$2 + 2 \neq 0 \pmod 6$, $3 + 3 = 0 \pmod 6$, $4 + 4 \neq 0 \pmod 6$, $5 + 5 \neq 0 \pmod 6$

Hence $\{0, 3\}$ is a subgroup.

For the three-element options, both elements other than the identity must be self-inverse, or they must be inverse pairs.

Since 3 is the only self-inverse element other than the identity, $\{0, 2, 3\}, \{0, 3, 4\}$ and $\{0, 3, 5\}$ can be discounted.

> **(3)** Check each possibility against the conditions. Using inverses is a good way of checking for a closed group.

$2 + 4 = 0 \pmod 6$ and $1 + 5 = 0 \pmod 6$, so $\{0, 1, 5\}$ and $\{0, 2, 4\}$ are also subgroups. ●————————

1   Determine the only possible orders of the subgroups of a group which has an order of 90. Fully justify your answer.

2   Which of the following groups *cannot* be a subgroup of G, which has order 30

   a A, order 5

   b B, order 3

   c C, order 12

   d D, order 10

3   Prove that no subgroups of order 6 exist for a group of order 92. Fully justify your answer.

4   Group $H = (\{0, 1, 2, 3, 4, 5, 6, 7, 8, 9, 10\}, +_{11})$

   Explain why H has only two subgroups, the trivial subgroup and the group itself.

5   A group $G = (\{e, p, q, r, s, t, u, v\}, \bullet)$ has the following Cayley table.

$\bullet$	e	p	q	r	s	t	u	v
e	e	p	q	r	s	t	u	v
p	p	q	u	t	v	s	e	r
q	q	u	e	s	r	v	p	t
r	r	t	s	u	p	e	v	q
s	s	v	r	p	u	q	t	e
t	t	s	v	e	q	p	r	u
u	u	e	p	v	t	r	q	s
v	v	r	t	q	e	u	s	p

   a   State the order of G

   b   Write down the orders of possible subgroups of G. Justify your answer.

   c   Use your answer to part **b** to find all the non-trivial proper subgroups of G

6   A group $J = (\{1, -1, i, -i\}, \times)$. This is a subgroup of the complex numbers under multiplication.

   Carmelita says that $(\{1, i, -i\}, \times)$ is a proper subgroup of J

   a   Explain why Carmelita is wrong.

   b   Identify all the proper subgroups of J

7   A group $G = (\{0, 1, 2, 3, 4, 5, 6, 7, 8\}, +_9)$. Explain why there are exactly three subgroups of G

8   The group, G, of all operations on a standard Rubik's cube has $43\,252\,003\,274\,489\,856\,000$ elements. Use Lagrange's theorem to work out the number of orders of possible subgroups of G

   Hint: Try writing the number as the product of prime factors. You do not need to write out all the possible orders.

Isomorphism

Isomorphism is an important concept in group theory. Suppose that you prove certain results for a group of order 4. If you encounter another group of order 4, your first thought is to start to prove these same results again for this different group. However, if you can show that the two groups are **isomorphic**, then the results proved for the first group automatically hold for the second group.

Key point

Two groups are **isomorphic** if there is a one-to-one mapping (an **isomorphism**) which associates each of the elements of one group with one of the elements of the other such that: If p maps to a and q maps to b, then the result of combining p and q under the binary operation of the first set maps to the result of combining a and b under the binary operation of the second set.

Example 1

A group G under the binary operation $\bullet$ has the Cayley table

$\bullet$	p	q	r	s
p	p	q	r	s
q	q	p	s	r
r	r	s	q	p
s	s	r	p	q

A second group $H = (\{i, -i, 1, -1\}, \times)$

Show that H is isomorphic to G and state the corresponding elements in each group.

The Cayley table for H is

$\times$	i	$-i$	1	-1
i	-1	1	i	$-i$
$-i$	1	-1	$-i$	i
1	i	$-i$	1	-1
-1	$-i$	i	-1	1

The identity element for H is 1 since $1 \times a = a \times 1 = a$

Elements 1 and -1 are self-inverse, so 1 corresponds to p and -1 to q

(Continued on the next page)

Reorder the columns and rows in the Cayley table:

×	1	−1	i	$-i$
1	1	−1	i	$-i$
−1	−1	1	$-i$	i
i	i	$-i$	−1	1
$-i$	$-i$	i	1	−1

By reordering the columns and rows in the Cayley table, you can see that the pattern of entries here is the same as in the Cayley table for G

Hence i corresponds to r and $-i$ corresponds to s

The groups are isomorphic.

The corresponding elements for each group are

$1 \leftrightarrow p, -1 \leftrightarrow q, i \leftrightarrow r$ and $-i \leftrightarrow s$

Note that this correspondence is not unique. Interchanging i and $-i$ would also give the same pattern of entries as in G

The notation $H \cong G$ is used to denote isomorphism between groups.

Exercise 10.3A Fluency and skills

1 Show that the group formed by the set of rotational symmetries of a square is also isomorphic to the groups in Example 1

2 **a** Show that the groups $A = (\{1, 2, 3, 4\}, \times_5)$ and $B = (\{0, 1, 2, 3\}, +_4)$ are isomorphic.

   b Are groups A and B also isomorphic to those in Example 1?

3 $M = \left\{ \begin{pmatrix} 1 & 0 \\ 0 & 1 \end{pmatrix}, \begin{pmatrix} 1 & 0 \\ 0 & -1 \end{pmatrix}, \begin{pmatrix} -1 & 0 \\ 0 & 1 \end{pmatrix}, \begin{pmatrix} -1 & 0 \\ 0 & -1 \end{pmatrix} \right\}$, matrix multiplication

$N = (\{1, 3, 5, 7\}, \times_8)$

   a Show that M and N are isomorphic.

   b Are M and N also isomorphic to the groups in Example 1?

4 Show that the group formed by the set of rotational symmetries of an equilateral triangle is isomorphic to the group $R = (\langle 4 \rangle, \times_7)$

Reasoning and problem-solving

Showing that two groups of order 3 or 4 are isomorphic (or not) is quite straightforward since it is simple to rearrange the columns and rows of one of the Cayley tables to see if the pattern of entries matches the other table. For groups of a larger order, a systematic approach is advised.

Strategy 1

To show that two groups are isomorphic

1 Identify the identity element in each group.

2 Find the self-inverse elements in each group.

3 Identify the elements in each group that are not self-inverse and choose an arbitrary mapping.

4 Choose an arbitrary pairing of the self-inverse elements and write down a possible mapping.

5 Rewrite the Cayley table for one of the groups using the possible mapping and check that the pattern of entries is the same as for the Cayley table of the other group.

Example 2

Groups *G* and *H* have Cayley tables as shown.

G

	a	*b*	*c*	*d*	*e*	*f*
a	*a*	*b*	*c*	*d*	*e*	*f*
b	*b*	*c*	*a*	*f*	*d*	*e*
c	*c*	*a*	*b*	*e*	*f*	*d*
d	*d*	*e*	*f*	*a*	*b*	*c*
e	*e*	*f*	*d*	*c*	*a*	*b*
f	*f*	*d*	*e*	*b*	*c*	*a*

H

	P	*Q*	*R*	*S*	*T*	*U*
P	*S*	*U*	*T*	*P*	*R*	*Q*
Q	*T*	*R*	*S*	*Q*	*U*	*P*
R	*U*	*S*	*Q*	*R*	*P*	*T*
S	*P*	*Q*	*R*	*S*	*T*	*U*
T	*Q*	*P*	*U*	*T*	*S*	*R*
U	*R*	*T*	*P*	*U*	*Q*	*S*

Show that *H* is isomorphic to *G*

In *G*, the identity element is *a*

In *H*, the identity element is *S*

> ① Identify the identity element in each group.

The self-inverse elements in *G* are *d*, *e* and *f*

The self-inverse elements in *H* are *P*, *T* and *U*

In *G*, *b* and *c* are not self-inverse.

In *H*, *Q* and *R* are not self-inverse.

> ② Identify the self-inverse elements in each group.

Choose an arbitrary mapping, say $b \leftrightarrow Q$

This means that $c \leftrightarrow R$

> ③ Identify the elements that are not self-inverse and choose an arbitrary mapping.

Choose an arbitrary mapping for the self-inverse elements:

Let $d \leftrightarrow P$; hence $e \leftrightarrow U$ and $f \leftrightarrow T$

A possible mapping is therefore $[b, c, d, e, f] \leftrightarrow [Q, R, P, U, T]$

The Cayley table for *H* is now

> ④ Choose an arbitrary pairing of the self-inverse elements and write down a possible mapping.

	S	*Q*	*R*	*P*	*U*	*T*
S	*S*	*Q*	*R*	*P*	*U*	*T*
Q	*Q*	*R*	*S*	*T*	*P*	*U*
R	*R*	*S*	*Q*	*U*	*T*	*P*
P	*P*	*U*	*T*	*S*	*Q*	*R*
U	*U*	*T*	*P*	*R*	*S*	*Q*
T	*T*	*P*	*U*	*Q*	*R*	*S*

The pattern of entries in the redrawn Cayley table for *H* now matches that for the Cayley table for *G*

Hence $H \cong G$

> ⑤ Redraw the Cayley table for one of the groups using the possible mapping and check the pattern of entries.

To show that two groups are *not* isomorphic, you need to establish at least one of the following

(1) That there are a different number of self-inverse elements in the two groups.

(2) That some of the elements in one group do not have the same period as in the other.

(3) That one group is cyclic and the other is not.

Example 3

Group S has a Cayley table as shown below.

	1	2	3	4	5	6
1	1	2	3	4	5	6
2	2	4	6	1	3	5
3	3	6	2	5	1	4
4	4	1	5	2	6	3
5	5	3	1	6	4	2
6	6	5	4	3	2	1

Show that S is not isomorphic to the two groups in Example 1

The identity element is 1

The only other self-inverse element in S is 6

G and H both have three self-inverse elements other than the identity.

Hence S is not isomorphic to G and H

There are a different number of self-inverse elements. (1)

You could also have shown that S has elements of period 6 (the elements 3 and 5) whereas G and H do not.

Exercise 10.3B Reasoning and problem-solving

1 Explain why all groups of order 2 are isomorphic to each other.

2 Explain why all groups of order 3 are isomorphic to each other.

3 Brice says that there must be four different isomorphisms of groups of order 4 since the three remaining elements can either all have period 2, one period 2 and two period 4, one period 4 and two period 2, or all have period 4 Explain why Brice is wrong and state the actual number of isomorphisms of groups of order 4

4 Leona says that groups of prime order have a single isomorphism, i.e. all groups of order 7, for example, are isomorphic to each other. Explain why Leona is correct in her assertion.

5 Explain why an abelian group cannot be isomorphic to a non-abelian group.

6 The group $G = (\{0, 1, 2, 3, 4, 5\}, +_6)$
The group H consists of the set of rotational symmetries of a regular hexagon.
Show that $G \cong H$

7 The group $S = (\{1, 2, 4, 7, 8, 11, 13, 14\}, \times_{15})$
Another group, M, has elements consisting of the set of rotations of angle $\dfrac{k\pi}{4}$, $k = 1, 2, 3, 4,$ 5, 6, 7, 8, of a unit square about the origin.
Show that S is not isomorphic to M

8 Show that the group of matrices of the form $\begin{pmatrix} 1-a & a \\ -a & 1+a \end{pmatrix}$ under the operation matrix multiplication is isomorphic to the group $G = (\mathbb{Z}, +)$

Hint: Since the groups are infinite, you need to specify a mapping connecting each element in one group with an element in the other group.

Chapter summary

- The conditions under which a set of mathematical objects form a group under a given binary operation are known as the axioms.

- These are closure, the existence of an identity element, associativity and the existence of an inverse element for each member of the set.

- A group $(S, \odot)$ is a non-empty set S with a binary operation $\odot$ such that:
  - $\odot$ is closed in S
  - $\odot$ is associative
  - there is an identity element such that $x \odot e = e \odot x = x$ for all x
  - each element has an inverse, x^{-1}, such that $x \odot x^{-1} = x^{-1} \odot x = e$

- The order of a group is equal to the number of elements in the group.

- The period (or order) of a particular element, x, of a group is the smallest non-negative integer n such that $x^n = e$, where e is the identity.

- An abelian group is a group with the additional property of commutativity between the elements of the group.

- To show that a given set forms a group under a given binary operation:
  - Write down the elements of the set.
  - Produce a Cayley table to show the combinations of each element under the given binary operation.
  - Check that the binary operation meets the axioms necessary to be a group.

- A subgroup of a group G is any subset H of G such that H itself is also a group under the same binary operation as G

- A non-trivial subgroup is any subgroup that is not the trivial subgroup.

- A proper subgroup is any subgroup that is not the group itself.

- Lagrange's theorem states that, for any finite group G, the order of every subgroup of G divides the order of G

- To find all the possible subgroups of a particular group:
  - Use Lagrange's theorem to find the order of the possible subgroups.
  - Use a systematic process to identify the possibilities.
  - Check each possibility against the conditions for being a subgroup.

- Two groups are isomorphic if there is a one-to-one mapping (an isomorphism) which associates each of the elements of one group with one of the elements of the other such that if p maps to a and q maps to b, then the result of combining p and q under the binary operation of the first set maps to the result of combining a and b under the binary operation of the second set.

- To show that two groups are isomorphic:
  - Identify the identity element in each group.
  - Find the self-inverse elements in each group.
  - Identify the elements in each group that are not self-inverse and choose an arbitrary mapping.
  - Choose an arbitrary pairing of the self-inverse elements and write down a possible mapping.
  - Rewrite the Cayley table for one of the groups using the possible mapping and check that the pattern of entries is the same as for the Cayley table of the other group.

- To show that two groups are not isomorphic, you need to establish at least one of the following:
  - That there are a different number of self-inverse elements in the two groups.
  - That some of the elements in one group do not have the same period as in the other.
  - That one group is cyclic and the other is not.

Check and review

You should now be able to…	Review Questions
Understand and use the language of groups including order, period, subgroup, proper, trivial, non-trivial.	1, 3
Understand and use the group axioms closure, identity, inverses and associativity, including the use of Cayley tables.	1, 2
Recognise and use finite and infinite groups and their subgroups, including groups of symmetries of regular polygons, cyclic groups and abelian groups.	1, 3, 4
Understand and use Lagrange's theorem.	3
Identify and use the generators of a group.	1
Recognise and find isomorphism between groups of finite order.	4

1 $G = (\{1, 2, 4, 5, 7, 8\}, \times_9)$

   a State the order of G

   b Draw a Cayley table for G

   c State the period of the element '5'

   d Explain why your answer to part **c** shows that G is cyclic.

   e Is G an abelian group? Explain your answer.

2 It is suggested that the set $S = \{1, 5, 7, 11\}$ forms a group under $\times_{12}$

By drawing a Cayley table or otherwise

  a Write down the identity element,

  b Show that S is closed under $\times_{12}$

  c Show that every element in S has an inverse,

  d Give at least two examples of the axiom of associativity holding for S

3 The group, S, formed by the set of all symmetries of an equilateral triangle has this Cayley table.

	r_0	r_1	r_2	m_1	m_2	m_3
r_0	r_0	r_1	r_2	m_1	m_2	m_3
r_1	r_1	r_2	r_0	m_2	m_3	m_1
r_2	r_2	r_0	r_1	m_3	m_1	m_2
m_1	m_1	m_3	m_2	r_0	r_2	r_1
m_2	m_2	m_1	m_3	r_1	r_0	r_2
m_3	m_3	m_2	m_1	r_2	r_1	r_0

  a State the order of possible subgroups of S

  b Write down the trivial subgroup of S

  c Find all proper subgroups of S

4 a Show that the groups $G = (\{1, 3, 7, 9\}, \times_{10})$ and $H = (\{0, 1, 2, 3\}, +_4)$ are isomorphic and write down a possible mapping.

  b Are the groups cyclic? Explain your reasoning.

  c Are the groups abelian? Explain your reasoning.

Did you know?

An automorphism is an isomorphism from a mathematical object to itself. One of the earliest group automorphisms was found by William Rowan Hamilton as he developed icosian calculus. This resulted in the development of the popular icosian game. The aim the game is to find a Hamiltonian cycle along the edges of a dodecahedron, visiting every vertex only once.

Research

The three general isomorphism theorems were formulated by Emmy Noether in 1927. Find out about them, particularly in the context of groups. You may also like to extend this research by looking at the lattice theorem and the Butterfly lemma.

Research

You can use the theories around zero knowledge proofs to discover whether two graphs are isomorphic.
Start by finding out about zero knowledge proofs. For example, look at the research paper *How to Explain Zero-Knowledge Protocols to Your Children* by Quisquater. In particular, well-known examples are the Ali Baba cave, and two-coloured balls with a colour-blind friend.

1   The group G has this Cayley table

*	a	b	c	d
a	c	a	d	b
b	a	b	c	d
c	d	c	b	a
d	b	d	a	c

     a   State, with a reason, which element is the identity element.   **[2]**

     b   Write down all of the elements that are self-inverse.   **[1]**

     c   Explain why G is an abelian group.   **[1]**

2   A finite group H has proper subgroups $\{a, b\}$, $\{b, d, e\}$ and $\{b, f, g, h, k\}$

     a   State, with a reason, which element of H is the identity.   **[2]**

     b   State, with a reason, the smallest possible order of H **[2]**

3   The group $G = (\{1, 3, 5, 7\}, \times_8)$

   The group $H = (\{1, 3, 7, 9\}, \times_{10})$

   By drawing Cayley tables for G and H, or otherwise, show that G and H
   are not isomorphic.   **[4]**

4   The cyclic group $C_n = (\langle 9 \rangle, \times_{64})$

     a   Explain what is meant by $\langle 9 \rangle$ **[1]**

     b   Find the value of n and justify your answer.   **[3]**

     c   State the order of all of the possible subgroups, giving a reason for your answer.   **[2]**

5   The binary operation $\circ$ is defined as $a \circ b = a + b + 3 \,[\text{mod } 6]$, where $a, b \in \mathbb{Z}$

     a   Show that the set $\{0, 1, 2, 3, 4, 5\}$ forms a group G under $\circ$ **[5]**

     b   Find all of the proper subgroups of G **[2]**

     c   Determine whether G is isomorphic to the group $K = (\langle 2 \rangle, \times_9)$ **[3]**

6 The group *G* has this Cayley table.

	a	*b*	*c*	*d*	*e*	*f*	*g*	*h*
a	c	e	b	f	a	h	d	g
b	e	c	a	g	b	d	h	f
c	b	a	e	h	c	g	f	d
d	f	g	h	a	d	c	e	b
e	a	b	c	d	e	f	g	h
f	h	d	g	c	f	b	a	e
g	d	h	f	e	g	a	b	c
h	g	f	d	b	h	e	c	a

    a Explain why element *e* is the identity element. [1]

Emilia says that {*e*, *d*, *g*} is a proper subgroup of *G*

    b Explain, with a reason, whether Emilia is correct. [2]

    c Show that *G* is cyclic and hence explain why *G* is not isomorphic to the group of symmetries of a square. [5]

7 The set *P* consists of the set of all integers under the binary operation • such that

$x \bullet y = x + y - 1$

    a Show that • is associative. [2]

    b Hence, show that *P* forms a group under • [4]

    c State, with a reason, whether the set of positive integers forms a group under • [2]

Mathematical formulae
For AS and A Level Further Maths

The following mathematical formulae will be provided for you.

Pure Mathematics

Summations

$$\sum_{r=1}^{n} r^2 = \frac{1}{6}n(n+1)(2n+1) \qquad \sum_{r=1}^{n} r^3 = \frac{1}{4}n^2(n+1)^2$$

Matrix transformations

Anticlockwise rotation through θ about O: $\begin{pmatrix} \cos\theta & -\sin\theta \\ \sin\theta & \cos\theta \end{pmatrix}$

Reflection in the line $y = (\tan\theta)x$: $\begin{pmatrix} \cos2\theta & \sin2\theta \\ \sin2\theta & -\cos2\theta \end{pmatrix}$

Area of a sector

$$A = \frac{1}{2}\int r^2 \, d\theta \qquad \text{(polar coordinates)}$$

Complex numbers

$$\{r(\cos\theta + i\sin\theta)\}^n = r^n(\cos n\theta + i\sin n\theta)$$

The roots of $z^n = 1$ are given by $z = e^{\frac{2\pi ki}{n}}$ for $k = 0, 1, 2, ..., n-1$

Maclaurin's and Taylor's Series

$$f(x) = f(0) + xf'(0) + \frac{x^2}{2!}f''(0) + ... + \frac{x^r}{r!}f^{(r)}(0) + ...$$

$$e^x = \exp(x) = 1 + x + \frac{x^2}{2!} + ... + \frac{x^r}{r!} + ... \qquad \text{for all } x$$

$$\ln(1+x) = x - \frac{x^2}{2} + \frac{x^3}{3} - ... + (-1)^{r+1}\frac{x^r}{r} + ... \qquad (-1 < x \leq 1)$$

$$\sin x = x - \frac{x^3}{3!} + \frac{x^5}{5!} - ... + (-1)^r \frac{x^{2r+1}}{(2r+1)!} + ... \qquad \text{for all } x$$

$$\cos x = 1 - \frac{x^2}{2!} + \frac{x^4}{4!} - ... + (-1)^r \frac{x^{2r}}{(2r)!} + ... \qquad \text{for all } x$$

$$\arctan x = x - \frac{x^3}{3} + \frac{x^5}{5} - ... + (-1)^r \frac{x^{2r+1}}{2r+1} + ... \qquad (-1 \leq x \leq 1)$$

Vectors

Vector products: $\mathbf{a} \times \mathbf{b} = |\mathbf{a}||\mathbf{b}| \sin \theta \,\hat{\mathbf{n}} = \begin{vmatrix} \mathbf{i} & \mathbf{j} & \mathbf{k} \\ a_1 & a_2 & a_3 \\ b_1 & b_2 & b_3 \end{vmatrix} = \begin{pmatrix} a_2 b_3 - a_3 b_2 \\ a_3 b_1 - a_1 b_3 \\ a_1 b_2 - a_2 b_1 \end{pmatrix}$

$\mathbf{a} \cdot (\mathbf{b} \times \mathbf{c}) = \begin{vmatrix} a_1 & a_2 & a_3 \\ b_1 & b_2 & b_3 \\ c_1 & c_2 & c_3 \end{vmatrix} = \mathbf{b} \cdot (\mathbf{c} \times \mathbf{a}) = \mathbf{c} \cdot (\mathbf{a} \times \mathbf{b})$

If A is the point with position vector $\mathbf{a} = a_1\mathbf{i} + a_2\mathbf{j} + a_3\mathbf{k}$ and the direction vector $\mathbf{b}$ is given by $\mathbf{b} = b_1\mathbf{i} + b_2\mathbf{j} + b_3\mathbf{k}$, then the straight line through A with direction vector $\mathbf{b}$ has cartesian equation

$$\frac{x - a_1}{b_1} = \frac{y - a_2}{b_2} = \frac{z - a_3}{b_3} (= \lambda)$$

The plane through A with normal vector $\mathbf{n} = n_1\mathbf{i} + n_2\mathbf{j} + n_3\mathbf{k}$ has cartesian equation $n_1 x + n_2 y + n_3 z + d = 0$ where $d = -\mathbf{a}.\mathbf{n}$

The plane through non-collinear points A, B and C has vector equation

$$\mathbf{r} = \mathbf{a} + \lambda(\mathbf{b} - \mathbf{a}) + \mu(\mathbf{c} - \mathbf{a}) = (1 - \lambda - \mu)\mathbf{a} + \lambda\mathbf{b} + \mu\mathbf{c}$$

The plane through the point with position vector $\mathbf{a}$ and parallel to $\mathbf{b}$ and $\mathbf{c}$ has equation

$$\mathbf{r} = \mathbf{a} + s\mathbf{b} + t\mathbf{c}$$

The perpendicular distance of (α, β, γ) from $n_1 x + n_2 y + n_3 z + d = 0$ is $\dfrac{|n_1 \alpha + n_2 \beta + n_3 \gamma + d|}{\sqrt{n_1^2 + n_2^2 + n_3^2}}$

Hyperbolic functions

$$\cosh^2 x - \sinh^2 x = 1$$

$$\sinh 2x = 2 \sinh x \cosh x$$

$$\cosh 2x = \cosh^2 x + \sinh^2 x$$

$$\operatorname{arcosh} x = \ln\left\{ x + \sqrt{x^2 - 1} \right\} \qquad (x \geq 1)$$

$$\operatorname{arsinh} x = \ln\left\{ x + \sqrt{x^2 + 1} \right\}$$

$$\operatorname{artanh} x = \frac{1}{2} \ln\left(\frac{1 + x}{1 - x} \right) \qquad (|x| < 1)$$

Conics

	Ellipse	Parabola	Hyperbola	Rectangular Hyperbola
Standard Form	$\dfrac{x^2}{a^2}+\dfrac{y^2}{b^2}=1$	$y^2=4ax$	$\dfrac{x^2}{a^2}-\dfrac{y^2}{b^2}=1$	$xy=c^2$
Parametric Form	$(a\cos\theta,\,b\sin\theta)$	$(at^2,\,2at)$	$(a\sec\theta,\,b\tan\theta)$ $(\pm a\cosh\theta,\,b\sinh\theta)$	$\left(ct,\dfrac{c}{t}\right)$
Eccentricity	$e<1$ $b^2=a^2(1-e^2)$	$e=1$	$e>1$ $b^2=a^2(e^2-1)$	$e=\sqrt{2}$
Foci	$(\pm ae,\,0)$	$(a,\,0)$	$(\pm ae,\,0)$	$\left(\pm\sqrt{2}c,\,\pm\sqrt{2}c\right)$
Directrices	$x=\pm\dfrac{a}{e}$	$x=-a$	$x=\pm\dfrac{a}{e}$	$x+y=\pm\sqrt{2}c$
Asymptotes	none	none	$\dfrac{x}{a}=\pm\dfrac{y}{b}$	$x=0,\,y=0$

Differentiation

$f(x)$	$f'(x)$		$f(x)$	$f'(x)$
$\arcsin x$	$\dfrac{1}{\sqrt{1-x^2}}$		$\cosh x$	$\sinh x$
$\arccos x$	$-\dfrac{1}{\sqrt{1-x^2}}$		$\tanh x$	$\operatorname{sech}^2 x$
$\arctan x$	$\dfrac{1}{1+x^2}$		$\operatorname{arsinh} x$	$\dfrac{1}{\sqrt{1+x^2}}$
$\sinh x$	$\cosh x$		$\operatorname{arcosh} x$	$\dfrac{1}{\sqrt{x^2-1}}$
			$\operatorname{artanh} x$	$\dfrac{1}{1-x^2}$

Mathematical formulae for AS and A Level Further Maths

Integration (+ constant; $a > 0$ where relevant)

$\mathbf{f}(x)$	$\int \mathbf{f}(x)\,\mathbf{d}x$
$\sinh x$	$\cosh x$
$\cosh x$	$\sinh x$
$\tanh x$	$\ln \cosh x$
$\dfrac{1}{\sqrt{a^2 - x^2}}$	$\arcsin\left(\dfrac{x}{a}\right) \quad (\lvert x \rvert < a)$
$\dfrac{1}{a^2 + x^2}$	$\dfrac{1}{a}\arctan\left(\dfrac{x}{a}\right)$
$\dfrac{1}{\sqrt{x^2 - a^2}}$	$\operatorname{arcosh}\left(\dfrac{x}{a}\right),\ \ln\{x + \sqrt{x^2 - a^2}\} \quad (x > a)$
$\dfrac{1}{\sqrt{a^2 + x^2}}$	$\operatorname{arsinh}\left(\dfrac{x}{a}\right),\ \ln\{x + \sqrt{x^2 + a^2}\}$
$\dfrac{1}{a^2 - x^2}$	$\dfrac{1}{2a}\ln\left\lvert\dfrac{a+x}{a-x}\right\rvert = \dfrac{1}{a}\operatorname{artanh}\left(\dfrac{x}{a}\right) \quad (\lvert x \rvert < a)$
$\dfrac{1}{x^2 - a^2}$	$\dfrac{1}{2a}\ln\left\lvert\dfrac{x-a}{x+a}\right\rvert$

Arc length

$$s = \int \sqrt{1 + \left(\frac{\mathrm{d}y}{\mathrm{d}x}\right)^2}\,\mathrm{d}x \qquad \text{(cartesian coordinates)}$$

$$s = \int \sqrt{\left(\frac{\mathrm{d}x}{\mathrm{d}t}\right)^2 + \left(\frac{\mathrm{d}y}{\mathrm{d}t}\right)^2}\,\mathrm{d}t \qquad \text{(parametric form)}$$

$$s = \int \sqrt{r^2 + \left(\frac{\mathrm{d}r}{\mathrm{d}\theta}\right)^2}\,\mathrm{d}\theta \qquad \text{(polar form)}$$

Full A Level

Surface area of revolution

$$s_x = 2\pi \int y \sqrt{1 + \left(\frac{dy}{dx}\right)^2}\, dx \qquad \text{(cartesian coordinates)}$$

$$s_x = 2\pi \int y \sqrt{\left(\frac{dx}{dt}\right)^2 + \left(\frac{dy}{dt}\right)^2}\, dt \qquad \text{(parametric form)}$$

$$s_x = 2\pi \int r \sin\theta \sqrt{r^2 + \left(\frac{dr}{d\theta}\right)^2}\, d\theta \qquad \text{(polar form)}$$

You are expected to know the following mathematical formulae, and they will not be provided for you.

Pure Mathematics

Quadratic Equations

$ax^2 + bx + c = 0$ has roots $\dfrac{-b \pm \sqrt{b^2 - 4ac}}{2a}$

Laws of indices

$a^x a^y \equiv a^{x+y}$

$a^x \div a^y \equiv a^{x-y}$

$(a^x)^y \equiv a^{xy}$

Laws of logarithms

$x = a^n \Leftrightarrow n = \log_a x$ for $a > 0$ and $x > 0$

$\log_a x + \log_a y \equiv \log_a xy$

$\log_a x - \log_a y \equiv \log_a \left(\dfrac{x}{y} \right)$

$k \log_a x \equiv \log_a (x)^k$

Coordinate geometry

A straight-line graph, gradient m passing through (x_1, y_1), has equation $y - y_1 = m(x - x_1)$

Straight lines with gradients m_1 and m_2 are perpendicular when $m_1 m_2 = -1$

Sequences

General term of an arithmetic progression: $u_n = a + (n-1)d$

General term of a geometric progression: $u_n = ar^{n-1}$

Trigonometry

In the triangle ABC:

Sine rule: $\dfrac{a}{\sin A} = \dfrac{b}{\sin B} = \dfrac{c}{\sin C}$

Cosine rule: $a^2 = b^2 + c^2 - 2bc \cos A$

Area $= \dfrac{1}{2} ab \sin C$

$\cos^2 A + \sin^2 A \equiv 1$

$\sec^2 A \equiv 1 + \tan^2 A$

$\operatorname{cosec}^2 A \equiv 1 + \cot^2 A$

$\sin 2A \equiv 2 \sin A \cos A$

$\cos 2A \equiv \cos^2 A - \sin^2 A$

$\tan 2A \equiv \dfrac{2 \tan A}{1 - \tan^2 A}$

Mensuration

Circumference and area of circle radius r and diameter d:

$$C = 2\pi r = \pi d \qquad A = \pi r^2$$

Pythagoras' Theorem:

In any right-angled triangle where a, b and c are the lengths of the sides and c is the hypotenuse, $c^2 = a^2 + b^2$

Area of a trapezium $= \dfrac{1}{2}(a+b)h$, where a and b are the lengths of the parallel sides and h is their perpendicular separation.

Volume of a prism = area of cross section $\times$ length

For a circle of radius r, where an angle at the centre of θ radians subtends an arc of length s and encloses an associated sector of area A:

$$s = r\theta \qquad A = \frac{1}{2}r^2\theta$$

Complex Numbers

For two complex numbers $z_1 = r_1 e^{i\theta_1}$ and $z_2 = r_2 e^{i\theta_2}$

$$z_1 z_2 = r_1 r_2\, e^{i(\theta_1 + \theta_2)}$$

$$\frac{z_1}{z_2} = \frac{r_1}{r_2} e^{i(\theta_1 - \theta_2)}$$

Loci in the Argand diagram:

$|z - a| = r$ is a circle radius r centred at a

$\arg(z - a) = \theta$ is a half line drawn from a at angle θ to a line parallel to the positive real axis.

Exponential Form: $e^{i\theta} = \cos\theta + i\sin\theta$

Matrices

For a 2 by 2 matrix $\begin{pmatrix} a & b \\ c & d \end{pmatrix}$ the determinant $\Delta = \begin{vmatrix} a & b \\ c & d \end{vmatrix} = ad - bc$

the inverse is $\dfrac{1}{\Delta}\begin{pmatrix} d & -b \\ -c & a \end{pmatrix}$

The transformation represented by matrix $\mathbf{AB}$ is the transformation represented by matrix $\mathbf{B}$ followed by the transformation represented by matrix $\mathbf{A}$.

For matrices $\mathbf{A}$, $\mathbf{B}$:

$$(\mathbf{AB})^{-1} = \mathbf{B}^{-1}\mathbf{A}^{-1}$$

Algebra

$$\sum_{r=1}^{n} r = \frac{1}{2} n (n+1)$$

For $ax^2 + bx + c = 0$ with roots α and β:

$$\alpha + \beta = -\frac{b}{a} \qquad \alpha \beta = \frac{c}{a}$$

For $ax^3 + bx^2 + cx + d = 0$ with roots α, β and γ:

$$\sum \alpha = -\frac{b}{a} \qquad \sum \alpha\beta = \frac{c}{a} \qquad \alpha\beta\gamma = -\frac{d}{a}$$

Hyperbolic functions

$$\cosh x \equiv \frac{1}{2}(e^x + e^{-x}) \qquad \sinh x \equiv \frac{1}{2}(e^x - e^{-x}) \qquad \tanh x \equiv \frac{\sinh x}{\cosh x}$$

Calculus and differential equations

Differentiation

Function	Derivative	Function	Derivative
x^n	nx^{n-1}	e^{kx}	ke^{kx}
$\sin kx$	$k \cos kx$	$\ln x$	$\dfrac{1}{x}$
$\cos kx$	$-k \sin kx$	$f(x) + g(x)$	$f'(x) + g'(x)$
$\sinh kx$	$k \cosh kx$	$f(x)g(x)$	$f'(x)g(x) + f(x)g'(x)$
$\cosh kx$	$k \sinh kx$	$f(g(x))$	$f'(g(x))g'(x)$

Integration

Function	Integral	Function	Integral
x^n	$\dfrac{1}{n+1}x^{n+1}+c, n \neq -1$	e^{kx}	$\dfrac{1}{k}e^{kx}+c$
$\cos kx$	$\dfrac{1}{k}\sin kx + c$	$\dfrac{1}{x}$	$\ln|x|+c, x \neq 0$
$\sin kx$	$-\dfrac{1}{k}\cos kx + c$	$f'(x)+g'(x)$	$f(x)+g(x)+c$
$\cosh kx$	$\dfrac{1}{k}\sinh kx + c$	$f'(g(x))g'(x)$	$f(g(x))+c$
$\sinh kx$	$\dfrac{1}{k}\cosh kx + c$		

Area under a curve $= \displaystyle\int_a^b y\,dx\,(y \geq 0)$

Volumes of revolution about the x and y axes:

$$V_x = \pi \int_a^b y^2\,dx \qquad V_y = \pi \int_c^d x^2\,dy$$

Simple Harmonic Motion: $\ddot{x} = -\omega^2 x$

Vectors

$$|x\mathbf{i}+y\mathbf{j}+z\mathbf{k}| = \sqrt{(x^2+y^2+z^2)}$$

Scalar product of two vectors $\mathbf{a} = \begin{pmatrix} a_1 \\ a_2 \\ a_3 \end{pmatrix}$ and $\mathbf{b} = \begin{pmatrix} b_1 \\ b_2 \\ b_3 \end{pmatrix}$ is

$$\begin{pmatrix} a_1 \\ a_2 \\ a_3 \end{pmatrix} . \begin{pmatrix} b_1 \\ b_2 \\ b_3 \end{pmatrix} = a_1 b_1 + a_2 b_2 + a_3 b_3 = |\mathbf{a}|\,|\mathbf{b}| \cos \theta$$

where θ is the acute angle between the vectors $\mathbf{a}$ and $\mathbf{b}$.

The equation of the line through the point with position vector $\mathbf{a}$ parallel to vector $\mathbf{b}$ is:

$$\mathbf{r} = \mathbf{a} + t\mathbf{b}$$

The equation of the plane containing the point with position vector $\mathbf{a}$ and perpendicular to vector $\mathbf{n}$ is:

$$(\mathbf{r} - \mathbf{a}) \cdot \mathbf{n} = 0$$

Mathematical notation
For AS and A Level Further Maths

You should understand the following notation for AS and A Level Further Maths, without need for further explanation. Notation from all strands of mathematics has been included for your reference.

Set Notation

$\in$	is an element of
$\notin$	is not an element of
$\subseteq$	is a subset of
$\subset$	is a proper subset of
$\{x_1, x_2,... \}$	the set with elements x_1, x_2, ...
$\{x: ... \}$	the set of all x such that ...
$n(A)$	the number of elements in set A
$\varnothing$	the empty set
ε	the universal set
A'	the complement of the set A
$\mathbb{N}$	the set of natural numbers, $\{1, 2, 3, ...\}$
$\mathbb{Z}$	the set of integers, $\{0, \pm1, \pm2, \pm3, ...\}$
$\mathbb{Z}^+$	the set of positive integers, $\{1, 2, 3, ...\}$
$\mathbb{Z}_0^+$	the set of non-negative integers, $\{0, 1, 2, 3, ...\}$
$\mathbb{R}$	the set of real numbers
$\mathbb{Q}$	the set of rational numbers, $\left\{\dfrac{p}{q} : p \in \mathbb{Z},\ q \in \mathbb{Z}^+\right\}$
$\cup$	union
$\cap$	intersection
(x, y)	the ordered pair x, y
$[a, b]$	the closed interval $\{x \in \mathbb{R} : a \le x \le b\}$
$[a, b)$	the interval $\{x \in \mathbb{R} : a \le x < b\}$
$(a, b]$	the interval $\{x \in \mathbb{R} : a < x \le b\}$
(a, b)	the open interval $\{x \in \mathbb{R} : a < x < b\}$
$\mathbb{C}$	the set of complex numbers

Miscellaneous Symbols

$=$	is equal to
$\neq$	is not equal to
$\equiv$	is identical to or is congruent to
$\approx$	is approximately equal to
∞	infinity
$\propto$	is proportional to
$<$	is less than
$\leqslant, \le$	is less than or equal to; is not greater than
$>$	is greater than
$\geqslant, \ge$	is greater than or equal to; is not less than
$\therefore$	therefore
$\because$	because
$p \Rightarrow q$	p implies q (if p then q)
$p \Leftarrow q$	p is implied by q (if q then p)
$p \Leftrightarrow q$	p implies and is implied by q (p is equivalent to q)
a	first term for an arithmetic or geometric sequence

l	last term for an arithmetic sequence
d	common difference for an arithmetic sequence
r	common ratio for a geometric sequence
S_n	sum to n terms of a sequence
S_∞	sum to infinity of a sequence

Operations

$a + b$	a plus b
$a - b$	a minus b
$a \times b,\ ab,\ a \cdot b$	a multiplied by b
$a \div b,\ \dfrac{a}{b}$	a divided by b
$\displaystyle\sum_{i=1}^{n} a_i$	$a_1 + a_2 + \ldots + a_n$
$\displaystyle\prod_{i=1}^{n} a_i$	$a_1 \times a_2 \times \ldots \times a_n$
$\sqrt{a}$	the non-negative square root of a
$|a|$	the modulus of a
$n!$	n factorial: $n! = n \times (n-1) \times \ldots \times 2 \times 1,\ n \in \mathbb{N};\ 0! = 1$
$\dbinom{n}{r},\ {}^nC_r,\ {}_nC_r$	the binomial coefficient $\dfrac{n!}{r!(n-r)!}$ for $n, r \in \mathbb{Z}_0^+,\ r \le n$ or $\dfrac{n(n-1)\ldots(n-r+1)}{r!}$ for $n \in \mathbb{Q},\ r \in \mathbb{Z}_0^+$

Functions

$f(x)$	the value of the function f at x
$\displaystyle\lim_{x \to a} f(x)$	the limit of $f(x)$ as x tends to a
$f : x \mapsto y$	the function f maps the element x to the element y
f^{-1}	the inverse function of the function f
gf	the composite function of f and g which is defined by $gf(x) = g(f(x))$
$\Delta x,\ \delta x$	an increment of x
$\dfrac{dy}{dx}$	the derivative of y with respect to x
$\dfrac{d^n y}{dx^n}$	the nth derivative of y with respect to x
$f'(x) \ldots,\ f^{(n)}(x)$	the first, ..., nth derivatives of $f(x)$ with respect to x
$\dot{x},\ \ddot{x},\ \ldots$	the first, second, ... derivatives of x with respect to t
$\displaystyle\int y\,dx$	the indefinite integral of y with respect to x
$\displaystyle\int_a^b y\,dx$	the definite integral of y with respect to x between the limits $x = a$ and $x = b$

Exponential and Logarithmic Functions

e	base of natural logarithms
e^x, $\exp x$	exponential function of x
$\log_a x$	logarithm to the base a of x
$\ln x$, $\log_e x$	natural logarithm of x

Trigonometric Functions

$\left.\begin{array}{l}\text{sin, cos, tan,}\\\text{cosec, sec, cot}\end{array}\right\}$ the trigonometric functions

$\left.\begin{array}{l}\sin^{-1}, \cos^{-1}, \tan^{-1}\\\text{arcsin, arccos, arctan}\end{array}\right\}$ the inverse trigonometric functions

°	degrees
rad	radians

$\left.\begin{array}{l}\text{cosec}^{-1}, \sec^{-1}, \cot^{-1}\\\text{arccosec, arcsec, arccot}\end{array}\right\}$ the inverse trigonometric functions

$\left.\begin{array}{l}\text{sinh, cosh, tanh}\\\text{cosech, sech, coth}\end{array}\right\}$ the hyperbolic functions

$\left.\begin{array}{l}\sinh^{-1}, \cosh^{-1}, \tanh^{-1}\\\text{cosech}^{-1}, \text{sech}^{-1}, \coth^{-1}\\\text{arsinh, arcosh, artanh}\\\text{arcosech, arsech, arcoth}\end{array}\right\}$ the inverse hyperbolic functions

Complex numbers

i, j	square root of -1
$x + iy$	complex number with real part x and imaginary part y
$r(\cos\theta + i\sin\theta)$	modulus argument form of a complex number with modulus r and argument θ
z	a complex number $z = x + iy = r(\cos\theta + i\sin\theta)$
$\text{Re}(z)$	the real part of z, $\text{Re}(z) = x$
$\text{Im}(z)$	the imaginary part of z, $\text{Im}(z) = y$
$|z|$	the modulus of z, $|z| = \sqrt{x^2 + y^2}$
$\arg(z)$	the argument of z, $\arg(z) = \theta$, $-\pi < \theta < \pi$
z^*	the complex conjugate of z, $x - iy$

Matrices

$\mathbf{M}$	a matrix $\mathbf{M}$
$\mathbf{0}$	zero matrix
$\mathbf{I}$	identity matrix
$\mathbf{M}^{-1}$	the inverse of the matrix $\mathbf{M}$
$\mathbf{M}^{\text{T}}$	the transpose of the matrix $\mathbf{M}$
$\det \mathbf{M}$ or $|\mathbf{M}|$	the determinant of the square matrix $\mathbf{M}$
$\mathbf{Mr}$	Image of the column vector $\mathbf{r}$ under the transformation associated with the matrix $\mathbf{M}$

Vectors

a, <u>a</u>, a̰	the vector **a**, <u>a</u>, a̰
$\overrightarrow{AB}$	the vector represented in magnitude and direction by the directed line segment AB
â	a unit vector in the direction of **a**
i, j, k	unit vectors in the directions of the Cartesian coordinate axes
$\lvert \mathbf{a} \rvert$, a	the magnitude of **a**
$\lvert \overrightarrow{AB} \rvert$, AB	the magnitude of $\overrightarrow{AB}$
$\begin{pmatrix} a \\ b \end{pmatrix}$, $a\mathbf{i} + b\mathbf{j}$	column vector and corresponding unit vector notation
r	position vector
s	displacement vector
v	velocity vector
a	acceleration vector
a·b	the scalar product of **a** and **b**
a × **b**	the vector product of **a** and **b**
a.b × **c**	the scalar triple product of **a**, **b** and **c**

Differential equations

ω	angular speed

Answers

Chapter 5

Exercise 5.1A

1 a $|z-4-3i|=4$

  b $\arg(z)=-\dfrac{\pi}{3}$

  c $\arg(z-3-2i)=\dfrac{3\pi}{4}$

  d $|z-1|=|z-6i|$

2 a i
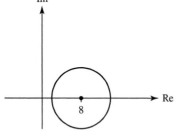

   ii $(x-8)^2+y^2=36$

  b i
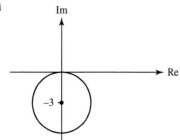

   ii $x^2+(y+3)^2=9$

  c i
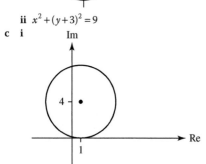

   ii $(x-1)^2+(y-4)^2=16$

  d i
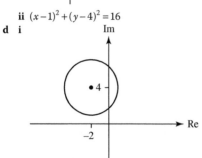

   ii $(x+2)^2+(y-4)^2=5$

  e i
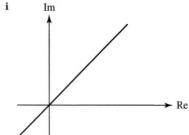

   ii $y=x$

  f i
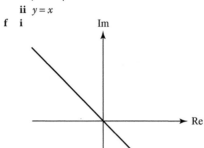

   ii $y=-x$

  g i
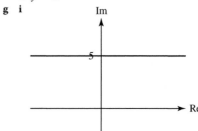

   ii $y=5$

  h i
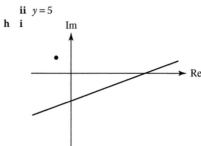

   ii $y=\dfrac{1}{2}x-\dfrac{9}{4}$

  i i
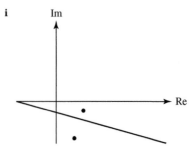

   ii $y=-\dfrac{1}{3}x-\dfrac{5}{3}$

j i

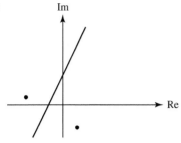

ii $y = \dfrac{7}{4}x + \dfrac{13}{8}$

3 a *C*
   b *D*
   c *B*
   d *A*

4 a i

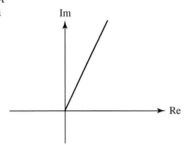

ii $y = \sqrt{3}x$

b i

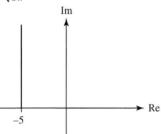

ii $x = -5$

c i

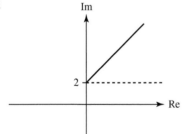

ii $y = x + 2$

d i

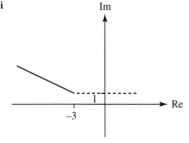

ii $\tan\left(\dfrac{\pi}{6}\right) = \dfrac{\sqrt{3}}{3}$

$y = -\dfrac{\sqrt{3}}{3}x + 1 + \sqrt{3}$

e i

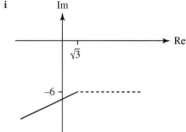

ii $\tan\left(\dfrac{\pi}{3}\right) = \sqrt{3}$

$y = \sqrt{3}x - 9$

5 a i $(x-1)^2 + y^2 = 4$
   ii Centre at $(1, 0)$, radius 2

   b i $\left(x - \dfrac{9}{4}\right)^2 + \left(y - \dfrac{1}{2}\right)^2 = \dfrac{45}{16}$

   ii Centre at $\left(\dfrac{9}{4}, \dfrac{1}{2}\right)$, radius $\dfrac{3\sqrt{5}}{4}$

   c i $\left(x + \dfrac{7}{4}\right)^2 + \left(y - \dfrac{5}{4}\right)^2 = \dfrac{85}{8}$

   ii Centre at $\left(-\dfrac{7}{4}, \dfrac{5}{4}\right)$, radius $\dfrac{\sqrt{170}}{4}$

   d i $(x-1)^2 + (y+6)^2 = 52$
   ii Centre at $(1, -6)$, radius $2\sqrt{13}$

   e i $(x-5)^2 + (y+7)^2 = 39$
   ii Centre at $(5, -7)$, radius $\sqrt{39}$

Exercise 5.1B

1 a

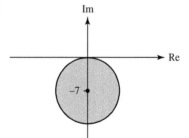

   b

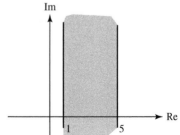

c

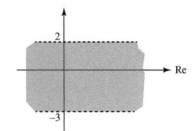

d

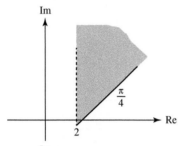

e

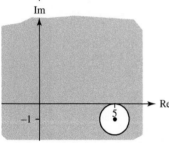

f

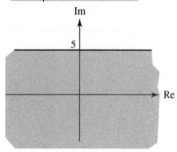

g

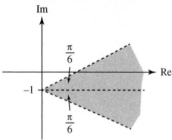

2 a

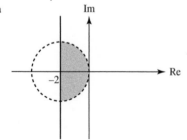

b

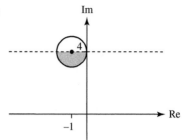

c

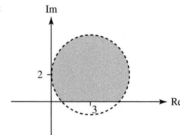

d

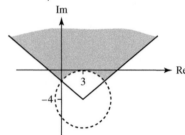

e

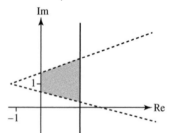

f

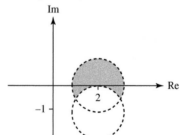

g

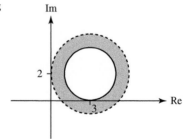

3 a i ii

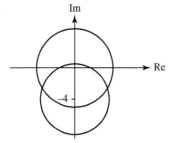

b $z = \pm\dfrac{\sqrt{311}}{8} - \dfrac{3}{8}i$

4 a i ii

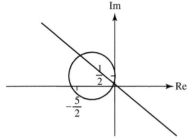

b $A = (-1, 1)$ or $A = (-2, 2)$

5 a e.g. $\{z \in \mathbb{C}: |z - 6 - 8i| \le 6\} \cap \{z \in \mathbb{C}: \text{Im}(z) < 8\}$

b $\left\{z \in \mathbb{C}: \dfrac{\pi}{6} < \arg(z + 2 + 2i) \le \dfrac{\pi}{4}\right\}$

6 a

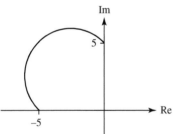

b $-\dfrac{5}{2} + \dfrac{5}{2}i$

c $-3 + (5 + \sqrt{21})i$

7 a

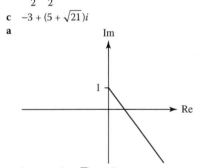

b $|x + iy + 4| = \sqrt{2}|x + iy|$

$(x + 4)^2 + y^2 = 2x^2 + 2y^2$

$x^2 + 8x + 16 + y^2 = 2x^2 + 2y^2$

$x^2 + y^2 - 8x - 16 = 0$

$(x - 4)^2 - 16 + y^2 - 16 = 0$

$(x - 4)^2 + y^2 = 32$

Therefore, a circle with centre $(4, 0)$ and radius $\sqrt{32}$

c $z_1 = \dfrac{5 + \sqrt{55}}{2} + \left(\dfrac{-3 - \sqrt{55}}{2}\right)i$ and

$z_2 = \dfrac{5 - \sqrt{55}}{2} + \left(\dfrac{-3 + \sqrt{55}}{2}\right)i$

8

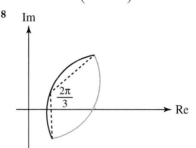

9 a $|z| = k|z - z_1|$

Let $z_1 = a + bi$

$|x + iy|^2 = k^2|x + iy - (a + bi)|^2$

$x^2 + y^2 = k^2(x - a)^2 + k^2(y - b)^2$

$x^2 + y^2 = k^2(x^2 - 2ax + a^2 + y^2 - 2by + b^2)$

$x^2(k^2 - 1) - 2k^2ax + y^2(k^2 - 1) - 2k^2by + k^2(a^2 + b^2) = 0$

$x^2 - \dfrac{2k^2ax}{k^2 - 1} + y^2 - \dfrac{2k^2by}{k^2 - 1} + \dfrac{k^2(a^2 + b^2)}{k^2 - 1} = 0$

$\left(x - \dfrac{k^2a}{k^2 - 1}\right)^2 - \dfrac{k^4a^2}{(k^2 - 1)^2} + \left(y - \dfrac{k^2b}{k^2 - 1}\right)^2$

$- \dfrac{k^4b^2}{(k^2 - 1)^2} + \dfrac{k^2(a^2 + b^2)}{k^2 - 1} = 0$

$\left(x - \dfrac{k^2a}{k^2 - 1}\right)^2 + \left(y - \dfrac{k^2b}{k^2 - 1}\right)^2$

$= \dfrac{k^4a^2}{(k^2 - 1)^2} + \dfrac{k^4b^2}{(k^2 - 1)^2} - \dfrac{k^2(a^2 + b^2)}{k^2 - 1}$

So a circle

b $\left(\dfrac{k^2a}{k^2 - 1}, \dfrac{k^2b}{k^2 - 1}\right)$

c $\dfrac{k}{k^2 - 1}\sqrt{a^2 + b^2}$

Exercise 5.2A

1 a $z = w + 1 \Rightarrow |w + 1| = 3$

Circle, centre $(-1, 0)$, radius 3

b $z = \dfrac{w}{3} \Rightarrow \left|\dfrac{w}{3}\right| = 3 \Rightarrow |w| = 9$

Circle, centre $(0, 0)$, radius 9

c $z^2 = \dfrac{w}{2} \Rightarrow \left|\dfrac{w}{2}\right| = |3|^2 \Rightarrow |w| = 18$

Circle, centre $(0, 0)$, radius 18

d $z = -iw \Rightarrow |-iw| = 3 \Rightarrow |w| = 3$

Circle, centre $(0, 0)$, radius 3

e $z = 2 + i - w \Rightarrow |2 + i - w| = 3 \Rightarrow |w - 2 - i| = 3$

Circle, centre $(2, 1)$, radius 3

f $|w| = |z|^3 \Rightarrow |w| = 27$

Circle, centre $(0, 0)$, radius 27

2 a $z = w - 5i \Rightarrow \arg(w - 5i) = \dfrac{\pi}{3}$

Half line from $(0, 5)$ angle of $\dfrac{\pi}{3}$

b $z = \dfrac{w-1-i}{4} \Rightarrow \arg\left(\dfrac{w-1-i}{4}\right) = \dfrac{\pi}{3}$

Half line from $(1, 1)$ angle of $\dfrac{\pi}{3}$

c $\arg(w) = \arg(z^3) = 3\arg(z)$

Half line from $(0, 0)$ angle of π

d $\arg(w) = \arg(iz) = \arg(i) + \arg(z)$

$\arg(w) = \dfrac{\pi}{2} + \dfrac{\pi}{3} = \dfrac{5\pi}{6}$

Half line from $(0, 0)$ angle of $\dfrac{5\pi}{6}$

e $z^2 = 2w - 1 \Rightarrow \arg(2w - 1) = \arg(z^2) = 2\arg(z)$

$\arg\left(w - \dfrac{1}{2}\right) = \dfrac{2}{3}\pi$

Half line from $\left(\dfrac{1}{2}, 0\right)$ angle of $\dfrac{2}{3}\pi$

f $2zw + iw = z - 1 \Rightarrow z = \dfrac{iw + 1}{1 - 2w}$

Minor arc anticlockwise from $(0, 1)$ to $\left(\dfrac{1}{2}, 0\right)$

3 a $|w - 3i| = |w|$

This is the perpendicular bisector of line joining $(0, 3)$ and $(0, 0)$, i.e. the line $v = \dfrac{3}{2}i$

b $|w - 2| = |w|$

This is the perpendicular bisector of the line joining $(2, 0)$ to $(0, 0)$, i.e. the line $u = 1$

c $\arg(w) = \dfrac{\pi}{12}$

d $\arg(w - 3i) - \arg(w) = \dfrac{\pi}{4}$

Major arc anticlockwise from $(0, 3)$ to $(0, 0)$

4 a i Half line from $(0, 6)$ at angle $\dfrac{\pi}{6}$

ii Half line from $(3, 0)$ at angle $\dfrac{\pi}{6}$

b $z = \dfrac{2}{w} \Rightarrow \arg\left(\dfrac{2}{w} - 2i\right) = \dfrac{\pi}{6}$

$\Rightarrow \arg\left(\dfrac{2 - 2wi}{w}\right) = \dfrac{\pi}{6}$

$\Rightarrow \arg\left(\dfrac{-2i(i + w)}{w}\right) = \dfrac{\pi}{6}$

$\Rightarrow \arg(-2i) + \arg\left(\dfrac{w + i}{w}\right) = \dfrac{\pi}{6}$

$\Rightarrow -\dfrac{\pi}{2} + \arg\left(\dfrac{w + i}{w}\right) = \dfrac{\pi}{6}$

$\Rightarrow \arg\left(\dfrac{w + i}{w}\right) = \dfrac{2\pi}{3}$

5 $wz - 3wi = 3 + z$

$\Rightarrow wz - z = 3 + 3wi$

$\Rightarrow z = \dfrac{3 + 3wi}{w - 1}$

$\arg\left(\dfrac{3 + 3wi}{w - 1} + 3\right) = -\dfrac{\pi}{3}$

$\Rightarrow \arg\left(\dfrac{3 + 3wi + 3(w - 1)}{w - 1}\right) = -\dfrac{\pi}{3}$

$\Rightarrow \arg\left(\dfrac{3wi + 3w}{w - 1}\right) = -\dfrac{\pi}{3}$

$\Rightarrow \arg\left(\dfrac{w(3i + 3)}{w - 1}\right) = -\dfrac{\pi}{3}$

$\Rightarrow \arg(3i + 3) + \arg\left(\dfrac{w}{w - 1}\right) = -\dfrac{\pi}{3}$

$\Rightarrow \dfrac{\pi}{4} + \arg\left(\dfrac{w}{w - 1}\right) = -\dfrac{\pi}{3}$

$\Rightarrow \arg\left(\dfrac{w}{w - 1}\right) = -\dfrac{7\pi}{12}$

6 a $\left|w - \dfrac{3}{2}\right| = |w - 1|$

Perpendicular bisector of line joining $\left(\dfrac{3}{2}, 0\right)$ to $(1, 0)$

b $|w - 1 - i| = |w - 1|$

Perpendicular bisector of line joining $(1, 1)$ to $(1, 0)$

c $\arg(w) - \arg(w - 1) = \dfrac{\pi}{3}$

Major arc anticlockwise from $(0, 0)$ to $(1, 0)$

d $\arg\left(w - \dfrac{3}{4}\right) - \arg(w - 1) = \dfrac{3\pi}{4}$

Minor arc anticlockwise from $\left(\dfrac{3}{4}, 0\right)$ to $(1, 0)$

7 a $\arg\left(w + \dfrac{3}{4}i\right) - \arg(w - 1) = \dfrac{\pi}{3}$

Major arc anticlockwise from $\left(0, -\dfrac{3}{4}\right)$ to $(1, 0)$

b $\arg(w + 2 - 4i) - \arg(w - 1) = -0.37$ rad

Major arc anticlockwise from $(-2, 4)$ to $(1, 0)$

Exercise 5.2B

1 $z = \dfrac{3i}{w}$

$\left|\dfrac{3i}{w} - 4\right| = 4$

$\left|\dfrac{3i - 4w}{w}\right| = 4$

$|3i - 4w| = 4|w|$

$|-4|\left|w - \dfrac{3}{4}i\right| = 4|w|$

$\left|w - \dfrac{3}{4}i\right| = |w|$ which is the equation of a line

$\left|u + iv - \dfrac{3}{4}i\right|^2 = |u + iv|^2$

$u^2 + \left(v - \dfrac{3}{4}\right)^2 = u^2 + v^2$

$-\dfrac{3}{2}v + \dfrac{9}{16} = 0 \Rightarrow v = \dfrac{3}{8}$

2 $w(z - 2) = z + 2 \Rightarrow z = \dfrac{2 + 2w}{w - 1}$

a $|z| = 2 \Rightarrow \left|\dfrac{2 + 2w}{w - 1}\right| = 2$

$|2 + 2w| = 2|w - 1|$

$|2||w + 1| = 2|w - 1|$

$|w + 1| = |w - 1|$

equation is $u = 0$

b $|z| = 3 \Rightarrow \left|\dfrac{2 + 2w}{w - 1}\right| = 3$

$|2 + 2w| = 3|w - 1|$

$$|2||w+1| = 3|w-1|$$
$$2|w+1| = 3|w-1|$$
$$2|u+iv+1| = 3|u+iv-1|$$
$$4((u+1)^2+v^2) = 9((u-1)^2+v^2)$$
$$4u^2+8u+4+4v^2 = 9u^2-18u+9+9v^2$$
$$5u^2+5v^2-26u+5 = 0$$
$$u^2+v^2-\frac{26}{5}u+1 = 0$$
$$\left(u-\frac{13}{5}\right)^2-\frac{169}{25}+v^2+1 = 0$$
$$\left(u-\frac{13}{5}\right)^2+v^2 = \frac{144}{25}$$

Centre at $\left(\frac{13}{5},0\right)$, radius $\frac{12}{5}$

3 a $zw-5iw = z+4i \Rightarrow z = \dfrac{i(4+5w)}{w-1}$

$$\left|\frac{i(4+5w)}{w-1}\right| = 2 \Rightarrow |5i|\left|w+\frac{4}{5}\right| = 2|w-1|$$

$$5\left|w+\frac{4}{5}\right| = 2|w-1|$$

$$\left|w+\frac{4}{5}\right| = \frac{2}{5}|w-1|$$

Therefore $A = \dfrac{2}{5}$

b $25\left|u+iv+\dfrac{4}{5}\right|^2 = 4|u+iv-1|^2$

$$25\left(\left(u+\frac{4}{5}\right)^2+v^2\right) = 4((u-1)^2+v^2)$$

$$25u^2+40u+16+25v^2 = 4u^2-8u+4+4v^2$$

$$21u^2+21v^2+48u+12 = 0$$

$$u^2+v^2+\frac{16}{7}u+\frac{4}{7} = 0$$

$$\left(u+\frac{8}{7}\right)^2-\frac{64}{49}+v^2+\frac{4}{7} = 0$$

$$\left(u+\frac{8}{7}\right)^2+v^2 = \frac{36}{49}$$

Hence a circle with centre $\left(-\dfrac{8}{7},0\right)$ and radius $\dfrac{6}{7}$

4 $Re : u = 1$

5 $w = \dfrac{z+3i}{4+iz}$

Q lies on the real axis so $w = u$

$$u = \frac{x+iy+3i}{4+i(x+iy)}$$

$$u = \frac{(x+(y+3)i)((4-y)-xi)}{((4-y)+xi)((4-y)-xi)}$$

$$= \frac{x(4-y)+x(y+3)+(y+3)(4-y)i-x^2i}{(4-y)^2+x^2}$$

$$Im : 0 = \frac{(y+3)(4-y)-x^2}{(4-y)^2+x^2}$$

$$(y+3)(4-y)-x^2 = 0$$

$$4y-y^2+12-3y-x^2 = 0$$

$$x^2+y^2-y-12 = 0$$
$$x^2+\left(y-\frac{1}{2}\right)^2-\frac{1}{4}-12 = 0$$
$$x^2+\left(y-\frac{1}{2}\right)^2 = \frac{49}{4}$$

Circle, centre $\left(0,\dfrac{1}{2}\right)$, radius $\dfrac{7}{2}$

6 a $x = -1$

b $u^2+\left(v-\dfrac{5}{6}\right)^2 = \dfrac{1}{36}$

Circle, centre $\left(0,\dfrac{5}{6}\right)$ and radius $\dfrac{1}{6}$

7 $(0, 0)$ or $(0, 4)$

8 $wz-iw = (2-i)z-3i$
$wz-(2-i)z = iw-3i$
$wz+(-2+i)z = iw-3i$
$(w-2+i)z = (w-3)i$

$$z = \frac{(w-3)i}{w-2+i}$$

$$z = \frac{(u+iv-3)i}{u+iv-2+i}$$

$$= \frac{-v+(u-3)i}{(u-2)+(v+1)i}$$

$$= \frac{(-v+(u-3)i)((u-2)-(v+1)i)}{((u-2)+(v+1)i)((u-2)-(v+1)i)}$$

Since line has equation $y = x$, the real and imaginary parts of z are equal.

i.e. $-v(u-2)+(u-3)(v+1) = v(v+1)+(u-3)(u-2)$
$\Rightarrow -uv+2v+uv+u-3v-3 = v^2+v+u^2-5u+6$
$\Rightarrow v^2+2v+u^2-6u+9 = 0$
$\Rightarrow (u-3)^2-9+(v+1)^2-1+9 = 0$
$\Rightarrow (u-3)^2+(v+1)^2 = 1$

So circle centre $3-i$ and radius 1

9 a $k = 3$ then image is a line

b i $9|u+iv+1|^2 = k^2|u+iv-1|$

$$9((u+1)^2+v^2) = k^2((u-1)^2+v^2)$$

$$9u^2+18u+9+9v^2 = k^2u^2-2k^2u+k^2+k^2v^2$$

$$(9-k^2)u^2+(9-k^2)v^2+(18+2k^2)u+9-k^2 = 0$$

$$u^2+v^2+\frac{2(9+k^2)}{9-k^2}u+1 = 0$$

$$\left(u+\frac{9+k^2}{9-k^2}\right)^2+v^2-\frac{(9+k^2)^2}{(9-k^2)^2}+1 = 0$$

$$\left(u+\frac{9+k^2}{9-k^2}\right)^2+v^2 = \frac{(9+k^2)^2-(9-k^2)^2}{(9-k^2)^2}$$

$$\left(u+\frac{9+k^2}{9-k^2}\right)^2+v^2 = \frac{36k^2}{(9-k^2)^2}$$

ii if $k < 3$ then centre $\left(\dfrac{9+k^2}{k^2-9},0\right)$,

radius $\sqrt{\dfrac{36k^2}{(9-k^2)^2}} = \dfrac{6k}{9-k^2}$

if $k > 3$ then centre $\left(\dfrac{9+k^2}{k^2-9},0\right)$,

radius $\sqrt{\dfrac{36k^2}{(9-k^2)^2}} = \dfrac{6k}{k^2-9}$

1 a i

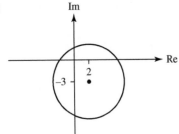

ii

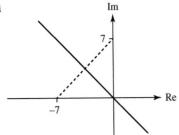

iii

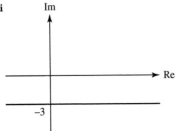

b i $(x-2)^2 + (y+3)^2 = 16$
  ii $y = -x$
  iii $y = -3$

2 a i

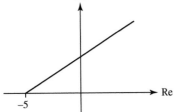

ii

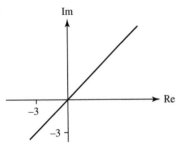

b i $y = \sqrt{3}x + 5\sqrt{3}$
  ii $y = x$

3 a

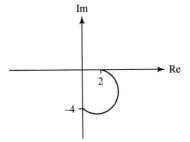

b

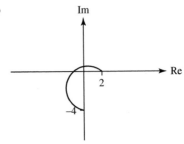

c

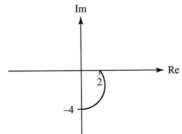

d

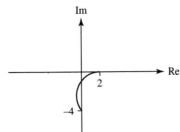

4 a i $\left(x - \dfrac{1}{3}\right)^2 + \left(y - \dfrac{8}{3}\right)^2 = \dfrac{20}{9}$

  ii $\left(x + \dfrac{3}{2}\right)^2 + \left(y + \dfrac{1}{2}\right)^2 = \dfrac{3}{2}$

b i Centre at $\left(\dfrac{1}{3}, \dfrac{8}{3}\right)$, radius $\dfrac{2\sqrt{5}}{3}$

  ii Centre at $\left(-\dfrac{3}{2}, -\dfrac{1}{2}\right)$, radius $\sqrt{\dfrac{3}{2}}$

5

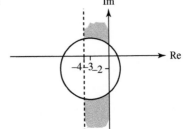

6

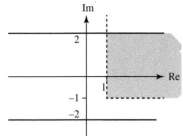

7

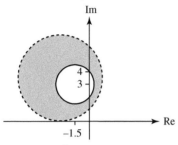

8 a i $|w| = |z|^2 \Rightarrow |w| = 25$

ii $2|w - i| = 5|w - 1|$

b i Circle centre origin, radius 25

ii Circle, centre $\left(\dfrac{25}{21}, -\dfrac{4}{21} \right)$, radius $\dfrac{10}{21}\sqrt{2}$

9 a $\arg(w) = \arg(4iz^3)$

$$= \arg(4i) + \arg(z^3)$$

$$= \dfrac{\pi}{2} + 3\arg(z)$$

$$= \dfrac{\pi}{2} + 3\left(-\dfrac{\pi}{4} \right)$$

$$= -\dfrac{\pi}{4}$$

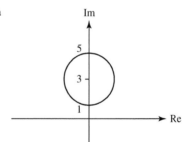

b $w = \dfrac{i - z}{z + 4} \Rightarrow wz + 4w = i - z$

$$z = \dfrac{i - 4w}{w + 1}$$

$$\arg\left(\dfrac{i - 4w}{w + 1} \right) = -\dfrac{\pi}{4} \Rightarrow \arg(i - 4w) - \arg(w + 1) = -\dfrac{\pi}{4}$$

$$\arg\left(-4\left(w - \dfrac{i}{4} \right) \right) - \arg(w + 1) = -\dfrac{\pi}{4}$$

$$\arg(-4) + \arg\left(w - \dfrac{i}{4} \right) - \arg(w + 1) = -\dfrac{\pi}{4}$$

$$\pi + \arg\left(w - \dfrac{i}{4} \right) - \arg(w + 1) = -\dfrac{\pi}{4}$$

$$\arg\left(w - \dfrac{i}{4} \right) - \arg(w + 1) = -\dfrac{5\pi}{4}$$

$$\arg\left(\dfrac{w - \dfrac{i}{4}}{w + 1} \right) = \dfrac{3\pi}{4}$$

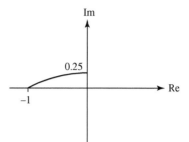

10 $w = \dfrac{6}{z + 1} \Rightarrow zw + w = 6 \Rightarrow z = \dfrac{6 - w}{w}$

$$|z + 5| = 4 \Rightarrow \left| \dfrac{6 - w}{w} + 5 \right| = 4$$

$$\left| \dfrac{6 - w + 5w}{w} \right| = 4$$

$$|6 + 4w| = 4|w|$$

$$|6 + 4(u + iv)| = 4|u + iv|$$

$$(6 + 4u)^2 + (4v)^2 = 16(u^2 + v^2)$$

$$36 + 48u + 16u^2 + 16v^2 = 16u^2 + 16v^2$$

$$48u = -36$$

$$u = -\dfrac{3}{4}$$

11 $3|u + iv - 2i| = 5|u + iv - 1|$

Assessment 5

1 a

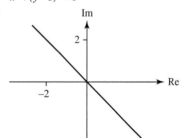

b $x^2 + (y - 3)^2 = 4$

2 a

Im

2

−2

Re

b $y = -x$

3 a

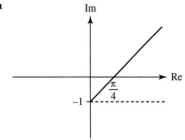

b $y = x - 1$

c $z = \dfrac{1+\sqrt{7}}{2} + \dfrac{-1+\sqrt{7}}{2}i$

4 a $|z+7| = \sqrt{2}|z-4i+1|$

$|x+iy+7| = \sqrt{2}|x+iy-4i+1|$

$(x+7)^2 + y^2 = 2(x+1)^2 + 2(y-4)^2$

$x^2 + 14x + 49 + y^2 = 2x^2 + 4x + 2 + 2y^2 - 16y + 32$

$x^2 - 10x + y^2 - 16y = 15$

$(x-5)^2 - 25 + (y-8)^2 - 64 = 15$

$(x-5)^2 + (y-8)^2 = 104$

So a circle

Centre (5, 8), radius $2\sqrt{26}$

b

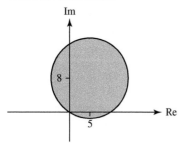

c $8 - 2\sqrt{26} \le \operatorname{Im}(w) \le 8 + 2\sqrt{26}$

5

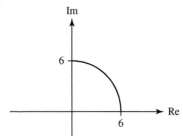

6 a

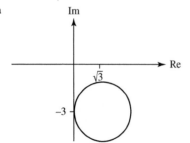

b $\sqrt{3} \le |z| \le 3\sqrt{3}$

7 a

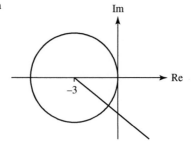

b $\left(-\dfrac{3}{2}, -\dfrac{3\sqrt{3}}{2} \right)$

8

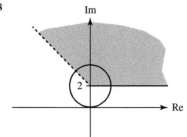

9 a

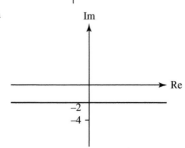

$y = -2$

b $z = 2 - 2i$

10 a

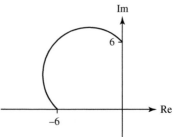

b Semi-circle so centre is midpoint of line segment joining 6i to −6 which is −3 + 3i

11 a $-6 - 6i$

b $z = \dfrac{4 - w}{2}$

$z + 1 = \dfrac{4 - w}{2} + 1$

$\quad = \dfrac{6 - w}{2}$

$|z + 1| = 2 \Rightarrow \left| \dfrac{6 - w}{2} \right| = 2$

$\qquad \Rightarrow |6 - w| = 4$

$\qquad \Rightarrow |w - 6| = 4$

So a circle

Centre (6, 0), radius 4

12 $w = \dfrac{i}{z} \Rightarrow z - 4 = \dfrac{i}{w} - 4 = \dfrac{i - 4w}{w}$

$|z - 4| = 4 \Rightarrow \left| \dfrac{i - 4w}{w} \right| = 4$

$|i - 4w| = 4|w|$

Let $w = u + iv$, then

$|i - 4(u + iv)| = 4|u + iv|$

$(-4u)^2 + (1 - 4v)^2 = 16u^2 + 16v^2$

$16u^2 + 16v^2 - 8v + 1 = 16u^2 + 16v^2$

$8v = 1$

So equation is $y = \dfrac{1}{8} \left(\text{or } v = \dfrac{1}{8} \right)$

13 a $z = 1 + iy \Rightarrow w = (1 + iy)^2 = 1 - y^2 + 2yi$

Let $w = u + iv$ then $u + iv = 1 - y^2 + 2yi$

Then $u = 1 - y^2$ and $v = 2y \Rightarrow y = \dfrac{v}{2}$

So $u = 1 - \left(\dfrac{v}{2} \right)^2 \Rightarrow v^2 = 4(1 - u)$

This is a parabola

b

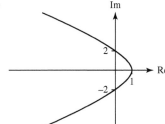

14

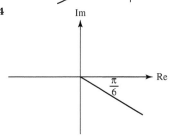

15 $w = 2z - 8 + 6i$

16 $wz + 3wi = z - 3$

$z - wz = 3wi + 3$

$z = \dfrac{3wi + 3}{1 - w}$

$|z| = 3 \Rightarrow \left| \dfrac{3wi + 3}{1 - w} \right| = 3$

$|3wi + 3| = 3|1 - w|$

Let $w = u + iv$, then

$|3(u + iv)i + 3| = 3|1 - (u + iv)|$

$|3ui - 3v + 3| = 3|1 - u - iv|$

$(3u)^2 + (3 - 3v)^2 = 9(1 - u)^2 + 9(-v)^2$

$9u^2 + 9 - 18v + 9v^2 = 9 - 18u + 9u^2 + 9v^2$

$9 - 18v = 9 - 18u \Rightarrow u = v$

So a line with equation $y = x$

17 $wz + w\sqrt{2}i = z - \sqrt{2}i$

$z = \dfrac{(w\sqrt{2} + \sqrt{2})i}{1 - w}$

$|z| = 2 \Rightarrow \left| \dfrac{(w\sqrt{2} + \sqrt{2})i}{1 - w} \right| = 2$

Let $w = u + iv$

$\left| (u + iv)\sqrt{2}i + \sqrt{2}i \right| = 2|1 - (u + iv)|$

$\left| -v\sqrt{2} + (u + 1)\sqrt{2}i \right| = 2|(1 - u) - vi|$

$(-v\sqrt{2})^2 + (\sqrt{2}(u + 1))^2 = 4(1 - u)^2 + 4v^2$

$2v^2 + 2u^2 + 4u + 2 = 4 - 8u + 4u^2 + 4v^2$

$0 = 2 - 12u + 2u^2 + 2v^2$

$u^2 + v^2 - 6u + 1 = 0$

$(u - 3)^2 - 9 + v^2 + 1 = 0$

$(u - 3)^2 + v^2 = 8$

Centre $(3, 0)$, radius $2\sqrt{2}$

18 If $w = z^2$ then $u + iv = (x + iy)^2 = x^2 + 2xyi - y^2$

Therefore Re : $u = x^2 - y^2$

Im : $v = 2xyi$

P lies on $y = x + 1$ therefore these become

$u = x^2 - (x + 1)^2 = -2x - 1$

and $v = 2x(x + 1) = 2x^2 + 2x$

Rearrange first equation to give $x = \dfrac{-1 - u}{2}$

Substitute into other equation: $v = 2\left(\dfrac{-1 - u}{2} \right)^2 + 2\left(\dfrac{-1 - u}{2} \right)$

$\Rightarrow v = \dfrac{2(1 + 2u + u^2)}{4} + \dfrac{-2 - 2u}{2}$

$= \dfrac{1 + 2u + u^2}{2} + \dfrac{-2 - 2u}{2}$

$= \dfrac{1 + 2u + u^2 - 2 - 2u}{2}$

$= \dfrac{u^2 - 1}{2}$

$\Rightarrow 2v = u^2 - 1$ as required

19 $|z| = 3 \Rightarrow z = 3e^{i\theta}$

Therefore $w = \dfrac{1}{3e^{i\theta}} + 3e^{i\theta}$

$= \dfrac{1}{3}e^{-i\theta} + 3e^{i\theta}$

$= \dfrac{1}{3}(\cos(-\theta) + i\sin(-\theta)) + 3(\cos\theta + i\sin\theta)$

$= \dfrac{1}{3}(\cos\theta - i\sin\theta) + 3(\cos\theta + i\sin\theta)$

$= \dfrac{10}{3}\cos\theta + \dfrac{8}{3}i\sin\theta$

Let $w = u + iv$

Then $u + iv = \dfrac{10}{3}\cos\theta + \dfrac{8}{3}\sin\theta$

$\Rightarrow u = \dfrac{10}{3}\cos\theta, \ v = \dfrac{8}{3}\sin\theta$

$\Rightarrow \cos\theta = \dfrac{3u}{10}, \ \sin\theta = \dfrac{3v}{8}$

$\cos^2\theta + \sin^2\theta = 1 \Rightarrow \left(\dfrac{3u}{10} \right)^2 + \left(\dfrac{3v}{8} \right)^2 = 1$

$\Rightarrow \dfrac{9u^2}{100} + \dfrac{9v^2}{64} = 1$

$\Rightarrow 576u^2 + 900v^2 = 6400$

$\Rightarrow 144u^2 + 225v^2 = 1600$

as required

Chapter 6

Exercise 6.1A

1. **a** $u_n = 1.02u_{n-1} + 1000$, $n \geq 2$, $u_1 = 2000$

   b £4100.80 in account after 2 years.

2. **a** $u_n = 1.1u_{n-1} - 1950$, $n \geq 2$, $u_1 = 18000$

   b 17685

   c The animals will eventually completely die out in this region.

3. **a** net migration = 200 − 1800 = −1600
   Initially 17 000 people so $u_1 = 17000$
   6 − 4 = 2 so net increase from births and deaths is
   $\dfrac{2}{1000} = 0.2\%$ so need to multiply previous term by
   100.2% = 1.002

   b The population is 13 865 at start of 2012.

   c The model predicts the population of the town will fall to zero but this is unlikely in practice.

4. **a** $u_n = 15(9^{n-1})$

   b $u_n = 8(-3)^{n-1}$

   c $u_n = 5(10^{n-1})$

   d $u_n = 128\left(-\dfrac{1}{2}\right)^{n-1}$

   e $u_n = 3^n$

   f $u_n = \dfrac{1}{49}(7^n)$ or $u_n = 7^{n-2}$

5. **a** $u_n = 4(2^{n-1}) - 1$

   b $u_n = 4(3^{n-1}) + 2$

   c $u_n = 3(6^{n-1}) - 1$

   d $u_n = 50\left(\dfrac{1}{2}\right)^{n-1} - 2$

   e $u_n = 4(-3)^n - 2$

   f $u_n = -5\left(\dfrac{1}{4}\right)^n + 4$

6. $u_n = 5 + \displaystyle\sum_{r=2}^{n} 8r$

   $= 5 + 8\left(\dfrac{n}{2}(n+1)\right) - 8$

   $= 5 + 4n(n+1) - 8$

   $= 4n^2 + 4n - 3$

7. $u_n = -2 + \displaystyle\sum_{r=2}^{n} 2r^2$

   $= -2 + 2\left(\dfrac{n}{6}(n+1)(2n+1)\right) - 2$

   $= -2 + \dfrac{n}{3}(2n^2 + 3n + 1) - 2$

   $= \dfrac{1}{3}(2n^3 + 3n^2 + n - 12)$

8. $u_n = 0 + \displaystyle\sum_{r=1}^{n-1} 3r(r+1)$

   $= \displaystyle\sum_{r=1}^{n-1}(3r^2 + 3r)$

   $= 3\left(\dfrac{(n-1)}{6}(n-1+1)(2(n-1)+1)\right) + 3\left(\dfrac{(n-1)}{2}(n-1+1)\right)$

   $= 3\left(\dfrac{n(n-1)}{6}(2n-1)\right) + 3\left(\dfrac{n(n-1)}{2}\right)$

   $= \dfrac{n(n-1)}{2}[2n-1+3]$

   $= \dfrac{n(n-1)}{2}[2n+2]$

   $= n(n-1)(n+1)$

9. $u_n = 2 + \displaystyle\sum_{r=1}^{n-1} r^3$

   $= 2 + \dfrac{1}{4}(n-1)^2(n-1+1)^2$

   $= \dfrac{1}{4}(8 + n^2(n-1)^2)$

   $= \dfrac{1}{4}(8 + n^4 - 2n^3 + n^2)$

10. $u_n = -3 + \displaystyle\sum_{r=1}^{n}(r^2 - 2r)$

    $= -3 + \dfrac{n}{6}(n+1)(2n+1) - 2\left(\dfrac{n}{2}\right)(n+1)$

    $= \dfrac{1}{6}(-18 + 2n^3 + 3n^2 + n - 6n^2 - 6n)$

    $= \dfrac{1}{6}(2n^3 - 3n^2 - 5n - 18)$

11. **a** $u_n = \dfrac{7}{2}(2^n) - n - 2$

    b $u_n = \dfrac{3}{4}(3^n) - \dfrac{1}{2}n + \dfrac{1}{4}$

    c $u_n = -\dfrac{2}{9}(-2)^n + n^2 + \dfrac{4}{3}n + \dfrac{2}{9}$

    d $u_n = -5(-1)^n + \dfrac{1}{2}n^2 - \dfrac{1}{2}n$

12. **a** $u_n = 1.03u_{n-1} - 12000$, $n \geq 1$, $u_0 = 200000$

    b Mortgage is £181 454.60 after 3 years

    c $u_n = -200000(1.03^n) + 400000$

    d 23 years and 5 months

13. **a** $a_1 = 1$, $a_2 = 3$

    b Solution is $a_n = 2^n - 1$
    Hence, $a_{10} = 1023$

Exercise 6.1B

1. Let $n = 1$ then $u_1 = 4^{1-1} = 1$
   so true for $n = 1$ since the initial condition is $u_1 = 1$
   Assume true for $n = k$ and let $n = k + 1$:
   $u_{k+1} = 4u_k$
   $= 4(4^{k-1})$

$$= 4^k$$

$$= 4^{(k+1)-1} \text{ as required}$$

so true for $n = k+1$

The solution is true for $n = 1$ and assuming true for $n = k$ implies it is true for $n = k+1$, hence it is true for all $n \in \mathbb{N}$

2 Let $n = 1$ then $u_1 = 7 \times 1 - 4 = 3$

so true for $n = 1$ since the initial condition is $u_1 = 3$

Assume true for $n = k$ and let $n = k+1$:

$$u_{k+1} = u_k + 7$$

$$= (7k - 4) + 7$$

$$= 7k + 3$$

$$= 7(k+1) - 4 \text{ as required}$$

so true for $n = k+1$

The solution is true for $n = 1$ and assuming true for $n = k$ implies it is true for $n = k+1$, hence it is true for all $n \in \mathbb{N}$

3 Let $n = 1$ then $u_1 = \frac{1}{2}(5^{1-1} + 1) = 1$

so true for $n = 1$ since the initial condition is $u_1 = 1$

Assume true for $n = k$ and let $n = k+1$:

$$u_{k+1} = 5u_k - 2$$

$$= 5\left(\frac{1}{2}(5^{k-1} + 1)\right) - 2$$

$$= \frac{1}{2} \times 5(5^{k-1}) + \frac{5}{2} - 2$$

$$= \frac{1}{2}(5^k) + \frac{1}{2}$$

$$= \frac{1}{2}(5^{(k+1)-1} + 1) \text{ as required}$$

so true for $n = k+1$

The solution is true for $n = 1$ and assuming true for $n = k$ implies it is true for $n = k+1$, hence it is true for all $n \in \mathbb{N}$

4 Let $n = 1$ then $u_1 = 2 - 3(2^{1-1}) = 2 - 3 = -1$

so true for $n = 1$ since the initial condition is $u_1 = -1$

Assume true for $n = k$ and let $n = k+1$:

$$u_{k+1} = \frac{1}{2}u_k + 1$$

$$= \frac{1}{2}(2 - 3(2^{1-k})) + 1$$

$$= 1 - \frac{3}{2}(2^{1-k}) + 1$$

$$= 2 - 3(2^{-k})$$

$$= 2 - 3(2^{1-(k+1)}) \text{ as required}$$

so true for $n = k+1$

The solution is true for $n = 1$ and assuming true for $n = k$ implies it is true for $n = k+1$, hence it is true for all $n \in \mathbb{N}$

5 Let $n = 1$ then $u_1 = \frac{1}{2}(1^2 + 1 - 2) = 0$

so true for $n = 1$ since the initial condition is $u_1 = 0$

Assume true for $n = k$ and let $n = k+1$:

$$u_{k+1} = u_k + k + 1$$

$$= \frac{1}{2}(k^2 + k - 2) + k + 1$$

$$= \frac{1}{2}(k^2 + k - 2 + 2k + 2)$$

$$= \frac{1}{2}(k^2 + 3k)$$

$$= \frac{1}{2}((k+1)^2 + (k+1) - 2) \text{ as required}$$

since $\frac{1}{2}((k+1)^2 + (k+1) - 2) = \frac{1}{2}(k^2 + 2k + 1 + k + 1 - 2)$

$$= \frac{1}{2}(k^2 + 3k)$$

so true for $n = k+1$

The solution is true for $n = 1$ and assuming true for $n = k$ implies it is true for $n = k+1$, hence it is true for all $n \in \mathbb{N}$

6 Let $n = 1$ then $u_1 = \frac{1}{3} \times 1 \times (1-1)(1-5) = 0$

so true for $n = 1$ since the initial condition is $u_1 = 0$

Assume true for $n = k$,

$$u_{k+1} = u_k + k^2 - 3k$$

$$= \frac{1}{3}k(k-1)(k-5) + k^2 - 3k$$

$$= \frac{1}{3}k[(k-1)(k-5) + k - 3]$$

$$= \frac{1}{3}k(k^2 - 6k + 5 + 3k - 9)$$

$$= \frac{1}{3}k(k^2 - 3k - 4)$$

$$= \frac{1}{3}k(k+1)(k-4)$$

$$= \frac{1}{3}((k+1)-1)(k+1)((k+1)-5) \text{ as required}$$

so true for $n = k+1$

The solution is true for $n = 1$ and assuming true for $n = k$ implies it is true for $n = k+1$, hence it is true for all $n \in \mathbb{N}$

7 Let $n = 0$ then $u_0 = \frac{1}{6}(0 - 0 - 0 - 6) = -1$

so true for $n = 0$ since the initial condition is $u_0 = -1$

Assume true for $n = k$,

$$u_{k+1} = u_k + 5k^2 - 4$$

$$= \frac{1}{6}(10k^3 - 15k^2 - 19k - 6) + 5k^2 - 4$$

$$= \frac{1}{6}(10k^3 - 15k^2 - 19k - 6 + 30k^2 - 24)$$

$$= \frac{1}{6}(10k^3 + 15k^2 - 19k - 30)$$

$$= \frac{1}{6}(10(k+1)^3 - 15(k+1)^2 - 19(k+1) - 6) \text{ as required}$$

since $10(k+1)^3 - 15(k+1)^2 - 19(k+1) - 6$

$$= 10k^3 + 30k^2 + 30k + 10 - 15k^2 - 30k - 15 - 19k - 19 - 6$$

$$= 10k^3 + 15k^2 - 19k - 30$$

so true for $n = k+1$

The solution is true for $n = 0$ and assuming true for $n = k$ implies it is true for $n = k+1$, hence it is true for all integers $n \geq 0$

8 Let $n = 0$ then $u_0 = \frac{1}{2}(5(3^0) - 0 - 1) = 2$

so true for $n = 0$ since the initial condition is $u_0 = 2$

Assume true for $n = k$,

$$u_{k+1} = 3u_k + 2k$$

$$= 3\left(\frac{1}{2}(5(3^k) - 2k - 1)\right) + 2k$$

$$= \frac{1}{2} \times 5 \times 3(3^k) - 3k - \frac{3}{2} + 2k$$

$$= \frac{1}{2} \times 5(3^{k+1}) - k - \frac{3}{2}$$

$$= \frac{1}{2}(5(3^{k+1}) - 2k - 3)$$

$$= \frac{1}{2}(5(3^{k+1}) - 2(k+1) - 1) \text{ as required}$$

so true for $n = k+1$

The solution is true for $n = 0$ and assuming true for $n = k$ implies it is true for $n = k+1$, hence it is true for all integers $n \geq 0$

9 Let $n=1$ then $u_1=3(1-1)!=3$

so true for $n=1$ since the initial condition is $u_1=3$

Assume true for $n=k$

$u_{k+1}=ku_k$

$\qquad =k(3(k-1)!)$

$\qquad =3k(k-1)!$

$\qquad =3k!$

$\qquad =3((k+1)-1)!$ as required

so true for $n=k+1$

The solution is true for $n=1$ and assuming true for $n=k$

implies it is true for $n=k+1$, hence it is true for all $n\in\mathbb{N}$

10 Let $n=1$ then $u_1=(1!)^2=1$

so true for $n=1$ since the initial condition is $u_1=1$

Assume true for $n=k$

$u_{k+1}=(k+1)^2u_k$

$\qquad =(k+1)^2(k!)^2$

$\qquad =((k+1)k!)^2$

$\qquad =((k+1)!)^2$ as required

so true for $n=k+1$

The solution is true for $n=1$ and assuming true for $n=k$

implies it is true for $n=k+1$, hence it is true for all $n\in\mathbb{N}$

11 $u_n=2-2\left(\dfrac{1}{2}\right)^n$

As $n\to\infty$, $\left(\dfrac{1}{2}\right)^n\to 0$, hence $u_n\to 2$

12 a $u_n\to 2+\dfrac{1-2k}{k+1}$

b The sequence diverges

c u_n oscillates between 2 and 1

13 a $20(2+n)$

b $R_n=R_{n-1}+n+1$, $R_1=3$

c Let $n=1$, then $R_1=\dfrac{1}{2}(1+3+2)=3$ which is R_1

Assume true for $n=k$ and let $n=k+1$,

$R_{k+1}=R_k+k+1+1$

$\qquad =\dfrac{1}{2}(k^2+3k+2)+k+2$

$\qquad =\dfrac{1}{2}(k^2+3k+2+2k+4)$

$\qquad =\dfrac{1}{2}(k^2+5k+6)$

$\qquad =\dfrac{1}{2}((k+1)^2+3(k+1)+2)$ as required

So true for $n=k+1$

The solution is true for $n=1$ and assuming true for $n=k$

implies it is true for $n=k+1$, hence it is true for all $n\in\mathbb{N}$

Exercise 6.2A

1 a $u_n=5(3^n)-4(-1)^n$, $n\geq 0$

b $u_n=(-1)^n-(-5)^n$, $n\geq 0$

c $u_n=(2+3n)2^n$, $n\geq 0$

d $u_n=\left(1-\dfrac{1}{2}n\right)(-4)^n$, $n\geq 0$

e $u_n=3^n\left(\cos\left(\dfrac{n\pi}{2}\right)+2\sin\left(\dfrac{n\pi}{2}\right)\right)$, $n\geq 0$

f $u_n=(\sqrt{2})^n\left(2\cos\left(\dfrac{n\pi}{4}\right)-2\sin\left(\dfrac{n\pi}{4}\right)\right)$, $n\geq 0$

or $2^{\left(\frac{n}{2}+1\right)}\left(\cos\left(\dfrac{n\pi}{4}\right)-\sin\left(\dfrac{n\pi}{4}\right)\right)$, $n\geq 0$

2 a $u_n=3(5^n)-(-3)^n$, $n\geq 0$

b $u_n=(3-n)7^n$, $n\geq 0$

c $u_n=(\sqrt{8})^n\left(\cos\left(\dfrac{3n\pi}{4}\right)+2\sin\left(\dfrac{3n\pi}{4}\right)\right)$, $n\geq 0$

3 a $u_n=5(2^n)-2(5^n)$

b $u_n=3(3^n)-(-5)^n$

c $u_n=(2-5n)8^n$

4 a $u_n=5(2^n)-\dfrac{1}{2}(-9)^n-\dfrac{1}{2}$

b $u_n=(2^n)+3(-9)^n-n-3$

c $u_n=5(2^n)-2(-9)^n-2n^2-10n-16$

5 a $u_n=(5-3n)5^n+2$

b $u_n=\dfrac{1}{4}(2n-1)5^n+\dfrac{1}{2}n+\dfrac{5}{4}$

c $u_n=(6-5n)5^n+n^2-\dfrac{45}{8}$

6 a $u_n=\dfrac{25}{12}+\dfrac{35}{12}(4^n)-\dfrac{9}{2}(3^n)$

b $u_n=\dfrac{1}{16}(15-23n)(-6)^n+\dfrac{1}{16}(2^n)$

c $u_n=2^n\left(\dfrac{1}{2}\cos\left(\dfrac{n\pi}{2}\right)-\sin\left(\dfrac{n\pi}{2}\right)\right)+\dfrac{1}{2}(2)^n$

Exercise 6.2B

1 a $u_n=\dfrac{7}{3}(2)^n+\dfrac{2}{3}(-7)^n+\dfrac{2}{9}n(2^n)$

or $u_n=\dfrac{1}{9}(2n+21)2^n+\dfrac{2}{3}(-7)^n$

b $u_n=-\dfrac{156}{46}(9)^n+\dfrac{156}{46}(2)^n+\dfrac{18}{7}n(9^n)$

c $u_n=\dfrac{23}{10}(5)^n+\dfrac{27}{10}(-5)^n-\dfrac{1}{2}n(5)^n$

2 a $u_n=(1-2n+2n^2)10^n$

b $u_n=(3-4n-n^2)(-3)^n$

c $u_n=\dfrac{n}{24}(7+5n)(12)^n$

3 $u_0=\dfrac{1}{8}(3+11-6)=1$ as given

$u_1=\dfrac{1}{8}(-3+33-6)=3$ as given

So true for $n=0$ and $n=1$

Assume true for $n=k$ and $n=k+1$

$u_{k+2}=2u_{k+1}+3u_k+3$

$\qquad =2\left(\dfrac{1}{8}(3(-1)^{k+1}+11(3)^{k+1}-6)\right)$

$\qquad +3\left(\dfrac{1}{8}(3(-1)^k+11(3)^k-6)\right)+3$

$\qquad =\dfrac{1}{8}\Big[6(-1)^{k+1}+22(3)^{k+1}-12+9(-1)^k+33(3)^k-18+24\Big]$

$$=\frac{1}{8}\left[\begin{array}{l}\dfrac{6}{-1}(-1)^{k+2}+\dfrac{22}{3}(3)^{k+2}-12+\dfrac{9}{(-1)^2}(-1)^{k+2}\\[4pt]+\dfrac{33}{(3)^2}(3)^{k+2}-18+24\end{array}\right]$$

$$=\frac{1}{8}\left[\begin{array}{l}-6(-1)^{k+2}+\dfrac{22}{3}(3)^{k+2}-12+9(-1)^{k+2}\\[4pt]+\dfrac{33}{9}(3)^{k+2}-18+24\end{array}\right]$$

$$=\frac{1}{8}\left[3(-1)^{k+2}+11(3)^{k+2}-6\right]\text{ as required}$$

So true for $n=0$ and $n=1$ and assuming true for $n=k$ and $n=k+1$ implies true for $n=k+2$, therefore true for all integers $n\geq0$

4 $u_0=\dfrac{1}{4}(5-1)=1$ as given

$u_1=\dfrac{1}{4}(5+1)\times2=3$ as given

So true for $n=0$ and $n=1$
Assume true for $n=k$ and $n=k+1$

$u_{k+2}=4u_k$

$$=4\left(\frac{1}{4}(5+(-1)^{k+1})2^k\right)$$

$$=(5+(-1)^{k+1})\,2^k$$

$$=\left(5+\frac{(-1)^{k+3}}{(-1)^2}\right)\frac{2^{k+2}}{2^2}$$

$$=\frac{1}{4}(5+(-1)^{k+3})2^{k+2}\quad\text{as required}$$

So true for $n=0$ and $n=1$ and assuming true for $n=k$ and $n=k+1$ implies true for $n=k+2$, therefore true for all integers $n\geq0$

5 $u_0=\dfrac{1}{11}(7+4)=1$ as given

$u_1=\dfrac{1}{11}(-35+24)=-1$ as given

So true for $n=0$ and $n=1$
Assume true for $n=k$ and $n=k+1$
$u_{k+2}=u_{k+1}+30u_k$

$$=\frac{1}{11}(7(-5)^{k+1}+4(6)^{k+1})+\frac{30}{11}(7(-5)^k+4(6)^k)$$

$$=\frac{1}{11}\left(\frac{7(-5)^{k+2}}{-5}+\frac{4(6)^{k+2}}{6}+\frac{210(-5)^{k+2}}{(-5)^2}+\frac{120(6)^{k+2}}{6^2}\right)$$

$$=\frac{1}{11}\left(-\frac{7}{5}(-5)^{k+2}+\frac{42}{5}(-5)^{k+2}+\frac{2}{3}(6)^{k+2}+\frac{10}{3}(6)^{k+2}\right)$$

$$=\frac{1}{11}\left(7(-5)^{k+2}+4(6)^{k+2}\right)\text{ as required}$$

So true for $n=0$ and $n=1$ and assuming true for $n=k$ and $n=k+1$ implies true for $n=k+2$, therefore true for all integers $n\geq0$

6 a $u_n=u_{n-1}+u_{n-2},\,n\geq2,\,u_0=1,\,u_1=1$

b $u_n=\left(\dfrac{5+\sqrt5}{10}\right)\left(\dfrac{1+\sqrt5}{2}\right)^n+\left(\dfrac{5-\sqrt5}{10}\right)\left(\dfrac{1-\sqrt5}{2}\right)^n$

c $u_0=\left(\dfrac{5+\sqrt5}{10}\right)\left(\dfrac{1+\sqrt5}{2}\right)^0+\left(\dfrac{5-\sqrt5}{10}\right)\left(\dfrac{1-\sqrt5}{2}\right)^0$

$$=\left(\dfrac{5+\sqrt5}{10}\right)+\left(\dfrac{5-\sqrt5}{10}\right)$$

$$=\frac{10}{10}=1\text{ as given}$$

$$u_1=\left(\frac{5+\sqrt5}{10}\right)\left(\frac{1+\sqrt5}{2}\right)^1+\left(\frac{5-\sqrt5}{10}\right)\left(\frac{1-\sqrt5}{2}\right)^1$$

$$=\frac{5+6\sqrt5+5}{20}+\frac{5-6\sqrt5+5}{20}$$

$$=\frac{20}{20}=1\text{ as given}$$

So true for $n=0$ and $n=1$

Assume true for $n=k$ and $n=k+1$

$u_{k+2}=u_{k+1}+u_k$

$$=\left(\frac{5+\sqrt5}{10}\right)\left(\frac{1+\sqrt5}{2}\right)^{k+1}+\left(\frac{5-\sqrt5}{10}\right)\left(\frac{1-\sqrt5}{2}\right)^{k+1}$$

$$+\left(\frac{5+\sqrt5}{10}\right)\left(\frac{1+\sqrt5}{2}\right)^{k}+\left(\frac{5-\sqrt5}{10}\right)\left(\frac{1-\sqrt5}{2}\right)^{k}$$

$$=\left(\frac{1+\sqrt5}{2}\right)^{k}\left[\left(\frac{5+\sqrt5}{10}\right)\left(\frac{1+\sqrt5}{2}\right)+\frac{5+\sqrt5}{10}\right]$$

$$+\left(\frac{1-\sqrt5}{2}\right)^{k}\left[\left(\frac{5-\sqrt5}{10}\right)\left(\frac{1-\sqrt5}{2}\right)+\frac{5-\sqrt5}{10}\right]$$

$$=\left(\frac{1+\sqrt5}{2}\right)^{k}\left(\frac{5+6\sqrt5+5}{20}+\frac{5+\sqrt5}{10}\right)$$

$$+\left(\frac{1-\sqrt5}{2}\right)^{k}\left(\frac{5-6\sqrt5+5}{20}+\frac{5-\sqrt5}{10}\right)$$

$$=\left(\frac{1+\sqrt5}{2}\right)^{k}\left(\frac{5+6\sqrt5+5+10+2\sqrt5}{20}\right)$$

$$+\left(\frac{1-\sqrt5}{2}\right)^{k}\left(\frac{5-6\sqrt5+5+10-2\sqrt5}{20}\right)$$

$$=\left(\frac{1+\sqrt5}{2}\right)^{k}\left(\frac{20+8\sqrt5}{20}\right)+\left(\frac{1-\sqrt5}{2}\right)^{k}\left(\frac{20-8\sqrt5}{20}\right)$$

$$=\left(\frac{5+\sqrt5}{10}\right)\left(\frac{1+\sqrt5}{2}\right)^{k+2}+\left(\frac{5-\sqrt5}{10}\right)\left(\frac{1-\sqrt5}{2}\right)^{k+2}$$

since $\left(\dfrac{1+\sqrt5}{2}\right)^2\left(\dfrac{5+\sqrt5}{10}\right)=\left(\dfrac{6+2\sqrt5}{4}\right)\left(\dfrac{5+\sqrt5}{10}\right)$

$$=\frac{40+16\sqrt5}{40}=\frac{20+8\sqrt5}{20}$$

and $\left(\dfrac{1-\sqrt5}{2}\right)^2\left(\dfrac{5-\sqrt5}{10}\right)=\left(\dfrac{6-2\sqrt5}{4}\right)\left(\dfrac{5-\sqrt5}{10}\right)$

$$=\frac{40-16\sqrt5}{40}=\frac{20-8\sqrt5}{20}$$

so true for $n=k+2$

The solution is true for $n=0$ and $n=1$ and assuming true for $n=k$ and $n=k+1$ implies it is true for $n=k+2$, hence it is true for all $n\in\mathbb{Z},\,n\geq0$

Review exercise 6

1 a $P_n=1.1P_{n-1}-35,\,P_1=450$

b $P_n=100(1.1)^{n-1}+350$

c No, for example, since population increases exponentially and will eventually run out of space/resources or interaction with other species will lead to greater predation. Cannot increase indefinitely.

2 a $u_1 = -2$, $u_2 = 0$, $u_3 = 2$

b $u_k = 2k - 4$

3 a $u_1 = 2$, $u_2 = 8$, $u_3 = 27$

b $u_n = \dfrac{13}{12}(3^n) - \dfrac{1}{2}n - \dfrac{3}{4}$

4 a $u_n = \dfrac{1}{6}(2n^3 - 3n^2 + n + 24)$

b 18

c Let $n = 1$, $u_1 = \dfrac{1}{6}(2 - 3 + 1 + 24) = 4$ and $u_1 = 4$ is given so true for $n = 1$

Assume true for $n = k$ and let $n = k + 1$

$u_{k+1} = u_k + k^2$

$= \dfrac{1}{6}(2k^3 - 3k^2 + k + 24) + k^2$

$= \dfrac{1}{6}(2k^3 - 3k^2 + k + 24 + 6k^2)$

$= \dfrac{1}{6}(2k^3 + 3k^2 + k + 24)$

$= \dfrac{1}{6}(2(k+1)^3 - 3(k+1)^2 + (k+1) + 24)$ as required

since $\dfrac{1}{6}(2(k+1)^3 - 3(k+1)^2 + (k+1) + 24)$

$= \dfrac{1}{6}(2k^3 + 6k^2 + 6k + 2 - 3k^2 - 6k - 3 + k + 1 + 24)$

$= \dfrac{1}{6}(2k^2 + 3k^2 + k + 24)$

so true for $n = k + 1$

The solution is true for $n = 1$ and assuming true for $n = k$ implies it is true for $n = k + 1$, hence it is true for all $n \in \mathbb{N}$

5 Let $n = 1$, $u_1 = 5(1)! = 5$ and $u_1 = 5$ is given so true for $n = 1$

assume true for $n = k$ and let $n = k + 1$

$u_{k+1} = (k+1)u_k$

$= (k+1)(5k!)$

$= 5(k+1)!$ as required

so true for $n = k + 1$

The solution is true for $n = 1$ and assuming true for $n = k$ implies it is true for $n = k + 1$, hence it is true for all $n \in \mathbb{N}$

6 a $S_n = 2000 + 1.05S_{n-1} + 0.01S_{n-2}$,

$n \geq 2$, $S_0 = 2000$, $S_1 = 4100$

b 6325

7 a $u_n = 5(8)^n - 4(11)^n$

b $u_n = (4 - 6n)(-6)^n$

c $u_n = \left(\sqrt{2}\right)^n \left(2\cos\left(\dfrac{3\pi n}{4}\right) + 5\sin\left(\dfrac{3\pi n}{4}\right)\right)$

8 a $u_n = \dfrac{1}{2}(2)^n + \dfrac{3}{4}(-7)^n - \dfrac{1}{4}$

b $u_n = \dfrac{5}{2}(2)^n - 4(-7)^n + n + \dfrac{5}{2}$

c $u_n = \dfrac{1}{10}(2)^n - (-7)^n + \dfrac{9}{10}(3)^n$

9 a $u_n = 3(2^n) - (3^n) - 2n(2^n)$

b Let $n = 0$, $u_0 = 3 - 1 = 2$ as given

let $n = 1$ then $u_1 = 3(2) - 3 - 2(2) = -1$ as given

so true for $n = 0$ and $n = 1$

Assume true for $n = k$ and $n = k + 1$

Let $n = k + 2$

$u_{k+2} = 5u_{k+1} - 6u_k + 2^{k+2}$

$= 5(3(2^{k+1}) - 3^{k+1} - 2(k+1)2^{k+1})$

$\quad - 6(3(2^k) - (3^k) - 2k(2^k)) + 2^{k+2}$

$= 15(2^{k+1}) - 5(3^{k+1}) - 10k(2^{k+1}) - 10(2^{k+1}) - 18(2^k)$

$\quad + 6(3^k) + 12k(2^k) + 2^{k+2}$

$= \dfrac{15}{2}(2^{k+2}) - \dfrac{5}{3}(3^{k+2}) - 5k(2^{k+2}) - 5(2^{k+2})$

$\quad - \dfrac{9}{2}(2^{k+2}) + \dfrac{2}{3}(3^{k+2}) + 3k(2^{k+2}) + 2^{k+2}$

$= (-1 - 2k)(2^{k+2}) - (3^{k+2})$

$= (3 - 2(k+2))(2^{k+2}) - (3^{k+2})$

$= 3(2^{k+2}) - (3^{k+2}) - 2(k+2)2^{k+2}$ as required

So true for $n = 0$ and $n = 1$ and assuming true for $n = k$ and $n = k + 1$ implies true for $n = k + 2$. Therefore true for all integers $n \geq 0$

10 Let $n = 0$, $u_0 = 0 + 0 + 13 - 13 = 0$ as given

Let $n = 1$ then $u_1 = 1 + 6 + 13 + 2(3 - 13) = 0$ as given

so true for $n = 0$ and $n = 1$

Assume true for $n = k$ and $n = k + 1$

Let $n = k + 2$

$u_{k+2} = 4u_{k+1} - 4u_k + (k+1)^2$

$= 4((k+1)^2 + 6(k+1) + 13 + (3(k+1) - 13)2^{k+1})$

$\quad - 4(k^2 + 6k + 13 + (3k - 13)2^k) + (k+1)^2$

$= 4\left(k^2 + 2k + 1 + 6k + 6 + 13 + \dfrac{3k-10}{2}(2^{k+2})\right)$

$\quad - 4\left(k^2 + 6k + 13 + \dfrac{3k-13}{4}(2^{k+2})\right) + k^2 + 2k + 1$

$= 4k^2 + 8k + 4 + 24k + 24 + 52 + (6k - 20)2^{k+2}$

$\quad - 4k^2 - 24k - 52 - (3k - 13)2^{k+2} + k^2 + 2k + 1$

$= k^2 + 10k + 29 + (3k - 7)2^{k+2}$

and $(k+2)^2 + 6(k+2) + 13 + (3(k+2) - 13)2^{k+2}$

$= k^2 + 4k + 4 + 6k + 12 + 13 + (3k - 7)2^{k+2}$

$= k^2 + 10k + 29 + (3k - 7)2^{k+2}$ as required

So true for $n = 0$ and $n = 1$ and assuming true for $n = k$ and $n = k + 1$ implies true for $n = k + 2$. Therefore true for all integers $n \geq 0$

Assessment 6

1 a 8, 29, 92, 281, 848

b $u_1 = 3A + B = 8$

$u_2 = 9A + B = 29$

$6A = 21$

$A = \dfrac{7}{2}$

$B = 8 - \dfrac{21}{2} = -\dfrac{5}{2}$

OR

$u_1 = 3u_0 + 5 = 8$

$u_0 = 1$

$u_0 = A + B = 1$

$u_1 = 3A + B = 8$

$2A = 7$

$A = \dfrac{7}{2}$, $B = -\dfrac{5}{2}$

c $u_1 = \dfrac{7}{2} \times 3 - \dfrac{5}{2} = 8$

so true for $n = 1$

Suppose true for $n = k$

Then $u_k = \dfrac{7}{2} \times 3^k - \dfrac{5}{2}$

and

$u_{k+1} = 3u_k + 5$

$= 3\left(\dfrac{7}{2} \times 3^k - \dfrac{5}{2}\right) + 5$

$= \dfrac{7}{2} \times 3^{k+1} - \dfrac{15}{2} + 5$

$= \dfrac{7}{2} \times 3^{k+1} - \dfrac{5}{2}$

True for $n = k + 1$

True for all positive integer n

2 a 3, 18, 78, 318, 1278

 b $p = 4, q = 6, r = 3$

3 a 3, 6, 12, 24, 48

 b $u_n = 3 \times 2^n$

 c $S_n = \displaystyle\sum_{r=0}^{n-1} u_r + u_n = S_{n-1} + 3 \times 2^n$

 d $S_n = 3(2^{n+1} - 1)$

4 a $u_n = \dfrac{17}{6} \times 7^n - \dfrac{5}{6}$

 b $u_0 = \dfrac{17}{6} - \dfrac{5}{6} = 2$

 True for $n = 0$

 Suppose true for $n = k$

 Then $u_k = \dfrac{17}{6} \times 7^k - \dfrac{5}{6}$

 and

 $u_{k+1} = 7u_k + 5$

 $= 7\left(\dfrac{17}{6} \times 7^k - \dfrac{5}{6}\right) + 5$

 $= \dfrac{17}{6} \times 7^{k+1} - \dfrac{35}{6} + 5$

 $= \dfrac{17}{6} \times 7^{k+1} - \dfrac{5}{6}$

 True for $n = k + 1$

 True for all positive integer n

5 a $u_1 = 12$

 $u_0 = 3$

 b $u_n = \dfrac{9}{4} \times 5^n + \dfrac{3}{4} = \dfrac{3}{4}(3 \times 5^n + 1)$

6 a 3, 5, 9, 15, 23

 b $u_n = n^2 + n + 3$

7 a 1, 6, 19, 56, 165

 b $u_n = 2 \times 3^n + n - 1$

 c $u_0 = 2 + 0 - 1 = 1$

 So true for $n = 0$

 Suppose true for $n = k$

 Then $u_k = 2 \times 3^k + k - 1$

 $u_{k+1} = 3u_k - 2(k+1) + 5$

 $= 6 \times 3^k + 3k - 3 - 2(k+1) + 5$

 $= 2 \times 3^{k+1} + k$

 $= 2 \times 3^{k+1} + (k+1) - 1$

 True for $n = k + 1$

 True for all positive integer n

8 a $u_n = 1.02u_{n-1} + 1020, u_0 = 0$

 b $u_n = 51000(1.02^n - 1)$

9 a $u_n = 2u_{n-1} + 2, n \geq 2$

 $u_1 = 1$

 b $u_n = \dfrac{3}{2} \times 2^n - 2 = 3 \times 2^{n-1} - 2$

c 1 572 862

d 3 145 685

e 2 097 150

10 a 0, 1, 1, 7, 13

 b $\lambda^n = \lambda^{n-1} + 6\lambda^{n-2}$

 $\lambda^2 - \lambda - 6 = 0$

 c $(\lambda - 3)(\lambda + 2) = 0$

 $\lambda = 3$ or $\lambda = -2$

 $u_n = A \times 3^n + B \times (-2)^n$

 d $u_0 = A + B = 0$

 $u_1 = 3A - 2B = 1$

 $A = \dfrac{1}{5}, B = -\dfrac{1}{5}$

 $u_n = \dfrac{3^n - (-2)^n}{5}$

11 a For example, to make a 6-digit number, you can put a 2, 3 or 4 in front of any 5-digit number, or you can put 12, 13, 14 in front of any 4-digit number.

 There is only 1 way to make a 0-digit number (by using none of the allowed integers), and there are clearly 4 ways to make a 1-digit number.

 b $\lambda^n = 3\lambda^{n-1} + 3\lambda^{n-2}$

 $\Rightarrow \lambda^2 - 3\lambda - 3 = 0$

 $\lambda = \dfrac{3 \pm \sqrt{9 + 12}}{2} = \dfrac{3 \pm \sqrt{21}}{2}$

 $u_n = A\left(\dfrac{3 + \sqrt{21}}{2}\right)^n + B\left(\dfrac{3 - \sqrt{21}}{2}\right)^n$

 c $u_n = \dfrac{21 + 5\sqrt{21}}{42}\left(\dfrac{3 + \sqrt{21}}{2}\right)^n + \dfrac{21 - 5\sqrt{21}}{42}\left(\dfrac{3 - \sqrt{21}}{2}\right)^n$

12 a For example, to make a line of 6 vehicles, you can add a car or a motorcycle to the back of any 5-vehicle line, or you can add a van to the back of any 4-vehicle line.

 There is only 1 sequence of 0 vehicles (the empty sequence), and there are clearly 2 possible sequences of 1 vehicle (either a car or a motorcycle).

 b $\lambda^n = 2\lambda^{n-1} + \lambda^{n-2}$

 $\lambda^2 - 2\lambda - 1 = 0$

 $\lambda = \dfrac{2 \pm \sqrt{8}}{2} = 1 \pm \sqrt{2}$

 $u_n = A(1 + \sqrt{2})^n + B(1 - \sqrt{2})^n$

 c $u_0 = A + B = 0$

 $u_1 = A + B + \sqrt{2}(A - B) = \sqrt{2}(A - B) = 2$

 $A = \dfrac{\sqrt{2}}{2}, B = -\dfrac{\sqrt{2}}{2},$

 $u_n = \dfrac{\sqrt{2}}{2}\left[(1 + \sqrt{2})^n - (1 - \sqrt{2})^n\right]$

 d Closed formula gives:

 $u_0 = \dfrac{\sqrt{2}}{2}\left[(1 + \sqrt{2})^0 - (1 - \sqrt{2})^0\right]$

 $= \dfrac{\sqrt{2}}{2} \times 0 = 0$

 and

 $u_1 = \dfrac{\sqrt{2}}{2}\left[(1 + \sqrt{2})^1 - (1 - \sqrt{2})^1\right]$

 $= \dfrac{\sqrt{2}}{2} \times 2\sqrt{2} = 2$

 so formula true for $n = 0, 1$

 Now suppose true for $n = k$ and $n = k - 1$

Then $u_{k+1} = 2u_k + u_{k-1}$

$$= 2 \times \frac{\sqrt{2}}{2}\left[(1+\sqrt{2})^k - (1-\sqrt{2})^k\right]$$

$$+ \frac{\sqrt{2}}{2}\left[(1+\sqrt{2})^{k-1} - (1-\sqrt{2})^{k-1}\right]$$

$$= \frac{\sqrt{2}}{2}(1+\sqrt{2})^{k-1}\left[2(1+\sqrt{2})+1\right]$$

$$- \frac{\sqrt{2}}{2}(1-\sqrt{2})^{k-1}\left[2(1-\sqrt{2})+1\right]$$

$$= \frac{\sqrt{2}}{2}(1+\sqrt{2})^{k-1}(3+2\sqrt{2}) - \frac{\sqrt{2}}{2}(1-\sqrt{2})^{k-1}(3-2\sqrt{2})$$

$$= \frac{\sqrt{2}}{2}\left(1+\sqrt{2}\right)^{k-1}\left(1+\sqrt{2}\right)^2 - \frac{\sqrt{2}}{2}\left(1-\sqrt{2}\right)^{k-1}\left(1-\sqrt{2}\right)^2$$

$$= \frac{\sqrt{2}}{2}\left(1+\sqrt{2}\right)^{k+1} - \frac{\sqrt{2}}{2}\left(1-\sqrt{2}\right)^{k+1}$$

$\Rightarrow$ true for $n = k+1$

$\Rightarrow$ true for all integer $n \geq 0$

13 a $\lambda^n = 6\lambda^{n-1} - 9\lambda^{n-2}$

$\lambda^2 - 6\lambda + 9 = 0$

$(\lambda - 3)^2 = 0$

b $u_n = (n-1)3^n$

c Closed formula gives $u_0 = -1$ and $u_1 = 0$
so formula true for $n = 0, 1$

Now suppose true for $n = k$ and $n = k-1$

$u_k = (k-1)3^k$ and $u_{k-1} = (k-2)3^{k-1}$

$u_{k+1} = 6u_k - 9u_{k-1}$

$$= 6(k-1)3^k - 9(k-2)3^{k-1}$$

$$= 3^{k-1}\left[18(k-1) - 9(k-2)\right]$$

$$= 3^{k-1} \times 9k$$

$$= k3^{k+1}$$

$\Rightarrow$ true for $n = k+1$

$\Rightarrow$ true for all integer $n \geq 0$

14 a $u_n = u_{n-1} + 2u_{n-2} - 2n^2$

$\lambda^2 - \lambda - 2 = 0$

$(\lambda - 2)(\lambda + 1) = 0$

$u_n = A \times 2^n + B \times (-1)^n$

$b_n = pn^2 + qn + r$

$b_n = b_{n-1} + 2b_{n-2} - 2n^2$

$pn^2 + qn + r = p(n-1)^2 + q(n-1) + r + 2p(n-2)^2$

$\qquad + 2q(n-2) + 2r - 2n^2$

$= (3p-2)n^2 + (3q-10p)n + 9p - 5q + 3r$

$p = 3p - 2$ and

$q = 3q - 10p$ and

$r = 9p - 5q + 3r$

$p = 1, \ q = 5, \ r = 8$

$u_n = A \times 2^n + B \times (-1)^n + n^2 + 5n + 8$

$u_0 = A + B + 8 = 8 \Rightarrow A = -B$

$u_1 = 2A - B + 14 = 3A + 14 = 5$

$A = -3, \ B = 3$

$u_n = 3\left[(-1)^n - 2^n\right] + n^2 + 5n + 8$

b Using recurrence relation:

$u_0 = 8$

$u_1 = 5$

$u_2 = 5 + 2 \times 8 - 2 \times 2^2 = 13$

$u_3 = 13 + 2 \times 5 - 2 \times 3^2 = 5$

$u_4 = 5 + 2 \times 13 - 2 \times 4^2 = -1$

Using closed formula:

$u_0 = 3 \times 0 + 8 = 8$

$u_1 = 3 \times (-1-2) + 1 + 5 + 8 = 5$

$u_2 = 3 \times (1-4) + 4 + 10 + 8 = 13$

$u_3 = 3 \times (-1-8) + 9 + 15 + 8 = 5$

$u_4 = 3 \times (1-16) + 16 + 20 + 8 = -1$

15 a 1, 3, 2, –8, –24, –16

b $\lambda^n = 2\lambda^{n-1} - 4\lambda^{n-2}$

$\lambda^2 = 2\lambda - 4$

$\lambda^2 - 2\lambda + 4 = 0$

c $\lambda = \dfrac{2 \pm \sqrt{4-16}}{2} = \dfrac{2 \pm i2\sqrt{3}}{2} = 1 \pm i\sqrt{3}$

$$= 2\left(\cos\frac{\pi}{3} \pm i\sin\frac{\pi}{3}\right)$$

$$u_n = 2^n\left(A\cos\frac{n\pi}{3} + B\sin\frac{n\pi}{3}\right)$$

d $u_0 = A = 1$

$u_1 = A + B\sqrt{3} = 3 \Rightarrow B\sqrt{3} = 2$

$B = \dfrac{2\sqrt{3}}{3}$

$$u_n = 2^n\left(\cos\frac{n\pi}{3} + \frac{2\sqrt{3}}{3}\sin\frac{n\pi}{3}\right)$$

e $u_0 = 2^0\left(\cos 0 + \dfrac{2\sqrt{3}}{3}\sin 0\right) = 1$

$$u_1 = 2^1\left(\cos\frac{\pi}{3} + \frac{2\sqrt{3}}{3}\sin\frac{\pi}{3}\right)$$

$$= 2\left(\frac{1}{2} + \frac{2\sqrt{3}}{3} \times \frac{\sqrt{3}}{2}\right) = 3$$

so true for $n = 0, 1$

Suppose true for $n = k$ and $n = k-1$

Then $u_{k+1} = 2u_k - 4u_{k-1}$

$$= 2^{k+1}\left(\cos\frac{k\pi}{3} + \frac{2\sqrt{3}}{3}\sin\frac{k\pi}{3}\right)$$

$$- 2^{k+1}\left[\cos\frac{(k-1)\pi}{3} + \frac{2\sqrt{3}}{3}\sin\frac{(k-1)\pi}{3}\right]$$

$$= 2^{k+1}\begin{bmatrix}\left(\cos\dfrac{k\pi}{3} - \cos\dfrac{(k-1)\pi}{3}\right) \\ + \dfrac{2\sqrt{3}}{3}\left(\sin\dfrac{k\pi}{3} - \sin\dfrac{(k-1)\pi}{3}\right)\end{bmatrix}$$

$$= 2^{k+1}\left[\left(\cos\frac{k\pi}{3} - \cos\frac{k\pi}{3}\cos\frac{\pi}{3} - \sin\frac{k\pi}{3}\sin\frac{\pi}{3}\right)\right.$$

$$\left. + \frac{2\sqrt{3}}{3}\left(\sin\frac{k\pi}{3} - \sin\frac{k\pi}{3}\cos\frac{\pi}{3} + \cos\frac{k\pi}{3}\sin\frac{\pi}{3}\right)\right]$$

$$= 2^{k+1}\left[\left(\cos\frac{k\pi}{3}\cos\frac{\pi}{3} - \sin\frac{k\pi}{3}\sin\frac{\pi}{3}\right)\right.$$

$$\left. + \frac{2\sqrt{3}}{3}\left(\sin\frac{k\pi}{3}\cos\frac{\pi}{3} + \cos\frac{k\pi}{3}\sin\frac{\pi}{3}\right)\right]$$

because $\cos\dfrac{\pi}{3} = \dfrac{1}{2}$

$$= 2^{k+1}\left[\cos\frac{(k+1)\pi}{3} + \frac{2\sqrt{3}}{3}\sin\frac{(k+1)\pi}{3}\right]$$

Therefore true for $n = k+1$

Therefore true for all integer $n \geq 0$

Chapter 7

Exercise 7.1A

1 a $I_n = \int x^n e^x \, dx = x^n e^x - \int nx^{n-1} e^x \, dx$

$\quad = x^n e^x - nI_{n-1}$

b $x^4 e^x - 4x^3 e^x + 12x^2 e^x - 24xe^x + 24e^x + c$

2 a $I_n = \int x^n e^{-\frac{x}{2}} \, dx = -2x^n e^{-\frac{x}{2}} + 2 \int nx^{n-1} e^{-\frac{x}{2}} \, dx$

$\quad = -2x^n e^{-\frac{x}{2}} + 2nI_{n-1}$

b $-2x^3 e^{-\frac{x}{2}} - 12x^2 e^{-\frac{x}{2}} - 48xe^{-\frac{x}{2}} - 96e^{-\left(\frac{x}{2}\right)} + c$

3 a $I_n = \int_0^1 x^n e^{3x} \, dx = \left[\frac{1}{3} x^n e^{3x}\right]_0^1 - \frac{1}{3} n \int_0^1 x^{n-1} e^{3x} \, dx$

$\quad = \frac{1}{3}(e^3 - 0) - \frac{1}{3} nI_{n-1}$

$\quad = \frac{1}{3} e^3 - \frac{n}{3} I_{n-1}$

b $\frac{11}{81} e^3 - \frac{8}{81}$

4 a $\int x(\ln x)^n \, dx = \frac{x^2}{2}(\ln x)^n - n \int \frac{x^2}{2} \frac{1}{x} (\ln x)^{n-1} \, dx$

$\quad = \frac{x^2}{2}(\ln x)^n - \frac{n}{2} \int x(\ln x)^{n-1} \, dx$

$\quad = \frac{x^2}{2}(\ln x)^n - \frac{n}{2} I_{n-1}$

b $\frac{x^2}{2}(\ln x)^2 - \frac{x^2}{2} \ln x + \frac{x^2}{4} + c$

5 a $I_n = \int_0^1 \frac{x^n}{\sqrt{1-x}} \, dx = \left[-2x^n (1-x)^{\frac{1}{2}}\right]_0^1 - \int_0^1 -2nx^{n-1}(1-x)^{\frac{1}{2}} \, dx$

$\quad = 0 + 2n \int_0^1 x^{n-1}(1-x)^{\frac{1}{2}} \, dx$

$\quad = 2n \int_0^1 x^{n-1}(1-x)(1-x)^{-\frac{1}{2}} \, dx$

$\quad = 2n \int_0^1 x^{n-1}(1-x)^{-\frac{1}{2}} - x^n (1-x)^{-\frac{1}{2}} \, dx$

$\quad = 2nI_{n-1} - 2nI_n$

$\quad I_n = \frac{2n}{1+2n} I_{n-1}$

b $\frac{2048}{3003}$

6 a $I_n = \int x^n \sin x \, dx = -x^n \cos x - \int -nx^{n-1} \cos x \, dx$

$\quad = -x^n \cos x + n \int x^{n-1} \cos x \, dx$

$\quad = -x^n \cos x + n\left(x^{n-1} \sin x - (n-1) \int x^{n-2} \sin x \, dx\right)$

$\quad = -x^n \cos x + nx^{n-1} \sin x - n(n-1)I_{n-2}$

b i $-x^4 \cos x + 4x^3 \sin x + 12x^2 \cos x - 24x \sin x$
$\quad -24 \cos x + c$

ii $-x^3 \cos x + 3x^2 \sin x + 6x \cos x - 6 \sin x + c$

7 a $I_n = \left[\frac{1}{2} x^n \sin 2x\right]_0^{\frac{\pi}{4}} - \frac{n}{2} \int_0^{\frac{\pi}{4}} x^{n-1} \sin 2x \, dx$

$\quad = \frac{1}{2}\left(\frac{\pi}{4}\right)^n - \frac{n}{2}\left(\left[-\frac{1}{2} x^{n-1} \cos 2x\right]_0^{\frac{\pi}{4}} + \frac{n-1}{2} \int_0^{\frac{\pi}{4}} x^{n-2} \cos 2x \, dx\right)$

$\quad = \frac{1}{2}\left(\frac{\pi}{4}\right)^n - \frac{n}{2}\left(\frac{n-1}{2}\right) I_{n-2}$

$\quad = \frac{1}{2}\left(\frac{\pi}{4}\right)^n - \frac{n(n-1)}{4} I_{n-2}$ as required

b i $\frac{1}{8192} \pi^6 - \frac{15}{1024} \pi^4 + \frac{45}{64} \pi^2 - \frac{45}{8}$

ii $\frac{1}{2048} \pi^5 - \frac{5}{128} \pi^3 + \frac{15}{16} \pi - \frac{15}{8}$

Exercise 7.1B

1 a $I_n = \int_0^{\frac{\pi}{2}} \cos x \cos^{n-1} x \, dx$

$\quad = \left[\sin x \cos^{n-1} x\right]_0^{\frac{\pi}{2}} - (n-1) \int_0^{\frac{\pi}{2}} -\sin^2 x \cos^{n-2} x \, dx$

$\quad = 0 + (n-1) \int_0^{\frac{\pi}{2}} (1 - \cos^2 x) \cos^{n-2} x \, dx$

$\quad = (n-1) \int_0^{\frac{\pi}{2}} \cos^{n-2} x - \cos^n x \, dx$

$\quad = (n-1)(I_{n-2} - I_n)$

$\quad I_n = \frac{n-1}{n} I_{n-2}$

b i $\frac{8}{15}$

ii $\frac{5}{32} \pi$

2 a $I_n = \int_{\frac{\pi}{2}}^{\pi} \sin x \sin^{n-1} x \, dx$

$\quad = \left[-\cos x \sin^{n-1} x\right]_{\frac{\pi}{2}}^{\pi} - (n-1) \int_{\frac{\pi}{2}}^{\pi} -\cos^2 x \sin^{n-2} x \, dx$

$\quad = 0 + (n-1) \int_{\frac{\pi}{2}}^{\pi} (1 - \sin^2 x) \sin^{n-2} x \, dx$

$\quad = (n-1) \int_{\frac{\pi}{2}}^{\pi} \sin^{n-2} x - \sin^n x \, dx$

$\quad = (n-1)(I_{n-2} - I_n)$

$\quad I_n = \frac{n-1}{n} I_{n-2}$

b **i** $\dfrac{16}{35}$

  ii $\dfrac{35}{256}\pi$

3 a $\dfrac{\tan^{n-1} x}{n-1} - I_{n-2}$

  b **i** $\dfrac{1}{5}\tan^5 x - \dfrac{1}{3}\tan^3 x + \tan x - x + c$

  ii $\dfrac{5}{12} - \dfrac{1}{2}\ln 2$

4 a $I_n = \displaystyle\int_0^1 x^n \sqrt{1+x^2}\,\mathrm{d}x = \int_0^1 x^{n-1} x \sqrt{1+x^2}\,\mathrm{d}x$

$= \left[\dfrac{1}{3} x^{n-1}(1+x^2)^{\frac{3}{2}}\right]_0^1 - \dfrac{n-1}{3}\displaystyle\int_0^1 x^{n-2}(1+x^2)^{\frac{3}{2}}\,\mathrm{d}x$

$= \left(\dfrac{1}{3}2\sqrt{2}-0\right) - \dfrac{n-1}{3}\displaystyle\int_0^1 x^{n-2}(1+x^2)(1+x^2)^{\frac{1}{2}}\,\mathrm{d}x$

$= \dfrac{2}{3}\sqrt{2} - \dfrac{n-1}{3}\displaystyle\int_0^1 x^{n-2}(1+x^2)^{\frac{1}{2}} + x^n(1+x^2)^{\frac{1}{2}}\,\mathrm{d}x$

$= \dfrac{2}{3}\sqrt{2} - \dfrac{n-1}{3}\left(I_{n-2} + I_n\right)$

$3I_n = 2\sqrt{2} - (n-1)I_{n-2} - (n-1)I_n$

$I_n = \dfrac{2\sqrt{2} - (n-1)I_{n-2}}{2+n}$

  b **i** $\dfrac{22\sqrt{2}-8}{105}$

  ii $\dfrac{7\sqrt{2}+3\ln\left(1+\sqrt{2}\right)}{48}$

5 a $I_n = \displaystyle\int_0^\pi \dfrac{\cos(nx)}{\cos x}\,\mathrm{d}x$

$= \displaystyle\int_0^\pi \dfrac{\cos((n-1)x + x)}{\cos x}\,\mathrm{d}x$

$= \displaystyle\int_0^\pi \dfrac{\cos(n-1)x \cos x - \sin(n-1)x \sin x}{\cos x}\,\mathrm{d}x$

$= \displaystyle\int_0^\pi \cos(n-1)x - \dfrac{\sin(n-1)x \sin x}{\cos x}\,\mathrm{d}x$

$= \dfrac{1}{n-1}\sin(n-1)x - \dfrac{1}{2}\displaystyle\int_0^\pi \dfrac{\cos(n-2)x - \cos nx}{\cos x}\,\mathrm{d}x$

$= \dfrac{1}{n-1}\sin(n-1)x - \dfrac{1}{2}\displaystyle\int_0^\pi \dfrac{\cos(n-2)x}{\cos x} - \dfrac{\cos nx}{\cos x}\,\mathrm{d}x$

$= \dfrac{1}{n-1}\sin(n-1)x - \dfrac{1}{2}I_{n-2} + \dfrac{1}{2}I_n$

$I_n = \left[\dfrac{1}{2(n-1)}\sin(n-1)x\right]_0^\pi - I_{n-2}$

$= 0 - I_{n-2}$

$= -I_{n-2}$ as required

  b $-\pi$

  c **i** $-\pi$ **ii** π

---

d Even values of n will reduce to I_0

$I_0 = \displaystyle\int_0^\pi \dfrac{\cos 0}{\cos x}\,\mathrm{d}x$

$= \displaystyle\int_0^\pi \dfrac{1}{\cos x}\,\mathrm{d}x$

Discontinuity at $x = \dfrac{\pi}{2}$

$\displaystyle\int_0^a \dfrac{1}{\cos x}\,\mathrm{d}x = \int_0^a \sec x\,\mathrm{d}x$

$= \ln(\tan x + \sec x)$

When $a \to \dfrac{\pi}{2}$, $\tan a \to \infty$ and $\sec a \to \infty$

So $\ln(\tan x + \sec x) \to \infty$

Therefore integral does not exist.

So I_n will not exist for even values of n

Exercise 7.2A

1 $\dfrac{\mathrm{d}y}{\mathrm{d}x} = x^{\frac{1}{2}}$

$s = \displaystyle\int_0^1 \sqrt{1 + \left(x^{\frac{1}{2}}\right)^2}\,\mathrm{d}x$

$= \displaystyle\int_0^1 \sqrt{1+x}\,\mathrm{d}x$

$= \left[\dfrac{2}{3}(1+x)^{\frac{3}{2}}\right]_0^1$

$= \dfrac{2}{3}\left(2\sqrt{2}-1\right)$

$= \dfrac{4}{3}\sqrt{2} - \dfrac{2}{3}$

2 19.7

3 $\dfrac{9}{8}$

4 $\dfrac{15}{16}$

5 $\dfrac{56}{27}$

6 a $\dfrac{\mathrm{d}}{\mathrm{d}x}(\ln(\sec x + \tan x)) = \dfrac{\sec x \tan x + \sec^2 x}{\sec x + \tan x}$

$= \dfrac{\sec x(\tan x + \sec x)}{\sec x + \tan x}$

$= \sec x$ as required

  b $\dfrac{1}{2}\ln\left(2+\sqrt{3}\right)$

7 $\dfrac{61}{6}$

8 $r^2 + \left(\dfrac{\mathrm{d}r}{\mathrm{d}\theta}\right)^2 = (3\sin\theta)^2 + (3\cos\theta)^2$

$= 9\sin^2\theta + 9\cos^2\theta$

$= 9$

Therefore, $s = \displaystyle\int_{\frac{\pi}{6}}^{\pi} \sqrt{9}\,d\theta$

$= \displaystyle\int_{\frac{\pi}{6}}^{\pi} 3\,d\theta$

$= \left[3\theta\right]_{\frac{\pi}{6}}^{\pi}$

$= 3\left(\pi - \dfrac{\pi}{6}\right)$

$= 3\left(\dfrac{5\pi}{6}\right)$

$= \dfrac{5\pi}{2}$

9 $= \dfrac{5\pi}{2}$

10 $\left(\dfrac{dx}{dt}\right)^2 + \left(\dfrac{dy}{dt}\right)^2 = (4\cos t)^2 + (-4\sin t)^2$

$= 16\cos^2 t + 16\sin^2 t$

$= 16$

At $(0, 4), t = 0$ and at $(2\sqrt{2}, 2\sqrt{2}), t = \dfrac{\pi}{4}$

Therefore, $s = \displaystyle\int_{0}^{\frac{\pi}{4}} \sqrt{16}\,dt$

$= \displaystyle\int_{0}^{\frac{\pi}{4}} 4\,dt$

$= \left[4t\right]_{0}^{\frac{\pi}{4}}$

$= 4\left(\dfrac{\pi}{4} - 0\right)$

$= \pi$

11 $\dfrac{14}{3}$

12 a $\dfrac{d}{dx}\left(x\sqrt{x^2+1} + \operatorname{arsinh} x\right) = \sqrt{x^2+1} + x\left(\dfrac{x}{\sqrt{x^2+1}}\right) + \dfrac{1}{\sqrt{x^2+1}}$

$= \sqrt{x^2+1} + \dfrac{x^2+1}{\sqrt{x^2+1}}$

$= \sqrt{x^2+1} + \sqrt{x^2+1}$

$= 2\sqrt{x^2+1}$ as required

b $r^2 + \left(\dfrac{dr}{d\theta}\right)^2 = \theta^2 + 1$

Therefore, $s = \displaystyle\int_{0}^{1} \sqrt{\theta^2+1}\,d\theta$

$= \dfrac{1}{2}\left[\theta\sqrt{\theta^2+1} + \operatorname{arsinh} \theta\right]_{0}^{1}$ (using part **a**)

$= \dfrac{1}{2}\left(\sqrt{2} + \operatorname{arsinh} 1\right) - \dfrac{1}{2}\left(0 + \operatorname{arsinh} 0\right)$

$= \dfrac{1}{2}\left(\sqrt{2} + \ln\left(1 + \sqrt{2}\right)\right)$ as required

13 $r^2 + \left(\dfrac{dr}{d\theta}\right)^2 = (\operatorname{cosec}\theta)^2 + (\operatorname{cosec}\theta\cot\theta)^2$

$= \operatorname{cosec}^2\theta + \operatorname{cosec}^2\theta\cot^2\theta$

$= \operatorname{cosec}^2\theta(1 + \cot^2\theta)$

$= \operatorname{cosec}^2\theta(\operatorname{cosec}^2\theta)$

$= \operatorname{cosec}^4\theta$

Therefore, $s = \displaystyle\int_{\frac{\pi}{3}}^{\frac{2\pi}{3}} \sqrt{\operatorname{cosec}^4\theta}\,d\theta$

$= \displaystyle\int_{\frac{\pi}{3}}^{\frac{2\pi}{3}} \operatorname{cosec}^2\theta\,d\theta$

$= \left[-\cot\theta\right]_{\frac{\pi}{3}}^{\frac{2\pi}{3}}$

$= \left(-\cot\left(\dfrac{2\pi}{3}\right)\right) - \left(-\cot\left(\dfrac{\pi}{3}\right)\right)$

$= \dfrac{1}{\sqrt{3}} - \left(-\dfrac{1}{\sqrt{3}}\right)$

$= \dfrac{2}{\sqrt{3}}$

$= \dfrac{2}{3}\sqrt{3}\left(k = \dfrac{2}{3}\right)$

Exercise 7.2B

1 a Let $6x = \sinh u$ then $\dfrac{dx}{du} = \dfrac{1}{6}\cosh u$

$s = \displaystyle\int \sqrt{1 + 36x^2}\,dx$

$= \displaystyle\int \sqrt{1 + \sinh^2 u}\left(\dfrac{1}{6}\cosh u\right)du$

$= \dfrac{1}{6}\displaystyle\int \sqrt{\cosh^2 u}\,(\cosh u)\,du$

$= \dfrac{1}{6}\displaystyle\int \cosh u(\cosh u)\,du$

$= \dfrac{1}{6}\displaystyle\int \cosh^2 u\,du$

$= \dfrac{1}{6}\displaystyle\int \dfrac{1}{2}(\cosh 2u + 1)\,du$

$= \dfrac{1}{12}\left(\dfrac{1}{2}\sinh 2u + u\right) + c$

$= \dfrac{1}{24}\sinh 2u + \dfrac{1}{12}u + c$

$= \dfrac{1}{24}(2\sinh u\cosh u) + \dfrac{1}{12}u + c$

$= \dfrac{1}{12}6x\sqrt{1 + (6x)^2} + \dfrac{1}{12}\operatorname{arsinh} 6x + c$

$= \dfrac{1}{2}x\sqrt{1 + 36x^2} + \dfrac{1}{12}\operatorname{arsinh} 6x + c$ as required

b $\dfrac{1}{2}\sqrt{37} + \dfrac{1}{12}\ln(6 + \sqrt{37})$

2 $\ln(1+\sqrt{2})+\sqrt{2}$

3 a $\dfrac{dy}{dx}=x^{-\frac{1}{2}}$

$$s=\int_0^4\sqrt{1+\left(x^{-\frac{1}{2}}\right)^2}\,dx$$

$$=\int_0^4\sqrt{1+\frac{1}{x}}\,dx$$

$$=\int_0^4\sqrt{\frac{x+1}{x}}\,dx \text{ as required}$$

b $\ln(2+\sqrt{5})+2\sqrt{5}$

4 $\dfrac{3}{2}$

5 $2(\sqrt{3}-1)$

6 $s=\displaystyle\int_0^1\sqrt{1+(-2x)^2}\,dx$

$$=\int_0^1\sqrt{1+4x^2}\,dx$$

Let $2x=\sinh u$ then $\dfrac{dx}{du}=\dfrac{1}{2}\cosh u$

When $x=0$, $u=0$ and when $x=1$, $u=\text{arsinh}\,2$

$$s=\int_0^{\text{arsinh}\,2}\sqrt{1+\sinh^2 u}\left(\frac{1}{2}\cosh u\right)du$$

$$=\frac{1}{2}\int_0^{\text{arsinh}\,2}\sqrt{\cosh^2 u}\,(\cosh u)du$$

$$=\frac{1}{2}\int_0^{\text{arsinh}\,2}\cosh^2 u\,du$$

$$=\frac{1}{2}\int_0^{\text{arsinh}\,2}\frac{1}{2}(\cosh 2u+1)\,du$$

$$=\frac{1}{4}\left[\frac{1}{2}\sinh 2u+u\right]_0^{\text{arsinh}\,2}$$

$$=\frac{1}{4}\left[\sinh u\cosh u+u\right]_0^{\text{arsinh}\,2}$$

$$=\frac{1}{4}\left[\sinh u\sqrt{1+\sinh^2 u}+u\right]_0^{\text{arsinh}\,2}$$

$$=\frac{1}{4}(2\sqrt{1+2^2}+\text{arsinh}\,2)-0$$

$$=\frac{1}{2}\sqrt{5}+\frac{1}{4}\ln(2+\sqrt{5})\text{ as required}$$

7 $r^2+\left(\dfrac{dr}{d\theta}\right)^2=(1+\cos\theta)^2+(-\sin\theta)^2$

$$=1+2\cos\theta+\cos^2\theta+\sin^2\theta$$
$$=2+2\cos\theta$$
$$=2(1+\cos\theta)$$

Therefore, $s=\displaystyle\int_{\frac{\pi}{3}}^{\frac{2\pi}{3}}\sqrt{2(1+\cos\theta)}\,d\theta$

$$=\int_{\frac{\pi}{3}}^{\frac{2\pi}{3}}\sqrt{2\left(2\cos^2\left(\frac{\theta}{2}\right)\right)}\,d\theta$$

$$=\int_{\frac{\pi}{3}}^{\frac{2\pi}{3}}\sqrt{4\cos^2\left(\frac{\theta}{2}\right)}\,d\theta$$

$$=\int_{\frac{\pi}{3}}^{\frac{2\pi}{3}}2\cos\left(\frac{\theta}{2}\right)d\theta$$

$$=\left[4\sin\left(\frac{\theta}{2}\right)\right]_{\frac{\pi}{3}}^{\frac{2\pi}{3}}$$

$$=\left(4\sin\frac{\pi}{3}\right)-\left(4\sin\frac{\pi}{6}\right)$$

$$=4\left(\frac{\sqrt{3}}{2}-\frac{1}{2}\right)$$

$$=2(\sqrt{3}-1)$$

8 $4k$

9 $r^2+\left(\dfrac{dr}{d\theta}\right)^2=(5-5\cos\theta)^2+(5\sin\theta)^2$

$$=25-50\cos\theta+25\cos^2\theta+25\sin^2\theta$$
$$=50-50\cos\theta$$
$$=50(1-\cos\theta)$$
$$=50\left(2\sin^2\left(\frac{\theta}{2}\right)\right)$$
$$=100\sin^2\left(\frac{\theta}{2}\right)$$

Therefore, $s=\displaystyle\int_0^{2\pi}\sqrt{100\sin^2\left(\frac{\theta}{2}\right)}\,d\theta$

$$=\int_0^{2\pi}10\sin\left(\frac{\theta}{2}\right)d\theta$$

$$=\left[-20\cos\left(\frac{\theta}{2}\right)\right]_0^{2\pi}$$

$$=(-20\cos\pi)-(-20\cos 0)$$
$$=(20)-(-20)$$
$$=40 \text{ as required}$$

10 $x=r\cos\theta,\ y=r\sin\theta$

$$\left(\frac{dx}{d\theta}\right)^2+\left(\frac{dy}{d\theta}\right)^2=(-r\sin\theta)^2+(r\cos\theta)^2$$

$$=r^2\sin^2\theta+r^2\cos^2\theta$$
$$=r^2(\sin^2\theta+\cos^2\theta)$$
$$=r^2$$

So circumference $= \displaystyle\int_{0}^{2\pi} \sqrt{r^2}\,d\theta$

$\qquad\qquad\quad = \displaystyle\int_{0}^{2\pi} r\,d\theta$

$\qquad\qquad\quad = \big[r\theta\big]_{0}^{2\pi}$

$\qquad\qquad\quad = r(2\pi - 0)$

$\qquad\qquad\quad = 2\pi r$ as required

11 $8k$

12 a $\quad k = 6\ln(2)$

   b $\quad \dfrac{15}{4}$ (3.75)

13 $r^2 + \left(\dfrac{dr}{d\theta}\right)^2 = (\sin 2\theta)^2 + (2\cos 2\theta)^2$

$\qquad\qquad\qquad = \sin^2 2\theta + 4\cos^2 2\theta$

$\qquad\qquad\qquad = (1 - \cos^2 2\theta) + 4\cos^2 2\theta$

$\qquad\qquad\qquad = 1 + 3\cos^2 \theta$

Therefore, $s = \displaystyle\int_{0}^{\frac{\pi}{2}} \sqrt{1 + 3\cos^2 2\theta}\,d\theta$

14 $\left(\dfrac{dx}{d\theta}\right)^2 + \left(\dfrac{dy}{d\theta}\right)^2 = (-a\sin\theta)^2 + (b\cos\theta)^2$

$\qquad\qquad\qquad\qquad = a^2 \sin^2\theta + b^2 \cos^2\theta$

$\qquad\qquad\qquad\qquad = a^2(1 - \cos^2\theta) + b^2 \cos^2\theta$

$\qquad\qquad\qquad\qquad = a^2 - (a^2 - b^2)\cos^2\theta$

$\qquad\qquad\qquad\qquad = a^2\left(1 - \dfrac{(a^2 - b^2)}{a^2}\cos^2\theta\right)$

$\qquad\qquad\qquad\qquad = a^2\left(1 - \left(1 - \dfrac{b^2}{a^2}\right)\cos^2\theta\right)$

$\qquad\qquad\qquad\qquad = a^2(1 - e^2 \cos^2\theta)$

The ellipse can be split into 4 sections of equal arc length.

Therefore, circumference $= 4\displaystyle\int_{0}^{\frac{\pi}{2}} \sqrt{a^2(1 - e^2\cos^2\theta)}\,d\theta$

$\qquad\qquad\qquad\qquad = 4a\displaystyle\int_{0}^{\frac{\pi}{2}} \sqrt{1 - e^2\cos^2\theta}\,d\theta$

$\qquad\qquad\qquad\qquad$ as required

Exercise 7.3A

1 a $\quad 24\sqrt{26}\pi$

   b Slant height of large cone $\sqrt{25^2 + 5^2} = 5\sqrt{26}$

      Slant height of small cone $\sqrt{5^2 + 1^2} = \sqrt{26}$

      Curved surface area of frustrum

      $= \pi(5 \times 5\sqrt{26} - 1 \times \sqrt{26})$

      $= \pi(25\sqrt{26} - \sqrt{26})$

      $= 24\sqrt{26}\pi$ as required

2 a $\quad 1 + \left(\dfrac{dy}{dx}\right)^2 = 1 + \left(\dfrac{1}{2\sqrt{x}}\right)^2$

$\qquad\qquad\qquad = 1 + \dfrac{1}{4x}$

$\qquad\qquad\qquad = \dfrac{4x + 1}{4x}$

$\qquad S = 2\pi \displaystyle\int_{0}^{1} \sqrt{x}\sqrt{\dfrac{4x + 1}{4x}}\,dx$

$\qquad\quad = 2\pi \displaystyle\int_{0}^{1} \sqrt{\dfrac{x(4x + 1)}{4x}}\,dx$

$\qquad\quad = 2\pi \displaystyle\int_{0}^{1} \sqrt{\dfrac{4x + 1}{4}}\,dx$

$\qquad\quad = 2\pi \displaystyle\int_{0}^{1} \dfrac{1}{2}\sqrt{4x + 1}\,dx$

$\qquad\quad = \pi \displaystyle\int_{0}^{1} \sqrt{4x + 1}\,dx$ as required

   b $\quad \dfrac{\pi}{6}(5\sqrt{5} - 1)$

3 $\dfrac{160}{3}\pi \left(k = \dfrac{160}{3}\right)$

4 π

5 $\dfrac{22}{9}\pi$

6 $\dfrac{9}{4}\pi(\pi - 2)$

7 $r^2 + \left(\dfrac{dr}{d\theta}\right)^2 = (1 - \cos\theta)^2 + (\sin\theta)^2$

$\qquad\qquad\qquad = 1 - 2\cos\theta + \cos^2\theta + \sin^2\theta$

$\qquad\qquad\qquad = 2(1 - \cos\theta)$

$S = 2\pi \displaystyle\int_{0}^{\frac{\pi}{2}} (1 - \cos\theta)\sin\theta\sqrt{2(1 - \cos\theta)}\,d\theta$

$\quad = 2\sqrt{2}\pi \displaystyle\int_{0}^{\frac{\pi}{2}} (1 - \cos\theta)^{\frac{3}{2}}\sin\theta\,d\theta$

$\quad = 2\sqrt{2}\pi \left[\dfrac{2}{5}(1 - \cos\theta)^{\frac{5}{2}}\right]_{0}^{\frac{\pi}{2}}$

$\quad = \dfrac{4}{5}\sqrt{2}\pi\left(\left(1 - \cos\left(\dfrac{\pi}{2}\right)\right)^{\frac{5}{2}} - (1 - \cos 0)^{\frac{5}{2}}\right)$

$\quad = \dfrac{4}{5}\sqrt{2}\pi(1 - 0)$

$\quad = \dfrac{4}{5}\sqrt{2}\pi$ as required

8 a 18π

b When $\theta = \dfrac{\pi}{4}$ the Cartesian coordinates are

$$x = 3\operatorname{cosec}\left(\dfrac{\pi}{4}\right)\cos\left(\dfrac{\pi}{4}\right) = 3 \text{ and } y = 3\operatorname{cosec}\left(\dfrac{\pi}{4}\right)\sin\left(\dfrac{\pi}{4}\right) = 3$$

When $\theta = \dfrac{\pi}{2}$ the Cartesian coordinates are

$$x = 3\operatorname{cosec}\left(\dfrac{\pi}{2}\right)\cos\left(\dfrac{\pi}{2}\right) = 0 \text{ and } y = 3\operatorname{cosec}\left(\dfrac{\pi}{2}\right)\sin\left(\dfrac{\pi}{2}\right) = 3$$

Curved surface area of cylinder $= 2\pi r h$
$$= 2\pi(3)(3)$$
$$= 18\pi \text{ as required}$$

9 $\dfrac{8\pi}{3}(5\sqrt{5}-1)$

10 a $\dfrac{\pi}{56}$

b $\dfrac{\pi}{108}(10\sqrt{10}-1)$

11 a $\dfrac{\pi}{4}\left(2\ln 3 + \dfrac{40}{9}\right)$

b $\pi\left(\ln 3 + \dfrac{20}{9}\right)$

Exercise 7.3B

1 a $\dfrac{3}{2}\pi$

b $\dfrac{dy}{dx} = -2e^{-x}$

$$S = 2\pi \int_0^{\ln 2} 2e^{-x}\sqrt{1+(-2e^{-x})^2}\,dx$$

$$= 2\pi \int_0^{\ln 2} 2e^{-x}\sqrt{1+4e^{-2x}}\,dx$$

$$= 4\pi \int_0^{\ln 2} e^{-x}\sqrt{1+4e^{-2x}}\,dx$$

c $\pi(\ln(2+\sqrt{5})-\sqrt{2}-\ln(1+\sqrt{2})+2\sqrt{5})$

2 a $V = -\pi \int_0^\pi (r\sin\theta)^2(-r\sin\theta)\,d\theta = \pi\int_0^\pi r^3\sin^3\theta\,d\theta$

$$= \pi\int_0^\pi r^3\sin\theta\sin^2\theta\,d\theta$$

$$= \pi\int_0^\pi r^3\sin\theta(1-\cos^2\theta)\,d\theta$$

$$= \pi r^3 \int_0^\pi \sin\theta - \sin\theta\cos^2\theta\,d\theta$$

$$= \pi r^3\left[-\cos\theta + \dfrac{1}{3}\cos^3\theta\right]_0^\pi$$

$$= \pi r^3\left(1-\dfrac{1}{3}\right) - \pi r^3\left(-1+\dfrac{1}{3}\right)$$

$$= \dfrac{4}{3}\pi r^3 \text{ as required}$$

b $S = 2\pi \int_0^\pi r\sin\theta\sqrt{(-r\sin\theta)^2 + (r\cos\theta)^2}\,d\theta = 2\pi\int_0^\pi r^2\sin\theta\,d\theta$

$$= 2\pi r^2\left[-\cos\theta\right]_0^\pi$$

$$= 2\pi r^2(1--1)$$

$$= 4\pi r^2 \text{ as required}$$

3 $\dfrac{2\pi}{3}\left(\dfrac{13\sqrt{13}}{8}-1\right)$

4 a $\sqrt{1-\cos\theta} = \sqrt{2\sin^2\dfrac{\theta}{2}}$

$$= \sqrt{2}\sin\dfrac{\theta}{2}$$

b 4

c $\dfrac{32}{3}\pi$

5 a $\pi\left(\dfrac{9}{2}\ln(2+\sqrt{3})-3\sqrt{3}\right)$

b $\sqrt{3}$

c $\pi(2\sqrt{3}-\ln(2+\sqrt{3}))$

6 a $\left(\dfrac{dx}{dt}\right)^2 + \left(\dfrac{dy}{dt}\right)^2 = \left(\dfrac{1}{t}\right)^2 + (t)^2$

$$= \dfrac{1}{t^2} + t^2$$

$$= \dfrac{1+t^4}{t^2}$$

Therefore, $S = 2\pi \int_1^2 \dfrac{1}{2}t^2\sqrt{\dfrac{1+t^4}{t^2}}\,dt$

$$= \pi\int_1^2 \dfrac{t^2}{t}\sqrt{1+t^4}\,dt$$

$$= \pi\int_1^2 t\sqrt{1+t^4}\,dt$$

b $\dfrac{\pi}{4}(\ln(4+\sqrt{17})+4\sqrt{17}-\ln(1+\sqrt{2})-\sqrt{2})$

7 $\pi(3\sqrt{10}-\sqrt{2}+\ln(3+\sqrt{10})-\ln(1+\sqrt{2}))$

8 $r^2 + \left(\dfrac{dr}{d\theta}\right)^2 = (e^{-\theta})^2 + (-e^{-\theta})^2$

$$= 2e^{-2\theta}$$

$$S = 2\pi\int_0^{\frac{\pi}{2}} e^{-\theta}\sin\theta\sqrt{2e^{-2\theta}}\,d\theta$$

$$= 2\sqrt{2}\pi\int_0^{\frac{\pi}{2}} e^{-\theta}\sin\theta e^{-\theta}\,d\theta$$

$$= 2\sqrt{2}\pi\int_0^{\frac{\pi}{2}} e^{-2\theta}\sin\theta\,d\theta$$

Let $I = \int_0^{\frac{\pi}{2}} e^{-2\theta}\sin\theta\,d\theta$

Let $u = e^{-2\theta}, \dfrac{dv}{d\theta} = \sin\theta$

Then $\dfrac{du}{d\theta} = -2e^{-2\theta}$, $v = -\cos\theta$

$I = \left[-e^{-2\theta}\cos\theta\right]_0^{\frac{\pi}{2}} - \displaystyle\int_0^{\frac{\pi}{2}} 2e^{-2\theta}\cos\theta \, d\theta$

$= 1 - 2\displaystyle\int_0^{\frac{\pi}{2}} e^{-2\theta}\cos\theta \, d\theta$

Let $u = e^{-2\theta}, \dfrac{dv}{d\theta} = \cos\theta$

Then $\dfrac{du}{d\theta} = -2e^{-2\theta}$, $v = \sin\theta$

So, $I = 1 - 2\left(\left[e^{-2\theta}\sin\theta\right]_0^{\frac{\pi}{2}} - \displaystyle\int_0^{\frac{\pi}{2}} -2e^{-2\theta}\sin\theta \, d\theta\right)$

$I = 1 - (2e^{-\pi} + 4I)$

$5I = 1 - 2e^{-\pi}$

$I = \dfrac{1}{5}(1 - 2e^{-\pi})$

Therefore, $S = 2\sqrt{2}\pi \times \dfrac{1}{5}(1 - 2e^{-\pi})$

$= \dfrac{2}{5}\sqrt{2}(1 - 2e^{-\pi})\pi$

9 $1 + \left(\dfrac{dy}{dx}\right)^2 = 1 + x^2$

So $S = 2\pi\displaystyle\int_0^2 \dfrac{1}{2}x^2\sqrt{1 + x^2}\, dx$

$= \pi\displaystyle\int_0^2 x^2\sqrt{1 + x^2}\, dx$

Let $x = \sinh u$, then $\dfrac{dx}{du} = \cosh u$

When $x = 0$, $u = 0$ and when $x = 2$, $u = \text{arsinh}\,2$

$S = \pi\displaystyle\int_0^{\text{arsinh}\,2} \sinh^2 u\sqrt{1 + \sinh^2 u}\, \cosh u \, du$

$= \pi\displaystyle\int_0^{\text{arsinh}\,2} \sinh^2 u\sqrt{\cosh^2 u}\, \cosh u \, du$

$= \pi\displaystyle\int_0^{\text{arsinh}\,2} \sinh^2 u\cosh u\cosh u \, du$

$= \pi\displaystyle\int_0^{\text{arsinh}\,2} \sinh^2 u\cosh^2 u \, du$

$= \pi\displaystyle\int_0^{\text{arsinh}\,2} \left(\sinh u\cosh u\right)^2 du$

$= \pi\displaystyle\int_0^{\text{arsinh}\,2} \left(\dfrac{1}{2}\sinh 2u\right)^2 du$

$= \dfrac{\pi}{4}\displaystyle\int_0^{\text{arsinh}\,2} \sinh^2 2u \, du$

$= \dfrac{\pi}{4}\displaystyle\int_0^{\text{arsinh}\,2} \dfrac{1}{2}(\cosh 4u - 1)\, du$

$= \dfrac{\pi}{8}\displaystyle\int_0^{\text{arsinh}\,2} \cosh 4u - 1 \, du$

$= \dfrac{\pi}{8}\left[\dfrac{1}{4}\sinh 4u - u\right]_0^{\text{arsinh}\,2}$

$= \dfrac{\pi}{8}\left[\dfrac{1}{2}\sinh 2u\cosh 2u - u\right]_0^{\text{arsinh}\,2}$

$= \dfrac{\pi}{8}\left[\sinh u\cosh u(\cosh^2 u + \sinh^2 u) - u\right]_0^{\text{arsinh}\,2}$

If $u = \text{arsinh}\,2$ then $\sinh u = 2$ and $\cosh u = \sqrt{1 + 2^2} = \sqrt{5}$

So $S = \dfrac{\pi}{8}(2\sqrt{5}(5 + 4) - \text{arsinh}\,2) - 0$

$= \dfrac{\pi}{8}(18\sqrt{5} - \ln(2 + \sqrt{5}))$

$= \left(\dfrac{9}{4}\sqrt{5} - \dfrac{1}{8}\ln(2 + \sqrt{5})\right)\pi$

Review exercise 7

1 a $I_n = \displaystyle\int x^n e^{-2x}\, dx = -\dfrac{1}{2}x^n e^{-2x} + \dfrac{n}{2}\displaystyle\int x^{n-1}e^{-2x}\, dx$

$= -\dfrac{1}{2}x^n e^{-2x} + \dfrac{n}{2}I_{n-1}$

b $e^{-2x}\left(-\dfrac{1}{2}x^3 - \dfrac{3}{4}x^2 - \dfrac{3}{4}x - \dfrac{3}{8}\right) + c$

$-\dfrac{1}{8}e^{-2x}(4x^3 + 6x^2 + 6x + 3) + c$

2 a $I_n = \displaystyle\int_0^\pi x^n\cos x\, dx = \left[x^n\sin x\right]_0^\pi - \displaystyle\int_0^\pi nx^{n-1}\sin x\, dx$

$= 0 - n\left(\left[-x^{n-1}\cos x\right]_0^\pi - (n-1)\displaystyle\int -x^{n-2}\cos x\, dx\right)$

$= -n(-\pi^{n-1}(-1) - 0 + (n-1)I_{n-2})$

$= -n(\pi^{n-1} + (n-1)I_{n-2})$

$= -n\pi^{n-1} - n(n-1)I_{n-2}$

b i $-6\pi^5 + 120\pi^3 - 720\pi$

ii $-5\pi^4 + 60\pi^2 - 240$

3 18.1 (to 3 sf)

4 $\ln(2 + \sqrt{5}) + 2\sqrt{5}$

5 $\dfrac{2\pi}{3}$

6 $\dfrac{\pi}{9}(2\sqrt{2} - 1)$

7 $\dfrac{dx}{d\theta} = -\sin\theta,\ \dfrac{dy}{d\theta} = \cos\theta$

$$S = 2\pi \int_{\frac{\pi}{2}}^{\frac{3\pi}{4}} \sin\theta \sqrt{(-\sin\theta)^2 + (\cos\theta)^2}\, d\theta$$

$$= 2\pi \int_{\frac{\pi}{2}}^{\frac{3\pi}{4}} \sin\theta \sqrt{\sin^2\theta + \cos^2\theta}\, d\theta$$

$$= 2\pi \int_{\frac{\pi}{2}}^{\frac{3\pi}{4}} \sin\theta\, d\theta$$

$$= 2\pi \left[-\cos\theta\right]_{\frac{\pi}{2}}^{\frac{3\pi}{4}}$$

$$= 2\pi \left(\frac{\sqrt{2}}{2} - 0\right)$$

$$= \sqrt{2}\pi$$

8 $\dfrac{\pi}{12}(13\sqrt{13} - 1)$

9 4π

Assessment 7

1 a $I_n = \displaystyle\int 1 \times (\ln x)^n\, dx$

$v' = \dfrac{n(\ln x)^{n-1}}{x}$

$I_n = x(\ln x)^n - \displaystyle\int x\, \dfrac{n(\ln x)^{n-1}}{x}\, dx$

$I_n = x(\ln x)^n - n I_{n-1}$

b $4(\ln 4)^3 - 12(\ln 4)^2 + 24(\ln 4) - 18$

2 a $I_n = \displaystyle\int \tanh^n x\, dx = \int (1 - \mathrm{sech}^2 x)\tanh^{n-2} x\, dx$

$= \displaystyle\int \tanh^{n-2} x\, dx - \int \mathrm{sech}^2 x \tanh^{n-2} x\, dx$

$= I_{n-2} - \dfrac{1}{n-1}\tanh^{n-1} x$

b $I_8 = x - \tanh x - \dfrac{1}{3}\tanh^3 x - \dfrac{1}{5}\tanh^5 x - \dfrac{1}{7}\tanh^7 x + c$

3 a $\dfrac{dy}{dx} = 6x$

$s = \displaystyle\int_0^1 \sqrt{1 + (6x)^2}\, dx$

$= \displaystyle\int_0^1 \sqrt{1 + 36x^2}\, dx$

Let $x = \dfrac{1}{6}\sinh u,\ \dfrac{dx}{du} = \dfrac{1}{6}\cosh u$

$= \displaystyle\int \sqrt{1 + 36\left(\frac{1}{6}\sinh u\right)^2}\left(\frac{1}{6}\cosh u\right) du$

$= \displaystyle\int \frac{1}{6}\cosh u \sqrt{1 + \sinh^2 u}\, du$

$= \dfrac{1}{6}\displaystyle\int \cosh u \sqrt{\cosh^2 u}\, du$

$= \dfrac{1}{6}\displaystyle\int \cosh^2 u\, du$

$= \dfrac{1}{12}\displaystyle\int (1 + \cosh(2u))\, du$

$= \dfrac{1}{12}\left[u + \dfrac{1}{2}\sinh(2u)\right]$

$= \dfrac{1}{12}\left[\mathrm{arsinh}(6x) + (6x)\sqrt{1 + (6x)^2}\,\right]_0^1$

(since $\dfrac{1}{2}\sinh(2u) = \dfrac{1}{2} 2\sinh u \cosh u = \sinh u \sqrt{1 + \sinh^2 u}$)

$= \dfrac{1}{12}\left(\mathrm{arsinh}(6) + (6)\sqrt{37}\right) - \dfrac{1}{12}\left(\mathrm{arsinh}(0) + \dfrac{1}{2}(0)\sqrt{1}\right)$

$= \dfrac{1}{12}(\ln(6 + \sqrt{37}) + 6\sqrt{37})$

b $\dfrac{\pi}{54}\left(37\sqrt{37} - 1\right) = 13.0$ (to 3 sf)

4 a $\dfrac{3a}{2}$ **b** $\dfrac{6\pi a^2}{5}$

5 a $I_n = x^n \sin x - \displaystyle\int nx^{n-1}\sin x\, dx$

$= x^n \sin x - n\left(-x^{n-1}\cos x + \displaystyle\int (n-1)x^{n-2}\cos x\, dx\right)$

$= x^n \sin x + nx^{n-1}\cos x - n(n-1)\displaystyle\int x^{n-2}\cos x\, dx$

$= x^n \sin x + nx^{n-1}\cos x - n(n-1)I_{n-2}$ as required

b $(x^3 - 6x)\sin x + (3x^2 - 6)\cos x + c$

c $-6\pi\left(\pi^4 - 20\pi^2 + 120\right)$

6 199 (to 3 sf)

7 a

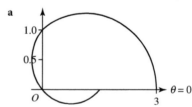

b $\dfrac{dr}{d\theta} = -2\sin\theta$

$s = \displaystyle\int_0^\pi \sqrt{(1 + 2\cos\theta)^2 + (-2\sin\theta)^2}\, d\theta$

$= \displaystyle\int_0^\pi \sqrt{1 + 4\cos\theta + 4\cos^2\theta + 4\sin^2\theta}\, d\theta$

$= \displaystyle\int_0^\pi \sqrt{1 + 4\cos\theta + 4}\, d\theta$

$= \displaystyle\int_0^\pi \sqrt{5 + 4\cos\theta}\, d\theta$ as required

8 a $$2\pi\int_0^2 y\sqrt{\left(\frac{dy}{dt}\right)^2+\left(\frac{dx}{dt}\right)^2}\,dt$$

$$=2\pi\int_0^2 2at\sqrt{(2a)^2+(2at)^2}\,dt$$

$$=8\pi a^2\int_0^2 t\sqrt{1+t^2}\,dt$$

b $8\pi a^2\left(\dfrac{5\sqrt{5}-1}{3}\right)$

c $$\int_0^2\sqrt{\left(\frac{dy}{dt}\right)^2+\left(\frac{dx}{dt}\right)^2}\,dt$$

$$=\int_0^2\sqrt{(2a)^2+(2at)^2}\,dt$$

$$=2a\int_0^2\sqrt{1+t^2}\,dt$$

d $a\left(\operatorname{arsinh}2+2\sqrt{5}\right)$

9 $2\sqrt{5}+\ln\left(2+\sqrt{5}\right)=5.92$ (to 3 sf)

10 a $$I_n=\int_0^{\frac{\pi}{2}}\sin^n x\,dx=\int_0^{\frac{\pi}{2}}\sin x\sin^{n-1}x\,dx$$

$$v'=(n-1)\sin^{n-2}x\cos x$$

$$I_n=\left[-\cos x\sin^{n-1}x\right]_0^{\frac{\pi}{2}}-\int_0^{\frac{\pi}{2}}-\cos x\times(n-1)\sin^{n-2}x\cos x\,dx$$

$$=\left[-\cos x\sin^{n-1}x\right]_0^{\frac{\pi}{2}}-\int_0^{\frac{\pi}{2}}-(1-\sin^2 x)\times(n-1)\sin^{n-2}x\,dx$$

$$=0+(n-1)\int_0^{\frac{\pi}{2}}\sin^{n-2}x\,dx-(n-1)\int_0^{\frac{\pi}{2}}\sin^n x\,dx$$

$$I_n=(n-1)I_{n-2}-(n-1)I_n$$

$$nI_n=(n-1)I_{n-2}$$

b $\dfrac{3\pi}{16}$ **c** $\dfrac{35}{256}\pi^2$

11 a

b $\dfrac{dr}{d\theta}=\cos(\theta)$

$$s=\int_0^\pi\sqrt{\sin^2(\theta)+\cos^2(\theta)}\,d\theta$$

$$=\int_0^\pi 1\,d\theta$$

$$=\left[\theta\right]_0^\pi$$

$$=\pi-0=\pi\ \text{ as required}$$

c $$S=2\pi\int_0^{\frac{\pi}{6}}\sin(\theta)\sin\theta\sqrt{\sin^2(\theta)+\cos^2(\theta)}\,d\theta$$

$$=2\pi\int_0^{\frac{\pi}{6}}\sin^2\theta\,d\theta$$

$$=2\pi\int_0^{\frac{\pi}{6}}\frac{1}{2}\left(1-\cos(2\theta)\right)d\theta$$

$$=\pi\int_0^{\frac{\pi}{6}}\left(1-\cos(2\theta)\right)d\theta$$

$$=\pi\left[\theta-\frac{1}{2}\sin(2\theta)\right]_0^{\frac{\pi}{6}}$$

$$=\pi\left(\frac{\pi}{6}-\frac{1}{2}\sin\left(\frac{\pi}{3}\right)\right)-0$$

$$=\pi\left(\frac{\pi}{6}-\frac{\sqrt{3}}{4}\right)$$

12 9π

Chapter 8

Exercise 8.1A

1 a $\lambda=2,-4$, corresponding eigenvectors $\begin{pmatrix}1\\0\end{pmatrix}$, $\begin{pmatrix}1\\-2\end{pmatrix}$

b $\lambda=2,-1$, corresponding eigenvectors $\begin{pmatrix}1\\1\end{pmatrix}$, $\begin{pmatrix}1\\4\end{pmatrix}$

2 a $\lambda=-3,1,5$, corresponding eigenvectors $\begin{pmatrix}5\\-3\\4\end{pmatrix}$, $\begin{pmatrix}1\\-1\\0\end{pmatrix}$, $\begin{pmatrix}0\\1\\0\end{pmatrix}$

b $\lambda=-2,2,3$, corresponding eigenvectors $\begin{pmatrix}1\\-1\\0\end{pmatrix}$, $\begin{pmatrix}3\\1\\-4\end{pmatrix}$, $\begin{pmatrix}3\\2\\0\end{pmatrix}$

3 a i $\lambda=3,7$, corresponding normalised eigenvectors $\begin{pmatrix}-\frac{4}{5}\\\frac{3}{5}\end{pmatrix}$ and $\begin{pmatrix}0\\1\end{pmatrix}$

ii $\lambda=-1,5$, corresponding normalised eigenvectors $\begin{pmatrix}\frac{1}{\sqrt{2}}\\\frac{1}{\sqrt{2}}\end{pmatrix}$ and $\begin{pmatrix}-\frac{5}{\sqrt{26}}\\\frac{1}{\sqrt{26}}\end{pmatrix}$

iii $\lambda = 5, 2, -4$, corresponding normalised eigenvectors

$$\begin{pmatrix} 1 \\ 0 \\ 0 \end{pmatrix}, \begin{pmatrix} \dfrac{6}{\sqrt{97}} \\ \dfrac{6}{\sqrt{97}} \\ -\dfrac{5}{\sqrt{97}} \end{pmatrix} \text{ and } \begin{pmatrix} 0 \\ 0 \\ 1 \end{pmatrix}$$

iv $\lambda = -7, 4, 9$, corresponding normalised eigenvectors

$$\begin{pmatrix} -\dfrac{44}{\sqrt{2418}} \\ \dfrac{19}{\sqrt{2418}} \\ \dfrac{11}{\sqrt{2418}} \end{pmatrix}, \begin{pmatrix} 0 \\ 1 \\ 0 \end{pmatrix} \text{ and } \begin{pmatrix} 0 \\ \dfrac{1}{\sqrt{26}} \\ \dfrac{5}{\sqrt{26}} \end{pmatrix}$$

b i Characteristic equation is $\lambda^2 - 10\lambda + 21 = 0$

Substitute the matrix:

$$\begin{pmatrix} 3 & 0 \\ 3 & 7 \end{pmatrix}^2 - 10\begin{pmatrix} 3 & 0 \\ 3 & 7 \end{pmatrix} + 21\begin{pmatrix} 1 & 0 \\ 0 & 1 \end{pmatrix}$$

$$= \begin{pmatrix} 9 & 0 \\ 30 & 49 \end{pmatrix} - \begin{pmatrix} 30 & 0 \\ 30 & 70 \end{pmatrix} + \begin{pmatrix} 21 & 0 \\ 0 & 21 \end{pmatrix}$$

$$= \begin{pmatrix} 9-30-21 & 0 \\ 30-30 & 49-70+21 \end{pmatrix}$$

$$= \begin{pmatrix} 0 & 0 \\ 0 & 0 \end{pmatrix} \text{ as required}$$

ii Characteristic equation is $\lambda^2 - 4\lambda - 5 = 0$

Substitute the matrix:

$$\begin{pmatrix} 4 & -5 \\ -1 & 0 \end{pmatrix}^2 - 4\begin{pmatrix} 4 & -5 \\ -1 & 0 \end{pmatrix} - 5\begin{pmatrix} 1 & 0 \\ 0 & 1 \end{pmatrix}$$

$$= \begin{pmatrix} 21 & -20 \\ -4 & 5 \end{pmatrix} - \begin{pmatrix} 16 & -20 \\ -4 & 0 \end{pmatrix} - \begin{pmatrix} 5 & 0 \\ 0 & 5 \end{pmatrix}$$

$$= \begin{pmatrix} 21-16-5 & -20+20 \\ -4+4 & 5-5 \end{pmatrix}$$

$$= \begin{pmatrix} 0 & 0 \\ 0 & 0 \end{pmatrix} \text{ as required}$$

iii Characteristic equation is $-\lambda^3 + 3\lambda^2 + 18\lambda - 40 = 0$

Substitute the matrix:

$$-\begin{pmatrix} 5 & -3 & 0 \\ 0 & 2 & 0 \\ 0 & -5 & -4 \end{pmatrix}^3 + 3\begin{pmatrix} 5 & -3 & 0 \\ 0 & 2 & 0 \\ 0 & -5 & -4 \end{pmatrix}^2$$

$$+ 18\begin{pmatrix} 5 & -3 & 0 \\ 0 & 2 & 0 \\ 0 & -5 & -4 \end{pmatrix} - 40\begin{pmatrix} 1 & 0 & 0 \\ 0 & 1 & 0 \\ 0 & 0 & 1 \end{pmatrix}$$

$$= -\begin{pmatrix} 125 & -117 & 0 \\ 0 & 8 & 0 \\ 0 & -60 & -64 \end{pmatrix} + 3\begin{pmatrix} 25 & -21 & 0 \\ 0 & 4 & 0 \\ 0 & 10 & 16 \end{pmatrix}$$

$$+ 18\begin{pmatrix} 5 & -3 & 0 \\ 0 & 2 & 0 \\ 0 & -5 & -4 \end{pmatrix} - 40\begin{pmatrix} 1 & 0 & 0 \\ 0 & 1 & 0 \\ 0 & 0 & 1 \end{pmatrix}$$

$$= \begin{pmatrix} -125+75+90-40 & 117-63-54 & 0 \\ 0 & -8+12+36-40 & 0 \\ 0 & 60+30-90 & 64+48-72-40 \end{pmatrix}$$

$$= \begin{pmatrix} 0 & 0 & 0 \\ 0 & 0 & 0 \\ 0 & 0 & 0 \end{pmatrix} \text{ as required}$$

iv Characteristic equation is $-\lambda^3 + 6\lambda^2 + 55\lambda - 252 = 0$

Substitute the matrix:

$$-\begin{pmatrix} -7 & 0 & 0 \\ 5 & 4 & 1 \\ 4 & 0 & 9 \end{pmatrix}^3 + 6\begin{pmatrix} -7 & 0 & 0 \\ 5 & 4 & 1 \\ 4 & 0 & 9 \end{pmatrix}^2$$

$$+ 55\begin{pmatrix} -7 & 0 & 0 \\ 5 & 4 & 1 \\ 4 & 0 & 9 \end{pmatrix} - 252\begin{pmatrix} 1 & 0 & 0 \\ 0 & 1 & 0 \\ 0 & 0 & 1 \end{pmatrix}$$

$$-\begin{pmatrix} -343 & 0 & 0 \\ 209 & 64 & 133 \\ 268 & 0 & 729 \end{pmatrix} + 6\begin{pmatrix} 49 & 0 & 0 \\ -11 & 16 & 13 \\ 8 & 0 & 81 \end{pmatrix}$$

$$+ 55\begin{pmatrix} -7 & 0 & 0 \\ 5 & 4 & 1 \\ 4 & 0 & 9 \end{pmatrix} - 252\begin{pmatrix} 1 & 0 & 0 \\ 0 & 1 & 0 \\ 0 & 0 & 1 \end{pmatrix}$$

$$= \begin{pmatrix} 343+294-385-252 & & 0 \\ -209-66+275 & & -64+96+220-252 \\ -268+48+220 & & 0 \end{pmatrix}$$

$$\begin{pmatrix} & 0 & \\ & -133+78+55 & \\ & -729+486+495-252 & \end{pmatrix}$$

$$= \begin{pmatrix} 0 & 0 & 0 \\ 0 & 0 & 0 \\ 0 & 0 & 0 \end{pmatrix} \text{ as required}$$

4 a $\lambda = \pm i$, corresponding eigenvectors are $\begin{pmatrix} 1 \\ i \end{pmatrix}, \begin{pmatrix} 1 \\ -i \end{pmatrix}$

b $\lambda = 1 \pm 2i$, corresponding eigenvectors are $\begin{pmatrix} 1 \\ i-1 \end{pmatrix}, \begin{pmatrix} 1 \\ -i-1 \end{pmatrix}$

c $\lambda = 3, 3 \pm i$, corresponding eigenvectors are $\begin{pmatrix} 1 \\ 1 \\ 1 \end{pmatrix}, \begin{pmatrix} 0 \\ 1 \\ 1+i \end{pmatrix},$

$$\begin{pmatrix} 0 \\ 1 \\ 1-i \end{pmatrix}$$

d $\lambda = 1, \dfrac{1}{2}(1 \pm i\sqrt{3})$, corresponding eigenvectors are $\begin{pmatrix} 0 \\ 0 \\ 1 \end{pmatrix},$

$$\begin{pmatrix} \frac{1}{2}(1+i\sqrt{3}) \\ 1 \\ 0 \end{pmatrix}, \begin{pmatrix} \frac{1}{2}(1-i\sqrt{3}) \\ 1 \\ 0 \end{pmatrix}$$

5 $\det\begin{pmatrix} 1-\lambda & 3 & -1 \\ -2 & 3-\lambda & 2 \\ 1 & 0 & 2-\lambda \end{pmatrix}$

$$= 1[6--1(3-\lambda)] + (2-\lambda)[(1-\lambda)(3-\lambda)--6]$$

$$= 9-\lambda+(2-\lambda)(\lambda^2-4\lambda+9)$$

$$= 9-\lambda+2\lambda^2-8\lambda+18-\lambda^3+4\lambda^2-9\lambda$$

$$= -\lambda^3+6\lambda^2-18\lambda+27$$

When $\lambda = 3$, $-\lambda^3 + 6\lambda^2 - 18\lambda + 27 = 0$ so 3 is an eigenvalue

$-\lambda^3 + 6\lambda^2 - 18\lambda + 27 = (\lambda - 3)(-\lambda^2 + 3\lambda - 9)$

$-\lambda^2 + 3\lambda - 9 = 0$ has no real solutions since
$b^2 - 4ac = 9 - 36 < 0$

Corresponding normalised eigenvector is $\begin{pmatrix} \dfrac{1}{\sqrt{3}} \\ \dfrac{1}{\sqrt{3}} \\ \dfrac{1}{\sqrt{3}} \end{pmatrix}$

6 a $\det\begin{pmatrix} -2-\lambda & 6 & -3 \\ 3 & 2-\lambda & 6 \\ 2 & 6 & -3-\lambda \end{pmatrix}$

$= (-2-\lambda)\big[(2-\lambda)(-3-\lambda) - 36\big]$
$\quad - 6\big[3(-3-\lambda) - 12\big] - 3\big[18 - 2(2-\lambda)\big]$

$= -\lambda^3 - 3\lambda^2 + 52\lambda + 168$

When $\lambda = -7$, $-\lambda^3 - 3\lambda^2 + 52\lambda + 168 = 0$ so -7 is an eigenvalue

$-\lambda^3 - 3\lambda^2 + 52\lambda + 168 = (\lambda + 7)(-\lambda^2 + 4\lambda + 24)$

$-\lambda^2 + 4\lambda + 24 = 0 \Rightarrow \lambda = 2 \pm 4\sqrt{7}$

b $\begin{pmatrix} 21 \\ -13 \\ 9 \end{pmatrix}$

7 a $\det\begin{pmatrix} 1-\lambda & 4 \\ 2 & -3-\lambda \end{pmatrix} = 0$

$\Rightarrow (1-\lambda)(-3-\lambda) - 8 = 0$

$\Rightarrow \lambda^2 + 2\lambda - 11 = 0$

$\begin{pmatrix} 1 & 4 \\ 2 & -3 \end{pmatrix}^2 + 2\begin{pmatrix} 1 & 4 \\ 2 & -3 \end{pmatrix} - 11\begin{pmatrix} 1 & 0 \\ 0 & 1 \end{pmatrix}$

$= \begin{pmatrix} 9 & -8 \\ -4 & 17 \end{pmatrix} + \begin{pmatrix} 2 & 8 \\ 4 & -6 \end{pmatrix} - \begin{pmatrix} 11 & 0 \\ 0 & 11 \end{pmatrix}$

$= \begin{pmatrix} 9+2-11 & -8+8-0 \\ -4+4-0 & 17+-6-11 \end{pmatrix}$

$= \begin{pmatrix} 0 & 0 \\ 0 & 0 \end{pmatrix}$ as required

b $\det\begin{pmatrix} 5-\lambda & 7 \\ -4 & 1-\lambda \end{pmatrix} = 0$

$\Rightarrow (5-\lambda)(1-\lambda) + 28 = 0$

$\Rightarrow \lambda^2 - 6\lambda + 33 = 0$

$\begin{pmatrix} 5 & 7 \\ -4 & 1 \end{pmatrix}^2 - 6\begin{pmatrix} 5 & 7 \\ -4 & 1 \end{pmatrix} + 33\begin{pmatrix} 1 & 0 \\ 0 & 1 \end{pmatrix}$

$= \begin{pmatrix} -3 & 42 \\ -24 & -27 \end{pmatrix} - \begin{pmatrix} 30 & 42 \\ -24 & 6 \end{pmatrix} + \begin{pmatrix} 33 & 0 \\ 0 & 33 \end{pmatrix}$

$= \begin{pmatrix} -3-30+33 & 42-42+0 \\ -24+24+0 & -27-6+33 \end{pmatrix}$

$= \begin{pmatrix} 0 & 0 \\ 0 & 0 \end{pmatrix}$ as required

c $\det\begin{pmatrix} 4-\lambda & 0 & 1 \\ 6 & 2-\lambda & 0 \\ 0 & 1 & -\lambda \end{pmatrix} = 0$

$-\lambda(4-\lambda)(2-\lambda) + 6 = 0$

$-\lambda^3 + 6\lambda^2 - 8\lambda + 6 = 0$

$-\begin{pmatrix} 4 & 0 & 1 \\ 6 & 2 & 0 \\ 0 & 1 & 0 \end{pmatrix}^3 + 6\begin{pmatrix} 4 & 0 & 1 \\ 6 & 2 & 0 \\ 0 & 1 & 0 \end{pmatrix}^2$

$-8\begin{pmatrix} 4 & 0 & 1 \\ 6 & 2 & 0 \\ 0 & 1 & 0 \end{pmatrix} + 6\begin{pmatrix} 1 & 0 & 0 \\ 0 & 1 & 0 \\ 0 & 0 & 1 \end{pmatrix}$

$= -\begin{pmatrix} 70 & 6 & 16 \\ 168 & 14 & 36 \\ 36 & 4 & 6 \end{pmatrix} + 6\begin{pmatrix} 16 & 1 & 4 \\ 36 & 4 & 6 \\ 6 & 2 & 0 \end{pmatrix}$

$-8\begin{pmatrix} 4 & 0 & 1 \\ 6 & 2 & 0 \\ 0 & 1 & 0 \end{pmatrix} + 6\begin{pmatrix} 1 & 0 & 0 \\ 0 & 1 & 0 \\ 0 & 0 & 1 \end{pmatrix}$

$= -\begin{pmatrix} 70 & 6 & 16 \\ 168 & 14 & 36 \\ 36 & 4 & 6 \end{pmatrix} + \begin{pmatrix} 96 & 6 & 24 \\ 216 & 24 & 36 \\ 36 & 12 & 0 \end{pmatrix}$

$-\begin{pmatrix} 32 & 0 & 8 \\ 48 & 16 & 0 \\ 0 & 8 & 0 \end{pmatrix} + \begin{pmatrix} 6 & 0 & 0 \\ 0 & 6 & 0 \\ 0 & 0 & 6 \end{pmatrix}$

$= \begin{pmatrix} -70+96-32+6 & -6+6-0-0 & -16+24-8+0 \\ -168+216-48+0 & -14+24-16+6 & -36+36-0+0 \\ -36+36-0+0 & -4+12-8 & -6+0-0+6 \end{pmatrix}$

$= \begin{pmatrix} 0 & 0 & 0 \\ 0 & 0 & 0 \\ 0 & 0 & 0 \end{pmatrix}$ as required

d $\det\begin{pmatrix} 1-\lambda & 0 & 0 \\ 2 & -\lambda & 0 \\ 0 & 1 & -\lambda \end{pmatrix} = 0 \Rightarrow (1-\lambda)\lambda^2 = 0$

$\left[\begin{pmatrix} 1 & 0 & 0 \\ 0 & 1 & 0 \\ 0 & 0 & 1 \end{pmatrix} - \begin{pmatrix} 1 & 0 & 0 \\ 2 & 0 & 0 \\ 0 & 1 & 0 \end{pmatrix}\right]\begin{pmatrix} 1 & 0 & 0 \\ 2 & 0 & 0 \\ 0 & 1 & 0 \end{pmatrix}^2$

$= \begin{pmatrix} 0 & 0 & 0 \\ -2 & 1 & 0 \\ 0 & -1 & 1 \end{pmatrix}\begin{pmatrix} 1 & 0 & 0 \\ 2 & 0 & 0 \\ 2 & 0 & 0 \end{pmatrix}$

$= \begin{pmatrix} 0 & 0 & 0 \\ 0 & 0 & 0 \\ 0 & 0 & 0 \end{pmatrix}$ as required

8 a 4

b $\begin{pmatrix} 0 \\ -2 \\ 1 \end{pmatrix}$ and $\begin{pmatrix} 1 \\ 5 \\ 0 \end{pmatrix}$

9 a $\lambda = 10, 10, -15$

b Corresponding eigenvectors are $\begin{pmatrix} 1 \\ 0 \\ 4 \end{pmatrix}$ or $\begin{pmatrix} 0 \\ 1 \\ 0 \end{pmatrix}$, $\begin{pmatrix} 1 \\ 0 \\ -1 \end{pmatrix}$

Exercise 8.1B

1 a $\lambda^2 - \lambda - 22 = 0$

C–H theorem $\Rightarrow \mathbf{A}^2 - \mathbf{A} - 22\mathbf{I} = 0$

b i $\begin{pmatrix} 16 & -5 \\ 4 & 29 \end{pmatrix}$

ii $\begin{pmatrix} -116 & -115 \\ 92 & 183 \end{pmatrix}$

iii $\dfrac{1}{22}\begin{pmatrix} -7 & -5 \\ 4 & 6 \end{pmatrix}$

2 $\dfrac{1}{21}\begin{pmatrix} 3 & 9 \\ 2 & -1 \end{pmatrix}$

3 a $\lambda^2 - k\lambda - 2 = 0$

b $\begin{pmatrix} k^3 + 4k & k^2 + 2 \\ 2k^2 + 4 & 2k \end{pmatrix}$

$\dfrac{1}{2}\begin{pmatrix} 0 & 1 \\ 2 & -k \end{pmatrix}$

4 a $\mathbf{M}^2 = \begin{pmatrix} a & 0 & 1 \\ -1 & 2 & 3 \\ -1 & 0 & -2 \end{pmatrix}\begin{pmatrix} a & 0 & 1 \\ -1 & 2 & 3 \\ -1 & 0 & -2 \end{pmatrix}$

$= \begin{pmatrix} a^2 + 0 - 1 & 0 + 0 + 0 & a + 0 - 2 \\ -a - 2 - 3 & 0 + 4 + 0 & -1 + 6 - 6 \\ -a + 0 + 2 & 0 + 0 + 0 & -1 + 0 + 4 \end{pmatrix}$

$= \begin{pmatrix} a^2 - 1 & 0 & a - 2 \\ -a - 5 & 4 & -1 \\ 2 - a & 0 & 3 \end{pmatrix}$ as required

b i When $a = 2$, $\mathbf{M} = \begin{pmatrix} 2 & 0 & 1 \\ -1 & 2 & 3 \\ -1 & 0 & -2 \end{pmatrix}$, $\mathbf{M}^2 = \begin{pmatrix} 3 & 0 & 0 \\ -7 & 4 & -1 \\ 0 & 0 & 3 \end{pmatrix}$

$\det\begin{pmatrix} 2 - \lambda & 0 & 1 \\ -1 & 2 - \lambda & 3 \\ -1 & 0 & -2 - \lambda \end{pmatrix} = 0$

$\Rightarrow (2 - \lambda)(2 - \lambda)(-2 - \lambda) + (0 - -(2 - \lambda)) = 0$

$\Rightarrow (2 - \lambda)(\lambda^2 - 4) + (2 - \lambda) = 0$

$\Rightarrow -\lambda^3 + 2\lambda^2 + 4\lambda - 8 + 2 - \lambda = 0$

$\Rightarrow -\lambda^3 + 2\lambda^2 + 3\lambda - 6 = 0$

$\Rightarrow \lambda^3 - 2\lambda^2 - 3\lambda + 6 = 0$

c $\mathbf{M}^3 - 2\mathbf{M}^2 - 3\mathbf{M} + 6\mathbf{I} = 0$

$\mathbf{M}^3 = 2\mathbf{M}^2 + 3\mathbf{M} - 6\mathbf{I}$

$= 2\begin{pmatrix} 3 & 0 & 0 \\ -7 & 4 & -1 \\ 0 & 0 & 3 \end{pmatrix} + 3\begin{pmatrix} 2 & 0 & 1 \\ -1 & 2 & 3 \\ -1 & 0 & -2 \end{pmatrix} - 6\begin{pmatrix} 1 & 0 & 0 \\ 0 & 1 & 0 \\ 0 & 0 & 1 \end{pmatrix}$

$= \begin{pmatrix} 6 & 0 & 3 \\ -17 & 8 & 7 \\ -3 & 0 & -6 \end{pmatrix}$ as required

d i $\begin{pmatrix} 9 & 0 & 0 \\ -49 & 16 & -7 \\ 0 & 0 & 9 \end{pmatrix}$

ii $\dfrac{1}{6}\begin{pmatrix} 4 & 0 & 2 \\ 5 & 3 & 7 \\ -2 & 0 & -4 \end{pmatrix}$

5 $\begin{pmatrix} \dfrac{1}{3} & -\dfrac{2}{3} & -\dfrac{1}{18} \\ 0 & \dfrac{1}{2} & \dfrac{1}{12} \\ 0 & 0 & -\dfrac{1}{6} \end{pmatrix}$

6 a $\mathbf{A}^3 - 3\mathbf{A}^2 + 5\mathbf{I} = 0 \Rightarrow \mathbf{A}^3 = 3\mathbf{A}^2 - 5\mathbf{I}$

$\mathbf{A}^4 = 3\mathbf{A}^3 - 5\mathbf{A}$

$= 3(3\mathbf{A}^2 - 5\mathbf{I}) - 5\mathbf{A}$

$= 9\mathbf{A}^2 - 5\mathbf{A} - 15\mathbf{I}$

b $\dfrac{1}{5}(3\mathbf{A} - \mathbf{A}^2)$

7 $\det\begin{pmatrix} 1 - \lambda & 3 & -2 \\ 2 & 1 - \lambda & 1 \\ 0 & 3 & -3 - \lambda \end{pmatrix} = 0$

$\Rightarrow (1 - \lambda)[(1 - \lambda)(-3 - \lambda) - 3] - 3[2(-3 - \lambda) - 0] - 2(6) = 0$

$(1 - \lambda)(\lambda^2 + 2\lambda - 6) + 6(3 + \lambda) - 12 = 0$

$\lambda^2 + 2\lambda - 6 - \lambda^3 - 2\lambda^2 + 6\lambda + 18 + 6\lambda - 12 = 0$

$\lambda^3 + \lambda^2 - 14\lambda = 0$

C–H theorem $\Rightarrow \mathbf{M}^3 + \mathbf{M}^2 - 14\mathbf{M} = 0$

$\mathbf{M}^3 = 14\mathbf{M} - \mathbf{M}^2$

$\mathbf{M}^4 = 14\mathbf{M}^2 - \mathbf{M}^3$

$= 14\mathbf{M}^2 - (14\mathbf{M} - \mathbf{M}^2)$

$= 15\mathbf{M}^2 - 14\mathbf{M}$

8 $\det\begin{pmatrix} 2 - \lambda & -1 & 0 \\ 4 & -1 - \lambda & -2 \\ 5 & 8 & 4 - \lambda \end{pmatrix} = 0$

$\Rightarrow (2 - \lambda)[(-1 - \lambda)(4 - \lambda) - -16] + 1[4(4 - \lambda) - -10] = 0$

$\Rightarrow (2 - \lambda)(\lambda^2 - 3\lambda + 12) + (26 - 4\lambda) = 0$

$2\lambda^2 - 6\lambda + 24 - \lambda^3 + 3\lambda^2 - 12\lambda + 26 - 4\lambda = 0$

$\lambda^3 - 5\lambda^2 + 22\lambda - 50 = 0$

$\mathbf{M}^3 - 5\mathbf{M}^2 + 22\mathbf{M} - 50\mathbf{I} = 0$

$\mathbf{M}^3 = 5\mathbf{M}^2 - 22\mathbf{M} + 50\mathbf{I}$

$\mathbf{M}^4 = 5\mathbf{M}^3 - 22\mathbf{M}^2 + 50\mathbf{M}$

$= 5(5\mathbf{M}^2 - 22\mathbf{M} + 50\mathbf{I}) - 22\mathbf{M}^2 + 50\mathbf{M}$

$= 3\mathbf{M}^2 - 60\mathbf{M} + 250\mathbf{I}$

9 C–H theorem $\Rightarrow \mathbf{A}^2 - 7\mathbf{A} = 0$

$\Rightarrow \mathbf{A}^2 = 7\mathbf{A}$

When $n = 2$, $\mathbf{A}^2 = 7^{2-1}\mathbf{A} = 7\mathbf{A}$ so true for $n = 2$

Assume true for $n = k$

let $n = k + 1$

$\mathbf{A}^{k+1} = \mathbf{A}\mathbf{A}^k$

$= \mathbf{A}(7^{k-1}\mathbf{A})$

$= 7^{k-1}\mathbf{A}^2$

$= 7^{k-1}(7\mathbf{A})$

$= 7^k\mathbf{A}$ so true for $n = k + 1$

1 a $P = \begin{pmatrix} -1 & -2 \\ 1 & 1 \end{pmatrix}$, $D = \begin{pmatrix} -3 & 0 \\ 0 & -1 \end{pmatrix}$

b $P = \begin{pmatrix} -1 & 6 \\ 1 & 1 \end{pmatrix}$, $D = \begin{pmatrix} -4 & 0 \\ 0 & 3 \end{pmatrix}$

c $P = \begin{pmatrix} 0 & 0 & -30 \\ -2 & 3 & 1 \\ 3 & 2 & 24 \end{pmatrix}$, $D = \begin{pmatrix} -7 & 0 & 0 \\ 0 & 6 & 0 \\ 0 & 0 & -4 \end{pmatrix}$

d $P = \begin{pmatrix} -4 & 0 & 0 \\ 8 & 13 & 0 \\ 1 & 1 & 1 \end{pmatrix}$, $D = \begin{pmatrix} -3 & 0 & 0 \\ 6 & 8 & 0 \\ 1 & 0 & -5 \end{pmatrix}$

2 a $\begin{pmatrix} 3 \\ 4 \end{pmatrix} \cdot \begin{pmatrix} 4 \\ -3 \end{pmatrix} = 12 - 12 = 0$ hence orthogonal

b $\begin{pmatrix} 2 \\ -3 \end{pmatrix} \cdot \begin{pmatrix} -12 \\ -8 \end{pmatrix} = -24 + 24 = 0$ hence orthogonal

c $\begin{pmatrix} 3 \\ -5 \\ 1 \end{pmatrix} \cdot \begin{pmatrix} 5 \\ 3 \\ 0 \end{pmatrix} = 15 - 15 + 0 = 0$ hence orthogonal

d $\begin{pmatrix} 2 \\ 3 \\ -1 \end{pmatrix} \cdot \begin{pmatrix} 5 \\ -4 \\ -2 \end{pmatrix} = 10 - 12 + 2 = 0$ hence orthogonal

3 a $\begin{pmatrix} -\frac{5}{13} \\ 0 \\ -\frac{12}{13} \end{pmatrix} \cdot \begin{pmatrix} 0 \\ -1 \\ 0 \end{pmatrix} = 0 + 0 + 0 = 0$ hence orthogonal

$\begin{pmatrix} -\frac{12}{13} \\ 0 \\ \frac{5}{13} \end{pmatrix} \cdot \begin{pmatrix} 0 \\ -1 \\ 0 \end{pmatrix} = 0 + 0 + 0 = 0$ hence orthogonal

$\begin{pmatrix} -\frac{5}{13} \\ 0 \\ -\frac{12}{13} \end{pmatrix} \cdot \begin{pmatrix} -\frac{12}{13} \\ 0 \\ \frac{5}{13} \end{pmatrix} = \frac{60}{169} + 0 - \frac{60}{169} = 0$ hence orthogonal

so **A** is orthogonal

b $AA^T = \begin{pmatrix} -\frac{5}{13} & 0 & -\frac{12}{13} \\ 0 & -1 & 0 \\ -\frac{12}{13} & 0 & \frac{5}{13} \end{pmatrix} \begin{pmatrix} -\frac{5}{13} & 0 & -\frac{12}{13} \\ 0 & -1 & 0 \\ -\frac{12}{13} & 0 & \frac{5}{13} \end{pmatrix}$

$= \begin{pmatrix} \frac{25}{169} + \frac{144}{169} & 0 & \frac{60}{169} - \frac{60}{169} \\ 0 & 1 & 0 \\ \frac{60}{169} - \frac{60}{169} & 0 & \frac{144}{169} + \frac{25}{169} \end{pmatrix}$

$= \begin{pmatrix} 1 & 0 & 0 \\ 0 & 1 & 0 \\ 0 & 0 & 1 \end{pmatrix} = I$ as required, so **A** is orthogonal

4 a $P = \begin{pmatrix} 0 & 1 \\ 1 & 0 \end{pmatrix}$, $D = \begin{pmatrix} 7 & 0 \\ 0 & 2 \end{pmatrix}$

b $P = \begin{pmatrix} \frac{2}{\sqrt{5}} & -\frac{1}{\sqrt{5}} \\ \frac{1}{\sqrt{5}} & \frac{2}{\sqrt{5}} \end{pmatrix}$, $D = \begin{pmatrix} 5 & 0 \\ 0 & -5 \end{pmatrix}$

c $D = \begin{pmatrix} 8 & 0 & 0 \\ 0 & -7 & 0 \\ 0 & 0 & 6 \end{pmatrix}$, $P = \begin{pmatrix} -\frac{1}{\sqrt{2}} & 0 & \frac{1}{\sqrt{2}} \\ \frac{1}{\sqrt{2}} & 0 & \frac{1}{\sqrt{2}} \\ 0 & 1 & 0 \end{pmatrix}$

1 a $\begin{pmatrix} 1 & 0 \\ 189 & 64 \end{pmatrix}$

b $\begin{pmatrix} 1 & 0 \\ 3(2^n) - 3 & 2^n \end{pmatrix}$

2 a $\begin{pmatrix} 5^4 & -2(5^4) \\ -2(5^4) & 4(5^4) \end{pmatrix}$

b $T^n = \frac{1}{5} \begin{pmatrix} 2 & 1 \\ 1 & -2 \end{pmatrix} \begin{pmatrix} 0 & 0 \\ 0 & 5 \end{pmatrix}^n \begin{pmatrix} 2 & 1 \\ 1 & -2 \end{pmatrix}$

$= \frac{1}{5} \begin{pmatrix} 2 & 1 \\ 1 & -2 \end{pmatrix} \begin{pmatrix} 0 & 0 \\ 0 & 5^n \end{pmatrix} \begin{pmatrix} 2 & 1 \\ 1 & -2 \end{pmatrix}$

$= \frac{1}{5} \begin{pmatrix} 0 & 5^n \\ 0 & -2(5^n) \end{pmatrix} \begin{pmatrix} 2 & 1 \\ 1 & -2 \end{pmatrix}$

$= 5^{n-1} \begin{pmatrix} 1 & -2 \\ -2 & 4 \end{pmatrix}$

3 a $U = \begin{pmatrix} -1 & 1 \\ 1 & 1 \end{pmatrix}$, $D = \begin{pmatrix} 3 & 0 \\ 0 & 7 \end{pmatrix}$

b $3^3 = 27$ and $7^3 = 343$

c Eigenvectors are $\begin{pmatrix} -1 \\ 1 \end{pmatrix}$ and $\begin{pmatrix} 1 \\ 1 \end{pmatrix}$

4 Only eigenvalue is $7^2 = 49$, eigenvectors are $\begin{pmatrix} 1 \\ -3 \end{pmatrix}$ and $\begin{pmatrix} 2 \\ 1 \end{pmatrix}$

5 Eigenvalues are $3^4 = 81$, $2^4 = 16$, $(-4)^4 = 256$

Normalised eigenvectors are $\begin{pmatrix} \frac{1}{\sqrt{2}} \\ 0 \\ \frac{1}{\sqrt{2}} \end{pmatrix}$, $\begin{pmatrix} \frac{2}{\sqrt{13}} \\ -\frac{3}{\sqrt{13}} \\ 0 \end{pmatrix}$, $\begin{pmatrix} \frac{1}{\sqrt{6}} \\ \frac{1}{\sqrt{6}} \\ \frac{2}{\sqrt{6}} \end{pmatrix}$

6 a
$$\begin{pmatrix} 101 & -37 & 0 \\ 74 & -10 & 0 \\ 0 & 0 & 1 \end{pmatrix}$$

b
$$\begin{pmatrix} 2(4^n)-3^n & 3^n-4^n & 0 \\ 2(4^n)-2(3^n) & 2(3^n)-4^n & 0 \\ 0 & 0 & 1 \end{pmatrix}$$

7 Let $n=1$, then $\begin{pmatrix} a & 0 & 0 \\ 0 & b & 0 \\ 0 & 0 & c \end{pmatrix}^1 = \begin{pmatrix} a & 0 & 0 \\ 0 & b & 0 \\ 0 & 0 & c \end{pmatrix} = \begin{pmatrix} a^1 & 0 & 0 \\ 0 & b^1 & 0 \\ 0 & 0 & c^1 \end{pmatrix}$

so true for $n=1$

Assume true for $n=k$ and let $n=k+1$:

$$\begin{pmatrix} a & 0 & 0 \\ 0 & b & 0 \\ 0 & 0 & c \end{pmatrix}^{k+1} = \begin{pmatrix} a & 0 & 0 \\ 0 & b & 0 \\ 0 & 0 & c \end{pmatrix}^{k}\begin{pmatrix} a & 0 & 0 \\ 0 & b & 0 \\ 0 & 0 & c \end{pmatrix}$$

$$= \begin{pmatrix} a^k & 0 & 0 \\ 0 & b^k & 0 \\ 0 & 0 & c^k \end{pmatrix}\begin{pmatrix} a & 0 & 0 \\ 0 & b & 0 \\ 0 & 0 & c \end{pmatrix}$$

$$= \begin{pmatrix} a^{k+1} & 0 & 0 \\ 0 & b^{k+1} & 0 \\ 0 & 0 & c^{k+1} \end{pmatrix}$$ so true for $n=k+1$

True for $n=1$ and assuming true for $n=k$ implies true for $n=k+1$, therefore, true for all positive integers n

8 a $\lambda=3, \pm2$

Corresponding normalised eigenvectors are

$$\begin{pmatrix} 0 \\ 1 \\ 0 \end{pmatrix}, \begin{pmatrix} \dfrac{\sqrt{3}}{2} \\ 0 \\ \dfrac{1}{2} \end{pmatrix}, \begin{pmatrix} \dfrac{1}{2} \\ 0 \\ -\dfrac{\sqrt{3}}{2} \end{pmatrix}$$

b
$$\begin{pmatrix} 64 & 0 & 0 \\ 0 & 729 & 0 \\ 0 & 0 & 64 \end{pmatrix}$$

9 Eigenvalues are 2 and −1, eigenvectors are $\begin{pmatrix} 1 \\ -1 \end{pmatrix}$ and $\begin{pmatrix} 4 \\ -1 \end{pmatrix}$

so $\mathbf{A} = \begin{pmatrix} 1 & 4 \\ -1 & -1 \end{pmatrix}\begin{pmatrix} 2 & 0 \\ 0 & -1 \end{pmatrix}\begin{pmatrix} -\dfrac{1}{3} & -\dfrac{4}{3} \\ \dfrac{1}{3} & \dfrac{1}{3} \end{pmatrix}$

therefore $\mathbf{A}^n = \begin{pmatrix} 1 & 4 \\ -1 & -1 \end{pmatrix}\begin{pmatrix} 2 & 0 \\ 0 & -1 \end{pmatrix}^n\begin{pmatrix} -\dfrac{1}{3} & -\dfrac{4}{3} \\ \dfrac{1}{3} & \dfrac{1}{3} \end{pmatrix}$

$$= \frac{1}{3}\begin{pmatrix} 1 & 4 \\ -1 & -1 \end{pmatrix}\begin{pmatrix} 2^n & 0 \\ 0 & (-1)^n \end{pmatrix}\begin{pmatrix} -1 & -4 \\ 1 & 1 \end{pmatrix}$$

$$= \frac{1}{3}\begin{pmatrix} 2^n & 4(-1)^n \\ -2^n & -1(-1)^n \end{pmatrix}\begin{pmatrix} -1 & -4 \\ 1 & 1 \end{pmatrix}$$

$$= \frac{1}{3}\begin{pmatrix} -2^n+4(-1)^n & -4(2^n)+4(-1)^n \\ 2^n-(-1)^n & 4(2^n)-(-1)^n \end{pmatrix}$$

a When n is even, $(-1)^n=1$ so

$$\mathbf{A}^n = \frac{1}{3}\begin{pmatrix} -2^n+4 & -4(2^n)+4 \\ 2^n-1 & 4(2^n)-1 \end{pmatrix} = \frac{1}{3}\begin{pmatrix} 4-2^n & 4-4(2^n) \\ 2^n-1 & 4(2^n)-1 \end{pmatrix}$$

b When n is odd, $(-1)^n=-1$

so $\mathbf{A}^n = \frac{1}{3}\begin{pmatrix} -2^n-4 & -4(2^n)-4 \\ 2^n+1 & 4(2^n)+1 \end{pmatrix}$

$$= \frac{1}{3}\begin{pmatrix} -2^n-4 & -4-2^{n+2} \\ 2^n+1 & 2^{n+2}+1 \end{pmatrix}$$

Review exercise 8

1 a $\lambda=2,-7$, corresponding eigenvectors are $\begin{pmatrix} 1 \\ 1 \end{pmatrix}\begin{pmatrix} 5 \\ -4 \end{pmatrix}$

b $\lambda=-9,-27$, corresponding eigenvectors are $\begin{pmatrix} 2 \\ 1 \end{pmatrix}\begin{pmatrix} -1 \\ 1 \end{pmatrix}$

2 a $\lambda=2,1,-1$, corresponding eigenvectors are

$$\begin{pmatrix} 1 \\ 8 \\ -5 \end{pmatrix}\begin{pmatrix} 0 \\ 1 \\ -1 \end{pmatrix}\begin{pmatrix} 0 \\ 1 \\ -2 \end{pmatrix}$$

b $\lambda=1,9,10$, corresponding eigenvectors are

$$\begin{pmatrix} -3 \\ 0 \\ 1 \end{pmatrix}\begin{pmatrix} 13 \\ -8 \\ 9 \end{pmatrix}\begin{pmatrix} 3 \\ 0 \\ 2 \end{pmatrix}$$

3 a $\det\begin{pmatrix} -1-\lambda & 0 & 2 \\ -1 & 2-\lambda & 0 \\ -4 & 0 & 3-\lambda \end{pmatrix} = (2-\lambda)[(-1-\lambda)(3-\lambda)--8]$

$(2-\lambda)(\lambda^2-2\lambda+5)=0 \Rightarrow \lambda=2$ or $\lambda^2-2\lambda+5=0$

Discriminant is $(-2)^2-4(5)=-16<0$ so no real solutions

b $\begin{pmatrix} 0 \\ 1 \\ 0 \end{pmatrix}$

4 a $\begin{pmatrix} 44 & -14 \\ -28 & 9 \end{pmatrix}$

b $\begin{pmatrix} -320 & 120 \\ 204 & -65 \end{pmatrix}$

c $\begin{pmatrix} 1 & 1 \\ 2 & \\ 2 & 3 \end{pmatrix}$

5 a $\begin{pmatrix} 5 & 3 & 1 \\ 11 & 8 & 0 \\ 1 & -1 & 4 \end{pmatrix}$

b $\det \begin{pmatrix} 1-\lambda & 1 & 0 \\ 4 & 2-\lambda & 1 \\ -1 & 0 & -2-\lambda \end{pmatrix} = 0$

$\Rightarrow (1-\lambda)(2-\lambda)(-2-\lambda) - (4(-2-\lambda) - -1) = 0$

$\Rightarrow -\lambda^3 + \lambda^2 + 8\lambda + 3 = 0$

c i $\begin{pmatrix} 16 & 11 & 1 \\ 43 & 27 & 8 \\ -7 & -1 & -9 \end{pmatrix}$

ii $\dfrac{1}{3}\begin{pmatrix} -4 & 2 & 1 \\ 7 & -2 & -1 \\ 2 & -1 & -2 \end{pmatrix}$

6 $\mathbf{P} = \begin{pmatrix} 0 & 4 & -1 \\ 0 & -10 & 0 \\ 1 & 1 & 1 \end{pmatrix},\ \mathbf{D} = \begin{pmatrix} 0 & 0 & 0 \\ 0 & 2 & 0 \\ 0 & 0 & -3 \end{pmatrix}$

7 $\mathbf{P} = \begin{pmatrix} 1 & 0 & 0 \\ 0 & -\dfrac{1}{\sqrt{2}} & \dfrac{1}{\sqrt{2}} \\ 0 & \dfrac{1}{\sqrt{2}} & \dfrac{1}{\sqrt{2}} \end{pmatrix},\ \mathbf{D} = \begin{pmatrix} -5 & 0 & 0 \\ 0 & 2 & 0 \\ 0 & 0 & 0 \end{pmatrix}$

8 Eigenvalues are $\lambda = 1, 0, 3$

Eigenvectors are $\begin{pmatrix} 0 \\ 0 \\ 1 \end{pmatrix}, \begin{pmatrix} 1 \\ -1 \\ 2 \end{pmatrix}, \begin{pmatrix} 2 \\ 1 \\ 1 \end{pmatrix}$

$\mathbf{M}^n = \dfrac{1}{3}\begin{pmatrix} 0 & 1 & 2 \\ 0 & -1 & 1 \\ 1 & 2 & 1 \end{pmatrix}\begin{pmatrix} 1 & 0 & 0 \\ 0 & 0 & 0 \\ 0 & 0 & 3 \end{pmatrix}^n\begin{pmatrix} -3 & 3 & 3 \\ 1 & -2 & 0 \\ 1 & 1 & 0 \end{pmatrix}$

$= \dfrac{1}{3}\begin{pmatrix} 0 & 1 & 2 \\ 0 & -1 & 1 \\ 1 & 2 & 1 \end{pmatrix}\begin{pmatrix} 1 & 0 & 0 \\ 0 & 0 & 0 \\ 0 & 0 & 3^n \end{pmatrix}\begin{pmatrix} -3 & 3 & 3 \\ 1 & -2 & 0 \\ 1 & 1 & 0 \end{pmatrix}$

$= \dfrac{1}{3}\begin{pmatrix} 0 & 0 & 2(3^n) \\ 0 & 0 & 3^n \\ 1 & 0 & 3^n \end{pmatrix}\begin{pmatrix} -3 & 3 & 3 \\ 1 & -2 & 0 \\ 1 & 1 & 0 \end{pmatrix}$

$= \dfrac{1}{3}\begin{pmatrix} 2(3^n) & 2(3^n) & 0 \\ 3^n & 3^n & 0 \\ 3^n-3 & 3^n+3 & 3 \end{pmatrix}$

$= \begin{pmatrix} 2(3^{n-1}) & 2(3^{n-1}) & 0 \\ 3^{n-1} & 3^{n-1} & 0 \\ 3^{n-1}-1 & 3^{n-1}+1 & 1 \end{pmatrix}$ as required

Assessment 8

1 a Eigenvalues are -2 and 8. Corresponding eigenvectors are

$\begin{pmatrix} 3 \\ 4 \end{pmatrix}, \begin{pmatrix} 1 \\ -2 \end{pmatrix}$

b Invariant lines are $y = \dfrac{4}{3}x$ and $y = -2x$

2 a Eigenvalues are $5 \pm i$. Corresponding eigenvectors are

$\begin{pmatrix} 1 \\ \dfrac{i-1}{2} \end{pmatrix}, \begin{pmatrix} 1 \\ \dfrac{-i-1}{2} \end{pmatrix}$

b Characteristic equation is $\lambda^2 - 10\lambda + 26 = 0$

$\mathbf{A}^2 - 10\mathbf{A} + 26\mathbf{I} = \begin{pmatrix} 6 & 2 \\ -1 & 4 \end{pmatrix}^2 - 10\begin{pmatrix} 6 & 2 \\ -1 & 4 \end{pmatrix} + 26\begin{pmatrix} 1 & 0 \\ 0 & 1 \end{pmatrix}$

$= \begin{pmatrix} 34 & 20 \\ -10 & 14 \end{pmatrix} - \begin{pmatrix} 60 & 20 \\ -10 & 40 \end{pmatrix} + \begin{pmatrix} 26 & 0 \\ 0 & 26 \end{pmatrix}$

$= \begin{pmatrix} 0 & 0 \\ 0 & 0 \end{pmatrix}$ as required

So $\mathbf{A}$ satisfies its own characteristic equation

3 a $\mathbf{P} = \begin{pmatrix} 3 & -1 \\ 1 & 1 \end{pmatrix},\ \mathbf{D} = \begin{pmatrix} -1 & 0 \\ 0 & 3 \end{pmatrix}$

b $\mathbf{M}^3 = \mathbf{P}\mathbf{D}^3\mathbf{P}^{-1}$

$= \begin{pmatrix} 3 & -1 \\ 1 & 1 \end{pmatrix}\begin{pmatrix} -1 & 0 \\ 0 & 3 \end{pmatrix}^3\dfrac{1}{4}\begin{pmatrix} 1 & 1 \\ -1 & 3 \end{pmatrix}$

$= \dfrac{1}{4}\begin{pmatrix} 3 & -1 \\ 1 & 1 \end{pmatrix}\begin{pmatrix} -1 & 0 \\ 0 & 27 \end{pmatrix}\begin{pmatrix} 1 & 1 \\ -1 & 3 \end{pmatrix}$

$= \dfrac{1}{4}\begin{pmatrix} 24 & -84 \\ -28 & 80 \end{pmatrix}$

$= \begin{pmatrix} 6 & -21 \\ -7 & 20 \end{pmatrix}$

4 $\mathbf{D} = \mathbf{P}^{-1}\mathbf{M}\mathbf{P} \Rightarrow \mathbf{P}\mathbf{D} = \mathbf{P}\mathbf{P}^{-1}\mathbf{M}\mathbf{P}$

$\Rightarrow \mathbf{P}\mathbf{D} = \mathbf{M}\mathbf{P}$

$\Rightarrow \mathbf{P}\mathbf{D}\mathbf{P}^{-1} = \mathbf{M}\mathbf{P}\mathbf{P}^{-1}$

$\Rightarrow \mathbf{P}\mathbf{D}\mathbf{P}^{-1} = \mathbf{M}$

$\Rightarrow \mathbf{M}^4 = (\mathbf{P}\mathbf{D}\mathbf{P}^{-1})^4$

$= \mathbf{P}\mathbf{D}\mathbf{P}^{-1}\mathbf{P}\mathbf{D}\mathbf{P}^{-1}\mathbf{P}\mathbf{D}\mathbf{P}^{-1}\mathbf{P}\mathbf{D}\mathbf{P}^{-1}$

$= \mathbf{P}\mathbf{D}\mathbf{I}\mathbf{D}\mathbf{I}\mathbf{D}\mathbf{I}\mathbf{D}\mathbf{P}^{-1}$

$= \mathbf{P}\mathbf{D}\mathbf{D}\mathbf{D}\mathbf{D}\mathbf{P}^{-1}$

$= \mathbf{P}\mathbf{D}^4\mathbf{P}^{-1}$ as required

5 a $\det\begin{pmatrix} 2-\lambda & 1 \\ -1 & 1-\lambda \end{pmatrix} = 0$

$\Rightarrow (2-\lambda)(1-\lambda) - -1 = 0$

$\Rightarrow \lambda^2 - 3\lambda + 3 = 0$

$\Rightarrow \left(\lambda - \dfrac{3}{2}\right)^2 - \dfrac{9}{4} = -3$

$\Rightarrow \left(\lambda - \dfrac{3}{2}\right)^2 = -\dfrac{3}{4}$

$\Rightarrow \lambda - \dfrac{3}{2} = \pm\dfrac{\sqrt{3}}{2}i$

Therefore eigenvalues of $\mathbf{M}$ are complex

b $\begin{pmatrix} 1 \\ -\dfrac{1}{2} + \dfrac{\sqrt{3}}{2}i \end{pmatrix}, \begin{pmatrix} 1 \\ -\dfrac{1}{2} - \dfrac{\sqrt{3}}{2}i \end{pmatrix}$

c Characteristic equation is $\lambda^2 - 3\lambda + 3 = 0$

So C–H theorem states that $M^2 - 3M + 3I = 0$

Verify:

$$M^2 - 3M + 3I = \begin{pmatrix} 2 & 1 \\ -1 & 1 \end{pmatrix}^2 - 3\begin{pmatrix} 2 & 1 \\ -1 & 1 \end{pmatrix} + 3\begin{pmatrix} 1 & 0 \\ 0 & 1 \end{pmatrix}$$

$$= \begin{pmatrix} 3 & 3 \\ -3 & 0 \end{pmatrix} - \begin{pmatrix} 6 & 3 \\ -3 & 3 \end{pmatrix} + \begin{pmatrix} 3 & 0 \\ 0 & 3 \end{pmatrix}$$

$$= \begin{pmatrix} 0 & 0 \\ 0 & 0 \end{pmatrix}$$

Therefore **M** satisfies the C–H theorem since it satisfies its own characteristic equation.

6 When $n = 1$, $A^n = \begin{pmatrix} 2 & 0 & 1 \\ 0 & 1 & 0 \\ 1 & 0 & 2 \end{pmatrix}^1 = \begin{pmatrix} 2 & 0 & 1 \\ 0 & 1 & 0 \\ 1 & 0 & 2 \end{pmatrix}$

And $\dfrac{1}{2}\begin{pmatrix} 3^1+1 & 0 & 3^1-1 \\ 0 & 2 & 0 \\ 3^1-1 & 0 & 3^1+1 \end{pmatrix} = \begin{pmatrix} 2 & 0 & 1 \\ 0 & 1 & 0 \\ 1 & 0 & 2 \end{pmatrix}$

So true for $n = 1$

Assume true for $n = k$ and let $n = k + 1$:

$$A^{k+1} = \begin{pmatrix} 2 & 0 & 1 \\ 0 & 1 & 0 \\ 1 & 0 & 2 \end{pmatrix}^{k+1} = \begin{pmatrix} 2 & 0 & 1 \\ 0 & 1 & 0 \\ 1 & 0 & 2 \end{pmatrix}^{k}\begin{pmatrix} 2 & 0 & 1 \\ 0 & 1 & 0 \\ 1 & 0 & 2 \end{pmatrix}$$

$$= \frac{1}{2}\begin{pmatrix} 3^k+1 & 0 & 3^k-1 \\ 0 & 2 & 0 \\ 3^k-1 & 0 & 3^k+1 \end{pmatrix}\begin{pmatrix} 2 & 0 & 1 \\ 0 & 1 & 0 \\ 1 & 0 & 2 \end{pmatrix}$$

$$= \frac{1}{2}\begin{pmatrix} 2(3^k+1)+3^k-1 & 0 & 3^k+1+2(3^k-1) \\ 0 & 2 & 0 \\ 2(3^k-1)+3^k+1 & 0 & 3^k-1+2(3^k+1) \end{pmatrix}$$

$$= \frac{1}{2}\begin{pmatrix} 3(3^k)+1 & 0 & 3(3^k)-1 \\ 0 & 2 & 0 \\ 3(3^k)-1 & 0 & 3(3^k)+1 \end{pmatrix}$$

$$= \frac{1}{2}\begin{pmatrix} 3^{k+1}+1 & 0 & 3^{k+1}-1 \\ 0 & 2 & 0 \\ 3^{k+1}-1 & 0 & 3^{k+1}+1 \end{pmatrix}$$

So true for $n = k$

Since true for $n = 1$ and assuming true for $n = k$ implies true for $n = k + 1$, therefore true for all $n \in \mathbb{N}$

7 a $\det\begin{pmatrix} 1-\lambda & 2 & 0 \\ 0 & -\lambda & 3 \\ 2 & 0 & 1-\lambda \end{pmatrix} = 0$

$\Rightarrow (1-\lambda)(-\lambda)(1-\lambda) - 2(0-6) + 0 = 0$

$\Rightarrow -\lambda^3 + 2\lambda^2 - \lambda + 12 = 0$

$\Rightarrow (\lambda-3)(-\lambda^2-\lambda-4) = 0$

$\Rightarrow \lambda = 3$ or $-\lambda^2-\lambda-4 = 0$

$b^2 - 4ac = (-1)^2 - 4(-1)(-4) = -15$

So no further real solutions
Hence 3 is the only real eigenvalue

b $\begin{pmatrix} \dfrac{1}{\sqrt{3}} \\[6pt] \dfrac{1}{\sqrt{3}} \\[6pt] \dfrac{1}{\sqrt{3}} \end{pmatrix}$

8 a C–H theorem states that a matrix satisfies its own characteristic equation, therefore $M^2 + 5M + 6I = 0$

Rearrange to give $M^2 = -5M - 6I$

Multiply both sides by **M** to give $M^3 = -5M^2 - 6IM$

$M^3 = -5(-5M - 6I) - 6M$

$= 25M + 30I - 6M$

$= 19M + 30I$

b $M^4 = -65M - 114I$

9 a $P = \begin{pmatrix} 1 & 3 & 0 \\ -2 & 2 & 1 \\ 1 & -3 & 0 \end{pmatrix}$, $D = \begin{pmatrix} 2 & 0 & 0 \\ 0 & -2 & 0 \\ 0 & 0 & 1 \end{pmatrix}$

b $\begin{pmatrix} 16 & 0 & 0 \\ -10 & 1 & -20 \\ 0 & 0 & 16 \end{pmatrix}$

10 $A^{-1} = \begin{pmatrix} \dfrac{4}{4+2a} & \dfrac{a}{4+2a} \\[8pt] \dfrac{2}{4+2a} & -\dfrac{1}{4+2a} \end{pmatrix}$

11 a $(3-\lambda)[(1-\lambda)(-2-\lambda)-0] - -1[2(-2-\lambda)-12] + 0 = 0$

$(3-\lambda)(-2-\lambda+2\lambda+\lambda^2) + 2(-2-\lambda) - 12 = 0$

$-6 - 3\lambda + 6\lambda + 3\lambda^2 + 2\lambda + \lambda^2 - 2\lambda^2 - \lambda^3 - 4 - 2\lambda - 12 = 0$

$-\lambda^3 + 2\lambda^2 + 3\lambda - 22 = 0$

$\lambda^3 - 2\lambda^2 - 3\lambda + 22 = 0$

b $c = -16, d = -44$

12 a $\det M = 1(1-2) + 2(0+1) + 3(0-1)$

$= -2 \neq 0$

Therefore **M** is non-singular

b $a = -\dfrac{1}{2}, b = \dfrac{3}{2}, c = 1$

c **M** must be non-singular in order to multiply through by M^{-1}

13 $A^n = \begin{pmatrix} a & b \\ b & -a \end{pmatrix}\begin{pmatrix} k & 0 \\ 0 & 0 \end{pmatrix}^n\begin{pmatrix} a & b \\ b & -a \end{pmatrix}$

$= \begin{pmatrix} a & b \\ b & -a \end{pmatrix}\begin{pmatrix} k^n & 0 \\ 0 & 0 \end{pmatrix}\begin{pmatrix} a & b \\ b & -a \end{pmatrix}$

$= \begin{pmatrix} a(k^n) & 0 \\ b(k^n) & 0 \end{pmatrix}\begin{pmatrix} a & b \\ b & -a \end{pmatrix}$

$= \begin{pmatrix} a^2(k^n) & ab(k^n) \\ ab(k^n) & b^2(k^n) \end{pmatrix}$

$= k^n\begin{pmatrix} a^2 & ab \\ ab & b^2 \end{pmatrix}$

14 a Normalised eigenvectors are $\widehat{v_1} = \begin{pmatrix} 1 \\ 0 \\ 0 \end{pmatrix}$, $\widehat{v_2} = \begin{pmatrix} 0 \\ -\dfrac{1}{\sqrt{2}} \\ \dfrac{1}{\sqrt{2}} \end{pmatrix}$

and $\widehat{v_3} = \begin{pmatrix} 0 \\ \dfrac{1}{\sqrt{2}} \\ \dfrac{1}{\sqrt{2}} \end{pmatrix}$

$\widehat{v_1} \cdot \widehat{v_2} = 0$

$\widehat{v_1} \cdot \widehat{v_3} = 0$

$\widehat{v_2} \cdot \widehat{v_3} = -\dfrac{1}{2} + \dfrac{1}{2} = 0$

Therefore they are all orthogonal

b $\begin{pmatrix} 2 & 0 & 0 \\ 0 & 0 & 1 \\ 0 & 1 & 0 \end{pmatrix}$

Chapter 9

Exercise 9.1A

1 a The units digit of $37\,894$ is 4 and $2|4$ since $4 = 2 \times 2$, therefore $2|37\,894$

b The sum of the digits is $1 + 6 + 8 + 1 + 5 = 21$ and $3|21$ since $21 = 7 \times 3$, therefore $3|16\,815$

c The sum of the digits is $9 + 9 + 8 + 7 + 8 + 4 = 45$ and $3|45$ since $45 = 15 \times 3$, therefore $3|998\,784$

d The units digit of $673\,225$ is 5 and $5|5$ since $n\,|\,n$ for all n, therefore $5|673\,225$

e The units digit of $18\,950$ is 0 and $5|0$ since $n\,|\,0$ for all n, therefore $5|18\,950$

f The units digit of $786\,010$ is 0, therefore $10|786\,010$

2 a The tens and units digits of $238\,764$ form the number 64, $4|64$ since $64 = 16 \times 4$, therefore $4|238\,764$

b The tens and units digits of $17\,508$ form the number 08, $4|8$ since $8 = 2 \times 4$, therefore $4|17\,508$

c $2|543\,522$ since the units digit is 2 and $2|2$
$3|543\,522$ since the sum of the digits is $5 + 4 + 3 + 5 + 2 + 2 = 21$ and $3|21$
Therefore since 2 and 3 divide $543\,522$, 6 must divide $543\,522$

d $2|4\,926\,036$ since the units digit is 6 and $2|6$
$3|4\,926\,036$ since the sum of the digits is $4 + 9 + 2 + 6 + 0 + 3 + 6 = 30$ and $3|30$
Therefore since 2 and 3 divide $4\,926\,036$, 6 must divide $4\,926\,036$

e The sum of the digits of $786\,015$ is $7 + 8 + 6 + 0 + 1 + 5 = 27$ and $9|27$ so $9|786\,015$

f The sum of the digits of $1\,397\,367$ is $1 + 3 + 9 + 7 + 3 + 6 + 7 = 36$ and $9|36$ so $9|1\,397\,367$

g The alternating sum of the digits of $519\,372\,711$ is $5 - 1 + 9 - 3 + 7 - 2 + 7 - 1 + 1 = 22$ and $11|22$ so $11|519\,372\,711$

h The alternating sum of the digits of $693\,088$ is $6 - 9 + 3 - 0 + 8 - 8 = 0$ and $11|0$ so $11|693\,088$

3 a $\gcd(85, 221) = 17$

b $\gcd(144, 120) = 24$

c $\gcd(243, 216) = 18$

d $\gcd(1092, 378) = 42$

4 a $\gcd(2673, 2727) = 27$

b $\gcd(2077, 1829) = 31$

c $\gcd(4199, 456) = 19$

d $\gcd(1260, 5460) = 60$

Exercise 9.1B

1 a $912 = 2 \times 336 + 240$
$336 = 1 \times 240 + 96$
$240 = 2 \times 96 + 48$
$96 = 2 \times 48 + 0$
Therefore $\gcd(912, 336) = 48$

b $48 = 3 \times 912 - 8 \times 336$
so $a = 3$, $b = -8$

2 a $864 = 2 \times 405 + 54$
$405 = 7 \times 54 + 27$
$54 = 2 \times 27 + 0$
Therefore $\gcd(864, 405) = 27$

b $27 = 15 \times 405 - 7 \times 864$
so $a = 15$, $b = -7$

3 a $x = -6, y = 5$

b $x = 3, y = -2$

c $x = 6, y = -7$

d $x = 4, y = -3$

e $x = -13, y = 14$

4 a $\gcd(92, 69) = 23$ so solutions exist

b $\gcd(65, 39) = 13$ and $13|26$ so solutions exist

c $\gcd(238, 88) = 2$ and $2 \nmid 11$ so solutions do not exist

d $\gcd(152, 95) = 19$ and $19|114$ so solutions exist

5 a $\gcd(234, 91) = 13$ and $13|52$ so solutions exist

b $a = 8, b = -20$

6 a $\gcd(648, 1593) = 27$ and $27|216$ so solutions exist

b $a = -216, b = 88$

7 If $c = \text{hcf}(a, b)$ then $ax + by = c$ for some integers x and y (Bezout)

Therefore $\dfrac{a}{c}x + \dfrac{b}{c}y = \dfrac{c}{c} \Rightarrow \dfrac{a}{c}x + \dfrac{b}{c}y = 1$ for some integers x and y

which implies that $\text{hcf}\left(\dfrac{a}{c}, \dfrac{b}{c}\right)\Big|1$

Therefore $\text{hcf}\left(\dfrac{a}{c}, \dfrac{b}{c}\right) = 1$ since the only factor of 1 is itself

So $\dfrac{a}{c}$ and $\dfrac{b}{c}$ are coprime

8 $a\,|\,bc \Rightarrow bc = ka$ for some integer k

$\text{hcf}(a, b) = 1 \Rightarrow ax + by = 1$ for some integers x and y

$ax + by = 1 \Rightarrow (ac)x + (bc)y = c$
$\Rightarrow (ac)x + (ka)y = c$ since $bc = ka$
$\Rightarrow a(cx + ky) = c$

Hence $a\,|\,c$

Exercise 9.2A

1 a 1   **b** 5   **c** 3
d 0   **e** 1   **f** 3
g 0   **h** 9

2 a 1   **b** 1   **c** 2
d 3   **e** 4   **f** 5
g 8   **h** 4

3 a $1 \,(\text{mod } 10)$ **b** $1 \,(\text{mod } 5)$
c $2 \,(\text{mod } 5)$ **d** $0 \,(\text{mod } 3)$
e $1 \,(\text{mod } 3)$ **f** $5 \,(\text{mod } 6)$

4 a $1 \pmod 4$ **b** $0 \pmod 2$

c $1 \pmod 4$ **d** $2 \pmod 3$

e $10 \pmod{11}$ **f** $64 \pmod 5$

5 a The final digit is 4

b The final digit is 5

c The final digit is 6

d The final digit is 1

e The final digit is 1

f The final digit is 4

Exercise 9.2B

1 For any natural number N,

$N = 10^n a_n + 10^{n-1} a_{n-1} + \ldots + 10^2 a_2 + 10 a_1 + a_0$

$N \equiv (10^n a_n + 10^{n-1} a_{n-1} + \ldots + 10^2 a_2 + 10 a_1) \pmod{10}$

$\qquad + a_0 \pmod{10}$

$\qquad \equiv 0 + a_0 \pmod{10}$ since

$10^n a_n + 10^{n-1} a_{n-1} + \ldots + 10^2 a_2 + 10 a_1$ is divisible by 10

$\qquad \equiv a_0 \pmod{10}$

Therefore $N \equiv 0 \pmod{10}$ if the units digit, a_0, equals 0

2 For any natural number N,

$N = 10^n a_n + 10^{n-1} a_{n-1} + \ldots + 10^2 a_2 + 10 a_1 + a_0$

$N \equiv (10^n a_n + 10^{n-1} a_{n-1} + \ldots + 10^2 a_2 + 10 a_1) \pmod 2$

$\qquad + a_0 \pmod 2$

$\qquad \equiv 0 + a_0 \pmod 2$ since $10^n a_n + 10^{n-1} a_{n-1} + \ldots + 10^2 a_2 + 10 a_1$

is divisible by 10 hence is divisible by 2

$\qquad \equiv a_0 \pmod 2$

Therefore $N \equiv 0 \pmod 2$ if the units digit, a_0, equals 0, 2, 4, 6, 8

3 For any natural number N,

$N = 10^n a_n + 10^{n-1} a_{n-1} + \ldots + 10^2 a_2 + 10 a_1 + a_0$

$10 a_1 \equiv 1 \times a_1 \pmod 3$

$\qquad \equiv a_1 \pmod 3$

$10 \equiv 1 \pmod 3 \Rightarrow 10^n \equiv 1 \pmod 3$ for all natural numbers n

Therefore,

$10^2 a_2 \equiv a_2 \pmod 3, 10^3 a_3 \equiv a_3 \pmod 3, \ldots, 10^n a_n \equiv a_n \pmod 3$,

$N \equiv 10^n a_n \pmod 3 + \ldots + 10^2 a_2 \pmod 3 + 10 a_1 \pmod 3$

$\qquad + a_0 \pmod 3$

$\qquad \equiv a_n + a_{n-1} + \ldots + a_1 + a_0 \pmod 3$

$N \equiv 0 \pmod 3$ if $a_n + a_{n-1} + \ldots + a_1 + a_0$ is divisible by 3

In other words, when the sum of the digits is divisible by 3

4 The final two digits are 81

5 a Need the value of $2^k \pmod{10}$

$2^k \equiv 2^{4v} \pmod{10}$ where $4v = k$ for some integer v since k divisible by 4

$\qquad \equiv (2^4)^v \pmod{10}$

$\qquad \equiv 16^v \pmod{10}$

$\qquad \equiv 6 \pmod{10}$ since 6 to any power has final digit 6

b The last digit is 2

6 For any natural number N,

$N = 10^n a_n + 10^{n-1} a_{n-1} + \ldots + 10^2 a_2 + 10 a_1 + a_0$

$10 \equiv -1 \pmod{11} \Rightarrow 10^n \equiv (-1)^n \pmod{11}$ for all natural numbers n

If n is even then:

$N \equiv 10^n a_n \pmod{11} + 10^{n-1} a_{n-1} \pmod{11} + \ldots$

$\qquad - 10 a_1 \pmod{11} + a_0 \pmod{11}$

$\qquad \equiv a_n \pmod{11} - a_{n-1} \pmod{11} + \ldots - a_1 \pmod{11} + a_0 \pmod{11}$

$\qquad \equiv a_n - a_{n-1} + \ldots + a_2 - a_1 + a_0 \pmod{11}$

If n is odd then:

$N \equiv 10^n a_n \pmod{11} + 10^{n-1} a_{n-1} \pmod{11} + \ldots$

$\qquad - 10 a_1 \pmod{11} + a_0 \pmod{11}$

$\qquad \equiv -a_n \pmod{11} + a_{n-1} \pmod{11} - \ldots - a_1 \pmod{11}$

$\qquad + a_0 \pmod{11}$

$\qquad \equiv -(a_n - a_{n-1} + \ldots - a_2 + a_1 - a_0) \pmod{11}$

So in both cases N is divisible by 11 if the alternating sum of the digits is divisible by 11

7 $a - a = 0$ and $n \mid 0$ for any integer n

Therefore $n \mid a - a$

So, by the definition of congruence modulo n, $a \equiv a \pmod n$ which is the reflective property of modulo arithmetic.

8 $a \equiv b \pmod n \Rightarrow n \mid (a - b)$

$b \equiv c \pmod n \Rightarrow n \mid (b - c)$

Therefore, $n \mid ((a - b) + (b - c))$

$((a - b) + (b - c)) = a - c$

So, $n \mid (a - c)$

$\Rightarrow a \equiv c \pmod n$ by definition of modulo arithmetic

9 $a \equiv b \pmod n \Rightarrow n \mid (a - b)$

$c \equiv d \pmod n \Rightarrow n \mid (c - d)$

Therefore, $n \mid ((a - b) - (c - d))$

$\Rightarrow n \mid (a - c) - (b - d)$

$\Rightarrow a - c \equiv b - d \pmod n$

10 a The remainder is 8

b The remainder is 3

c The remainder is 1

d The remainder is 3

11 a The least residue is 3

b The least residue is 1

c The least residue is 361

d The least residue is 47

12 Let $a = 25$, $p = 23$ then a and p are coprime so $a^{p-1} \equiv 1 \pmod p$ gives $25^{22} \equiv 1 \pmod{23}$ so the remainder is 1

13 a 17 is a prime number, therefore Fermat's little theorem tells you that $59^{17} \equiv 59 \pmod{17}$

$\qquad \equiv 8 \pmod{17}$

So, the remainder from $59^{17} \div 17$ is 8

b 19 is a prime number, therefore Fermat's little theorem tells you that $63^{19} \equiv 63 \pmod{19}$

$\qquad \equiv 6 \pmod{19}$

So, the remainder from $63^{19} \div 19$ is 6

c 37 is a prime number, therefore Fermat's little theorem tells you that $18\,529^{37} \equiv 18\,529 \pmod{37}$

$\qquad \equiv 018 \pmod{37}$

So, the remainder from $18\,529^{37} \div 37$ is 018

d 163 is a prime number, therefore Fermat's little theorem tells you that $2445^{163} \equiv 2445 \pmod{163}$

$\qquad \equiv 0 \pmod{163}$

So, the remainder from $2445^{163} \div 163$ is 0

14 a 2

b 0

15 Let $a = 1$, $a^1 = 1$ and we know that $a \equiv a \pmod{p}$ so true for $a = 1$

Assume true for $a = k$ and let $a = k + 1$

$$(k+1)^p = k^p + \binom{p}{1}k^{p-1} + \binom{p}{2}k^{p-2} + \ldots + \binom{p}{p-1}k + 1$$

$\binom{p}{r} = \dfrac{p!}{r!(p-r)!}$, therefore, $p \mid \binom{p}{r}$ for all integers r such that $1 \le r \le p - 1$

This implies that $(k+1)^p \equiv k^p + 1 \pmod{p}$

But, we have assumed that $k^p \equiv k \pmod{p}$ therefore, $(k+1)^p \equiv k+1 \pmod{p}$

True for $a = 1$ and assuming true for $a = k$ implies true for $a = k + 1$, therefore, must be true for all positive integers a

Exercise 9.3A

1 a $x = 2$ **b** $x = 3$

  c $x = 2$ **d** $x = 1$

  e $x = 5$ **f** $x = 7$

2 a 8   **b** 14

  c 3   **d** 13

  e 51   **f** 29

3 a $x \equiv 15 \pmod{37}$

  b $x \equiv 105 \pmod{157}$

  c $x \equiv 7 \pmod{24}$

  d $x \equiv 190 \pmod{263}$

  e $x \equiv 24 \pmod{139}$

  f $x \equiv 381 \pmod{397}$

4 a $x \equiv 14 \pmod{27}$

  b $x \equiv 17 \pmod{82}$

  c $x \equiv 19 \pmod{85}$

  d $x \equiv 68 \pmod{126}$

  e $x \equiv 57 \pmod{225}$

  f $x \equiv 67 \pmod{379}$

5 a $\gcd(5, 25) = 5$ but $5 \nmid 1$

  b $\gcd(14, 133) = 7$ but $7 \nmid 1$

  c $\gcd(9, 27) = 9$ but $9 \nmid 2$

  d $\gcd(8, 128) = 8$ but $8 \nmid 3$

  e $\gcd(21, 168) = 21$ but $21 \nmid 3$

  f $\gcd(48, 192) = 16$ but $16 \nmid 8$

Exercise 9.3B

1 a $x \equiv 9 \pmod{126}$, $x \equiv 30 \pmod{126}$,

    $x \equiv 51 \pmod{126}$, $x \equiv 72 \pmod{126}$,

    $x \equiv 93 \pmod{126}$, $x \equiv 114 \pmod{126}$

  b $x \equiv 30 \pmod{165}$, $x \equiv 85 \pmod{165}$, $x \equiv 140 \pmod{165}$

  c $x \equiv 117 \pmod{462}$, $x \equiv 348 \pmod{462}$

  d $x \equiv 7 \pmod{285}$, $x \equiv 26 \pmod{285}$,

    $x \equiv 45 \pmod{285}$, $x \equiv 64 \pmod{285}$

    $x \equiv 83 \pmod{285}$, $x \equiv 102 \pmod{285}$

    $x \equiv 121 \pmod{285}$, $x \equiv 140 \pmod{285}$

$x \equiv 159 \pmod{285}$, $x \equiv 178 \pmod{285}$

$x \equiv 197 \pmod{285}$, $x \equiv 216 \pmod{285}$

$x \equiv 235 \pmod{285}$, $x \equiv 254 \pmod{285}$

$x \equiv 273 \pmod{285}$

2 3 solutions

3 no solutions

4 11 solutions

5 a $x \equiv 3 \pmod{5}$

  b $x \equiv 2 \pmod{4}$

  c $x \equiv 5 \pmod{12}$

  d $x \equiv 8 \pmod{15}$

  e $x \equiv 16 \pmod{68}$, $x \equiv 33 \pmod{68}$,

    $x \equiv 50 \pmod{68}$, $x \equiv 67 \pmod{68}$

  f $x \equiv 16 \pmod{90}$, $x \equiv 34 \pmod{90}$,

    $x \equiv 52 \pmod{90}$, $x \equiv 70 \pmod{90}$, $x \equiv 88 \pmod{90}$

Exercise 9.4A

1 120

2 479 001 600

3 142 506

4 189

5 a 77 520

  b 6048

  c 27 720

  d 13 230

  e 366

6 19 448

7 a 3024

  b 6561

8 a 665 280

  b 2 985 984

9 a i 181 440

   ii 4 782 969

  b 2880

  c i 50 400

   ii 1 476 225

10 a 2 220 075

  b 675 675

  c 6930

  d 4 624 620

Exercise 9.4B

1 792

2 43 758

3 1 set of size 0

  5 sets of size 1

  10 sets of size 2

  10 sets of size 3

  5 sets of size 4

  1 set of size 5

  $1 + 5 + 10 + 10 + 5 + 1 = 32$ as required

4 1 set of size 0

  7 sets of size 1

  21 sets of size 2

  35 sets of size 3

  35 sets of size 4

  21 set of size 5

  7 sets of size 6

  1 set of size 7

  $1 + 7 + 21 + 35 + 35 + 21 + 7 + 1 = 128$ as required

5 131 072

6 16 777 216

7 524 287

8 2 097 151

9 24 576

10 465

11 523 128

12 $2^{n+1} - 2^n$

$= 2^n(2-1)$

$= 2^n$

13 $2^{2n} - 2^n = (2^n)^2 - 2^n$

14 $2^{2n} - 2^n = (2^n)^2 - 2^n = 2^n(2^n - 1)$

15 $n \times n!$

16 $n!(n^2 + 3n + 1)$

17 $^kC_r + {}^kC_{r-1} = \dfrac{k!}{r!(k-r)!} + \dfrac{k!}{(r-1)!(k-(r-1))!}$

$= \dfrac{k!}{r!(k-r)!} + \dfrac{k!}{(r-1)!(k-r+1)!}$

$= \dfrac{k!(r-1)!(k-r)!(k-r+1) + k!r(r-1)!(k-r)!}{r!(k-r)!(r-1)!(k-r+1)!}$

$= \dfrac{k!(r-1)!(k-r+1)! + k!r!(k-r)!}{r!(k-r)!(r-1)!(k-r+1)!}$

since $(k-r+1)! = (k-r)!(k-r+1)$

and $r! = r(r-1)!$

$= \dfrac{k!(k-r+1) + k!r}{r!(k-r+1)!}$

by cancelling common factors of numerator and denominator

$= \dfrac{k!(k+1)}{r!(k-r+1)!}$

since $(k+1)! = k!(k+1)$

$= {}^{k+1}C_r$

18 n

Review exercise 9

1 hcf is 11

2 $1159 = 2 \times 551 + 57$

$551 = 9 \times 57 + 38$

$57 = 1 \times 38 + 19$

$38 = 2 \times 19$

so hcf(57, 551) = 19

$19 = 57 - 38$

$= 57 - (551 - 9 \times 57)$

$= 10 \times 57 - 551$

$= 10 \times (1159 - 2 \times 551) - 551$

$19 = 10 \times 1159 - 21 \times 551$

3 a The units digit is 0 and 2|0 so 1980 is divisible by 2

  b The sum of the digits is $1 + 9 + 8 + 0 = 18$ and 3|18 so 1980 is divisible by 3

  c The final two digits form the number 80 and 4|80 so 1980 is divisible by 4

  d The units digit is 0 and 5|0 so 1980 is divisible by 5

  e We have shown it is divisible by both 2 and 3, therefore 1980 is divisible by 6

  f The sum of the digits is 18 and 9|18 so 1980 is divisible by 9

  g The final digit is 0 so 1980 is divisible by 10

  h The alternating sum of the digits is $1 - 9 + 8 - 0 = 0$ and 11|0 so 1980 is divisible by 11

4 a 2 (mod 5)

  b 1 (mod 4)

5 a 2 (mod 3)

  b 8 (mod 10)

6 $x = 17$ (mod 72)

7 $x \equiv 4$ (mod 65), $x \equiv 9$ (mod 65), $x \equiv 14$ (mod 65),

$x \equiv 19$ (mod 65), $x \equiv 24$ (mod 65), $x \equiv 29$ (mod 65),

$x \equiv 34$ (mod 65), $x \equiv 39$ (mod 65), $x \equiv 44$ (mod 65),

$x \equiv 49$ (mod 65), $x \equiv 54$ (mod 65), $x \equiv 59$ (mod 65),

$x \equiv 64$ (mod 65)

8 The remainder is 8

9 4 (mod 13)

10 1 081 575

11 a 2520

  b 16 807

12 330 750

13 190

14 a 16 384

  b 2002

  c 15 subsets in total

Assessment 9

1 a Sum of digit is 21 which is divisible by 3 so 2892 is divisible by 3

2892 is even so divisible by 2, hence 2892 is divisible by 6

  b hcf is 12

2 a $6 - 1 + 8 - 2 = 11$

which is divisible by 11 so 6182 is divisible by 11

  b 6182 and 1911 are coprime.

3 $a = -8$ and $b = 9$

4 a $x = 3, y = -8$

  b $x = 185, y = -498$ and $x = 367, y = 988$

5 a 6 (mod 7)

  b 3 (mod 13)

  c 1 (mod 11)

6 Use of Fermat's little therorem with $p = 11$: $2^{10} \equiv 1$ (mod 11)

$2^{45} \equiv (2^{10})^4 (2^5) \equiv (1)^4 (2^5) \equiv 32 \equiv 10$ (mod 11)

$10 + 1 \equiv 11 \equiv 0$ (mod 11)

7 Least positive residue = 10 (mod 13)

8 a $x \equiv 5$ (mod 12)

  b The hcf of 6 and 30 does not divide 1

9 a 100 000

  b 30 240

  c 15 120

  d $\dfrac{5}{9}$

10 a 117 600

  b 25 401 600

11 a 32 767

  b 5005

  c 120

Chapter 10

Exercise 10.1A

1 a

$\times_5$	0	1	2	3	4
0	0	0	0	0	0
1	0	1	2	3	4
2	0	2	4	1	3
3	0	3	1	4	2
4	0	4	3	2	1

b Yes

c 1

d 1 and 4 are self-inverse, 2 is the inverse of 3 and vice versa. 0 has no inverse.

e S does not form a group since not every element has an inverse.

2 a

$+_6$	0	1	2	3	4	5
0	0	1	2	3	4	5
1	1	2	3	4	5	0
2	2	3	4	5	0	1
3	3	4	5	0	1	2
4	4	5	0	1	2	3
5	5	0	1	2	3	4

b Yes

c 0

d S forms a group since modular addition is associative, every element has an inverse (e.g. the inverse of 5 is 1), and parts **b** and **c** give us that the operation is closed and has an identity element.

e Yes: $x +_6 y = y +_6 x$ for all x, y. (The Cayley table has a line of symmetry down the leading diagonal.)

3 a

•	0	1	2	3
0	0	1	2	3
1	1	0	1	2
2	2	1	0	1
3	3	2	1	0

b Yes

c 0

d No: Inverse axiom is ok but $(2 \cdot 1) \cdot 3 \neq 2 \cdot (1 \cdot 3)$ so not associative.

4 Closed: $\begin{pmatrix} 1 & p \\ 0 & 1 \end{pmatrix}\begin{pmatrix} 1 & q \\ 0 & 1 \end{pmatrix} = \begin{pmatrix} 1 & p+q \\ 0 & 1 \end{pmatrix}$ which is also a member of the set S

Identity: $\mathbf{I} = \begin{pmatrix} 1 & 0 \\ 0 & 1 \end{pmatrix}$ is a member of the set S, and for any element s of S, $s\mathbf{I} = \mathbf{I}s = s$

Associativity: Matrix multiplication is associative.

Inverse: The inverse of $\begin{pmatrix} 1 & p \\ 0 & 1 \end{pmatrix}$ is $\begin{pmatrix} 1 & -p \\ 0 & 1 \end{pmatrix}$ which is also a member of set S

Commutativity: $\begin{pmatrix} 1 & p \\ 0 & 1 \end{pmatrix}\begin{pmatrix} 1 & q \\ 0 & 1 \end{pmatrix} = \begin{pmatrix} 1 & p+q \\ 0 & 1 \end{pmatrix}$ and

$\begin{pmatrix} 1 & q \\ 0 & 1 \end{pmatrix}\begin{pmatrix} 1 & p \\ 0 & 1 \end{pmatrix} = \begin{pmatrix} 1 & p+q \\ 0 & 1 \end{pmatrix}$ so the set forms an Abelian group under the operation of matrix multiplication.

5 For example, $1, 2 \in \mathbb{N}$ but $1 - 2 = -1 \notin \mathbb{N}$

6 a 6

b 2

7 a Closed: If x and y are integers then $x + y - 2$ is an integer. Identity: $x \cdot e = x \Rightarrow x + e - 2 = x \Rightarrow e = 2$. Conversely, $2 \cdot x = 2 + x - 2 = x$
Associativity: $(x \cdot y) \cdot z = (x + y - 2) + z - 2 = x + y + z - 4$; $x \cdot (y \cdot z) = x + (y + z - 2) - 2 = x + y + z - 4$

Inverse: $x \cdot x^{-1} = e \Rightarrow x + x^{-1} - 2 = 2 \Rightarrow x^{-1} = 4 - x$ which is also an integer.

b $1 \in \mathbb{Z}^+$, but $1 \cdot 1 = 1 + 1 - 2 = 0 \notin \mathbb{Z}^+$. Hence T is not closed under •.

Exercise 10.1B

1 a Define the symmetries:
Given that the centre of the square is the origin,
r_0 = rotation of 0° about the origin (i.e. the square is in its initial orientation)
r_1 = rotation of 90° anticlockwise about the origin
r_2 = rotation of 180° anticlockwise about the origin
r_3 = rotation of 270° anticlockwise about the origin
m_1 = reflection in the x-axis
m_2 = reflection in the line $y = x$
m_3 = reflection in the y-axis
m_4 = reflection in the line $y = -x$
Draw up a Cayley table:

	r_0	r_1	r_2	r_3	m_1	m_2	m_3	m_4
r_0	r_0	r_1	r_2	r_3	m_1	m_2	m_3	m_4
r_1	r_1	r_2	r_3	r_0	m_2	m_3	m_4	m_1
r_2	r_2	r_3	r_0	r_1	m_3	m_4	m_1	m_2
r_3	r_3	r_0	r_1	r_2	m_4	m_1	m_2	m_3
m_1	m_1	m_4	m_3	m_2	r_0	r_3	r_2	r_1
m_2	m_2	m_1	m_4	m_3	r_1	r_0	r_3	r_2
m_3	m_3	m_2	m_1	m_4	r_2	r_1	r_0	r_3
m_4	m_4	m_3	m_2	m_1	r_3	r_2	r_1	r_0

Identity element: r_0
Inverses: The mirror lines are self-inverse, as are r_0 and r_2. r_1 is the inverse of r_3 and vice versa.
Associativity: Since the binary operation is a composition of mappings, the operation is associative.
Closure: Every combination of symmetries is in the original set of symmetries.
The order of the group is 8

b $C_4 = \{r_0, r_1, r_2, r_3\}$
Generators are r_1 and r_3

2 a

	r_0	r_1	r_2	r_3	r_4	r_5
r_0	r_0	r_1	r_2	r_3	r_4	r_5
r_1	r_1	r_2	r_3	r_4	r_5	r_0
r_2	r_2	r_3	r_4	r_5	r_0	r_1
r_3	r_3	r_4	r_5	r_0	r_1	r_2
r_4	r_4	r_5	r_0	r_1	r_2	r_3
r_5	r_5	r_0	r_1	r_2	r_3	r_4

Generators are r_1 and r_5

b Yes

3 a The set of all symmetries of a regular pentagon.

b There is the identity element, r_0, plus four other rotations through multiples of 72° and five lines of symmetry, one through each vertex and the midpoint of its opposite side. Hence the group has at least 10 elements.

Conversely, select one vertex v of the pentagon, and consider an adjacent vertex w. Any symmetry of the pentagon maps v to one of 5 vertices of the pentagon, 5 possibilities.

Following this mapping, w must still be adjacent to v, either immediately clockwise, or immediately anticlockwise, so 2 possibilities.

These 5×2 possibilities uniquely determine the action of the symmetry on all vertices; hence there can be at most 10 elements of the group. Hence the group has 10 elements.

c For each group of symmetries there will be n rotations through multiples of $\dfrac{360°}{n}$ plus n lines of symmetry. For odd n, these will be through each vertex and the midpoint of its opposite side and for even n there will be $\dfrac{n}{2}$ lines through pairs of opposite vertices and $\dfrac{n}{2}$ lines through the midpoints of opposite sides. Hence the group has at least $2n$ elements.

Conversely, select one vertex v of the n-gon, and consider an adjacent vertex w. Any symmetry of the n-gon maps v to one of n vertices of the n-gon, so n possibilities. Following this mapping, w must still be adjacent to v, either immediately clockwise or immediately anticlockwise, so 2 possibilities. These two possibilities uniquely determine the action of the symmetry on all vertices; hence there can be at most $2n$ elements of the group. Hence the group has exactly $2n$ elements.

4 a $\{1, 2, 3, 4, 5, 6\}$

b Yes

5 a

$+_7$	0	1	2	3	4	5	6
0	0	1	2	3	4	5	6
1	1	2	3	4	5	6	0
2	2	3	4	5	6	0	1
3	3	4	5	6	0	1	2
4	4	5	6	0	1	2	3
5	5	6	0	1	2	3	4
6	6	0	1	2	3	4	5

b 7

c She is correct. Any element coprime to 7 is a generator under modular addition so in this case all of the elements except 0 are possible generators of the group.

6 a $\left\{ \begin{pmatrix} 0 & 1 \\ -1 & 0 \end{pmatrix}, \begin{pmatrix} -1 & 0 \\ 0 & -1 \end{pmatrix}, \begin{pmatrix} 0 & -1 \\ 1 & 0 \end{pmatrix}, \begin{pmatrix} 1 & 0 \\ 0 & 1 \end{pmatrix} \right\}$, 4

b The group of rotational symmetries of the unit square.

7 a a

b c or d

8 a A rotation through $0°$ about the centre of the circle.

b Since the binary operation is a composition of mappings, the operation is associative.

c **i** A rotation through $327.9°$

   ii A reflection in a line of symmetry inclined at $\theta°$

d rot since a combination of any two rotations is another rotation.

e Any combination of rotations and reflections leads to either another rotation or reflection and since the set of elements contains every rotation and every reflection, the resulting combination must be contained within the set.

Exercise 10.2A

1 H is non-empty since there exist (infinitely many) elements in H

The identity element of G under the binary operation of addition is 0 and $0 \in \mathbb{Z}$

H is closed since if x and y are integers, then so is their sum $x + y$. Hence if $x, y \in \mathbb{Z}$ then $x + y \in \mathbb{Z}$

The inverse of an element x is x^{-1} which is $-x$ under the binary operation of addition. Since the negation of an integer is also an integer, it follows that if $x \in \mathbb{Z}$ then $x^{-1} \in \mathbb{Z}$

Hence H is a subgroup of G

2 The Cayley table of all symmetries of an equilateral triangle is

	r_0	r_1	r_2	m_1	m_2	m_3
r_0	r_0	r_1	r_2	m_1	m_2	m_3
r_1	r_1	r_2	r_0	m_2	m_3	m_1
r_2	r_2	r_0	r_1	m_3	m_1	m_2
m_1	m_1	m_3	m_2	r_0	r_2	r_1
m_2	m_2	m_1	m_3	r_1	r_0	r_2
m_3	m_3	m_2	m_1	r_2	r_1	r_0

The group of rotations is given by

	r_0	r_1	r_2
r_0	r_0	r_1	r_2
r_1	r_1	r_2	r_0
r_2	r_2	r_0	r_1

This contains the identity element r_0 and is non-empty. r_0 is self-inverse and r_1 and r_2 form an inverse pair. The set of rotations is closed since every combined element is one of the original elements. Therefore, the group of rotations is a subgroup of the group of all symmetries.

3 $\{1\}$ and $\{1, 4\}$

4 $\{0, 2\}$ and $\{0, 1, 2, 3\}$

5 a The Cayley table for C_4:

	c_0	c_1	c_2	c_3
c_0	c_0	c_1	c_2	c_3
c_1	c_1	c_2	c_3	c_0
c_2	c_2	c_3	c_0	c_1
c_3	c_3	c_0	c_1	c_2

$\{c_0, c_1\}$, $\{c_0, c_3\}$, $\{c_0, c_1, c_2\}$, $\{c_0, c_1, c_3\}$ and $\{c_0, c_2, c_3\}$ are not closed, e.g. $c_3 c_2 = c_1$

$\{c_0, c_2\}$ is closed, contains the identity element c_0 and both elements are self-inverse so this is the only non-trivial proper subgroup of C_4

b The Cayley tables for Q4 and Q5 have exactly the same structure indicating that H is equivalent to C_4

6 $\{a\}$, $\{a, b\}$, $\{a, c\}$ and $\{a, d\}$

7 $N = \left\{ \begin{pmatrix} 1 & 0 \\ 0 & 1 \end{pmatrix}, \begin{pmatrix} -1 & 0 \\ 0 & -1 \end{pmatrix} \right\}$ contains the identity matrix and is non-empty.

$$\begin{pmatrix} 1 & 0 \\ 0 & 1 \end{pmatrix}\begin{pmatrix} -1 & 0 \\ 0 & -1 \end{pmatrix} = \begin{pmatrix} -1 & 0 \\ 0 & -1 \end{pmatrix}$$

$$\begin{pmatrix} -1 & 0 \\ 0 & -1 \end{pmatrix}\begin{pmatrix} 1 & 0 \\ 0 & 1 \end{pmatrix} = \begin{pmatrix} -1 & 0 \\ 0 & -1 \end{pmatrix}$$

$$\begin{pmatrix} -1 & 0 \\ 0 & -1 \end{pmatrix}\begin{pmatrix} -1 & 0 \\ 0 & -1 \end{pmatrix} = \begin{pmatrix} 1 & 0 \\ 0 & 1 \end{pmatrix}$$

Hence the set is closed under matrix multiplication. Both matrices are self-inverse hence N is a subgroup of M

Exercise 10.2B

1 By Lagrange's theorem, only groups with order that is a factor of 90 can be subgroups so the only possibilities are: 1, 2, 3, 5, 6, 9, 10, 15, 18, 30, 45, 90

2 **c** C, order 12

Since 12 is not a factor of 30

3 6 does not divide 92, therefore by Lagrange's theorem, 6 cannot be the order of a possible subgroup.

4 There are 11 elements in H and since 11 is prime, the only orders of possible subgroups are 1 and 11. The only subgroup of order 1 is the trivial subgroup, since any subgroup must contain the identity element, and the only subgroup of order 11 is the group itself, since it must contain every element. Hence the only subgroups are the trivial subgroup and the group itself.

5 **a** 8

b Orders of possible subgroups by Lagrange's theorem are 1, 2, 4, 8 (the factors of 8).

c $\{e, q\}$ and $\{e, q, p, u\}$

6 **a** There are three elements in Carmelita's proposed subgroup and since 3 is not a factor or 4, by Lagrange's theorem, Carmelita must be wrong. (Also accept as an answer that $-i \times -i = 1$ and 1 is not an element of Carmelita's proposed subgroup, so it's not closed.)

b $\{1\}$ and $\{1, -1\}$

7 There are nine elements so the order of G is 9. Hence possible subgroups should be of orders 1, 3 or 9.

Order 1: The trivial subgroup $\{0\}$

Order 9: The group itself, G

Order 3: There are no self-inverse elements under $+_9$ so a subgroup of order 3 will consist of the identity, an element and its inverse. There are four such sets: $\{0, 1, 8\}$, $\{0, 2, 7\}$, $\{0, 3, 6\}$ and $\{0, 4, 5\}$. However, all except $\{0, 3, 6\}$ are not closed under the group operation. Hence there is a single subgroup of order 3. Hence there are three subgroups in total.

8 $43\,252\,003\,274\,489\,856\,000 = 2^{27} \times 3^{14} \times 5^3 \times 7^2 \times 11$

$(27 + 1)(14 + 1)(3 + 1)(2 + 1)(1 + 1) = 10\,080$ so

$43\,252\,003\,274\,489\,856\,000$ has $10\,080$ factors and by Lagrange's theorem this gives the number of orders of possible subgroups.

Exercise 10.3A

1 Draw a Cayley table for the group:

	r_0	r_1	r_2	r_3
r_0	r_0	r_1	r_2	r_3
r_1	r_1	r_2	r_3	r_0
r_2	r_2	r_3	r_0	r_1
r_3	r_3	r_0	r_1	r_2

r_0 is the identity element. r_2 is self-inverse. Rearranging the columns and rows gives

	r_0	r_2	r_1	r_3
r_0	r_0	r_2	r_1	r_3
r_2	r_2	r_0	r_3	r_1
r_1	r_1	r_3	r_2	r_0
r_3	r_3	r_1	r_0	r_2

Now it is clear to see that the pattern of entries is the same as for the groups in example 1, for instance via the mapping $r_0 \mapsto 1$, $r_2 \mapsto -1$, $r_1 \mapsto i$, $r_3 \mapsto -i$ hence the groups are isomorphic.

2 **a** Write out the Cayley tables for each group:

$\times_5$	1	2	3	4
1	1	2	3	4
2	2	4	1	3
3	3	1	4	2
4	4	3	2	1

$+_4$	0	1	2	3
0	0	1	2	3
1	1	2	3	0
2	2	3	0	1
3	3	0	1	2

The self-inverse element in $+_4$ is 2 so rearrange the columns and rows:

$+_4$	0	1	3	2
0	0	1	3	2
1	1	2	0	3
3	3	0	2	1
2	2	3	1	0

Now it is clear to see the pattern of entries is the same for both groups, for instance via the mapping between A and B given by $1 \mapsto 0$, $2 \mapsto 1$, $3 \mapsto 3$, $4 \mapsto 2$ hence the groups are isomorphic.

b Yes

3 **a** For group M, let the four matrices be a, b, c and d respectively. Hence the Cayley table for M is

$\times$	a	b	c	d
a	a	b	c	d
b	b	a	d	c
c	c	d	a	b
d	d	c	b	a

For group N, the Cayley table is

	1	3	5	7
1	1	3	5	7
3	3	1	7	5
5	5	7	1	3
7	7	5	3	1

The identity elements are a and 1 respectively and since all elements in both groups are self-inverse, the groups are isomorphic to each other, for instance via the mapping $a \mapsto 1$, $b \mapsto 3$, $c \mapsto 5$, $d \mapsto 7$

b No

4 The Cayley table for the rotations of the equilateral triangle is

	r_0	r_1	r_2
r_0	r_0	r_1	r_2
r_1	r_1	r_2	r_0
r_2	r_2	r_0	r_1

For group R the Cayley table is

$\times_7$	4	2	1
4	2	1	4
2	1	4	2
1	4	2	1

Since the identity elements are r_0 and 1, rearrange the rows/columns in the table for $\times_7$:

$\times_7$	1	4	2
1	1	4	2
4	4	2	1
2	2	1	4

Now it is clear to see the matching patterns of entries in the two tables, for instance via the mapping $r_0 \mapsto 1, r_1 \mapsto 4, r_2 \mapsto 2$, hence the two groups are isomorphic.

Exercise 10.3B

1 All groups of order 2 consist of the identity element and one other self-inverse element of period 2 so they must be isomorphic.

2 All groups of order 3 consist of the identity element and two other elements of period 3 (period 2 is not allowed since 2 does not divide into 3 and the period of any element must divide into the order of its group). The groups are therefore cyclic with elements which map to e, a and a^2.

3 Period 4 elements must occur in pairs, paired with their inverse. Hence one or three elements of period 4 cannot happen. There are thus **two** different isomorphisms of groups of order 4, one with all elements other than the identity of order 2 (the Klein 4-group) and one with two elements of order 4 (the C_4 group).

4 Groups of order p, where p is prime, have an identity element of period 1 and all remaining elements must have period p since p has just two factors, 1 and p. Let G and H be two such groups of order p, and select an element $g \in G$ and $h \in H$, both of order p. Then the mapping $a^i \mapsto b^i$ gives a one-to-one mapping which respects the operations of G and H, hence giving an isomorphism. Hence all groups of order p are isomorphic to the cyclic group C_p.

5 Let G be a non-abelian group, and H an abelian group. Since G is not abelian there are elements a, $b \in G$ such that $ab \neq ba$. Suppose there were an isomorphism between G and H with $a \mapsto x$, $b \mapsto y$. Then $ab \mapsto xy$, $ba \mapsto yx$, and since H is abelian $xy = yx$. This means that ab and ba map to the same element of H despite being different elements of G, so the mapping cannot have been one-to-one. Hence no isomorphism exists.

6 The Cayley table for G:

$+_6$	0	1	2	3	4	5
0	0	1	2	3	4	5
1	1	2	3	4	5	0
2	2	3	4	5	0	1
3	3	4	5	0	1	2
4	4	5	0	1	2	3
5	5	0	1	2	3	4

The Cayley table for H:

	r_0	r_1	r_2	r_3	r_4	r_5
r_0	r_0	r_1	r_2	r_3	r_4	r_5
r_1	r_1	r_2	r_3	r_4	r_5	r_0
r_2	r_2	r_3	r_4	r_5	r_0	r_1
r_3	r_3	r_4	r_5	r_0	r_1	r_2
r_4	r_4	r_5	r_0	r_1	r_2	r_3
r_5	r_5	r_0	r_1	r_2	r_3	r_4

It is evident that the two Cayley tables have the same pattern of entries, for instance via the mapping $i \mapsto r_i$, therefore the two groups are isomorphic.

7 M is a cyclic group since when $k = 1$, the period of the element is 8 (8 successive rotations of $\frac{\pi}{4}$ will map the unit square back to itself). In particular the only self-inverse element of M is the rotation by π, so M only has one self-inverse element. However, in S the elements 4, 11 and 14 are all self-inverse. Hence the groups cannot be isomorphic.

8 0, which is the identity element of G

Consider a mapping between the sets, say a maps to

$\begin{pmatrix} 1-a & a \\ -a & 1+a \end{pmatrix}$ for all $a \in \mathbb{Z}$. This means that p maps to

$\begin{pmatrix} 1-p & p \\ -p & 1+p \end{pmatrix}$ and q maps to $\begin{pmatrix} 1-q & q \\ -q & 1+q \end{pmatrix}$. This mapping is clearly one-to-one.

You must now show that the product of these two matrices

is $\begin{pmatrix} 1-(p+q) & (p+q) \\ -(p+q) & 1+(p+q) \end{pmatrix}$, i.e. $p + q$ maps to this matrix product.

$\begin{pmatrix} 1-p & p \\ -p & 1+p \end{pmatrix}\begin{pmatrix} 1-q & q \\ -q & 1+q \end{pmatrix}$

$= \begin{pmatrix} (1-p)(1-q)-pq & (1-p)q+p(1+q) \\ -p(1-q)-q(1+p) & -pq+(1+p)(1+q) \end{pmatrix}$

$= \begin{pmatrix} 1-p-q & p+q \\ -p-q & 1+p+q \end{pmatrix} = \begin{pmatrix} 1-(p+q) & (p+q) \\ -(p+q) & 1+(p+q) \end{pmatrix}$

as required.

Hence the two groups are isomorphic.

Review exercise 10

1 a 6

   b

$\times_9$	1	2	4	5	7	8
1	1	2	4	5	7	8
2	2	4	8	1	5	7
4	4	8	7	2	1	5
5	5	1	2	7	8	4
7	7	5	1	8	4	7
8	8	7	5	4	7	1

   c 6

   d 5 has period equal to the order of the group; hence G is the group generated by 5 and hence the group is cyclic.

   e Yes: The Cayley table has a line of symmetry down the leading diagonal (or G is a cyclic group and cyclic groups are abelian).

2 a 1

  b Since all of the entries in the Cayley table are elements of S, the set is closed under the operation $\times_{12}$

  c All of the elements are self-inverse since for $a \in S$, $a^2 = 1$

  d For instance:
  $(5 \times 7) \times 11 = 11 \times 11 = 1 \pmod{12}$ and
  $5 \times (7 \times 11) = 5 \times 5 = 1 \pmod{12}$
  $(11 \times 7) \times 5 = 5 \times 5 = 1 \pmod{12}$ and
  $11 \times (7 \times 5) = 11 \times 11 = 1 \pmod{12}$

3 a 1, 2, 3 and 6

  b $\{r_0\}$

  c $\{r_0\}$, $\{r_0, m_1\}$, $\{r_0, m_2\}$, $\{r_0, m_3\}$ and $\{r_0, r_1, r_2\}$

4 a The Cayley tables are

$\times_{10}$	1	3	7	9
1	1	3	7	9
3	3	9	1	7
7	7	1	9	3
9	9	7	3	1

$\times_4$	0	1	2	3
0	0	1	2	3
1	1	2	3	0
2	2	3	0	1
3	3	0	1	2

  The self-inverse element in $+_4$ is 2 so swapping the order of columns and rows gives

$+_4$	0	1	3	2
0	0	1	3	2
1	1	2	0	3
3	3	0	2	1
2	2	3	1	0

  Now the pattern of elements in the two groups are the same, hence $G \cong H$

  A possible mapping is $[1, 3, 7, 9] \leftrightarrow [0, 1, 3, 2]$

  b Yes: 1 and 3 are generators of H and 3 and 7 are generators of G

  c Yes: the Cayley tables have a line of symmetry along the leading diagonal. Also the groups are cyclic, and cyclic groups are abelian.

Assessment 10

1 a b

  Since $b * x = x * b = x$ for all elements x

  b b, c

  c Symmetric in the leading diagonal

2 a b

  since it is the only element in all the subgroups

  b 30

  since it is the lowest common multiple of 2, 3 and 5

3

$\times_8$	1	3	5	7
1	1	3	5	7
3	3	1	7	5
5	5	7	1	3
7	7	5	3	1

$\times_{10}$	1	3	7	9
1	1	3	7	9
3	3	9	1	7
7	7	1	9	3
9	9	7	3	1

All elements in $\times_8$ are self-inverse, $\times_{10}$ has only two self-inverse elements, therefore not isomorphic.

4 a It means that 9 is a *generator* of the group.

  b $9^2 = 17 \pmod{64}$
  $9^3 = 25 \pmod{64}$
  $9^4 = 33 \pmod{64}$
  $9^5 = 41 \pmod{64}$
  $9^6 = 49 \pmod{64}$
  $9^7 = 57 \pmod{64}$
  $9^8 = 1 \pmod{64}$
  Since 1 is the multiplicative identity,
  $n = 8$

  c 1, 2, 4, 8
  Since by Lagrange's theorem, the order of the subgroup must be a factor of the group order.

5 a

$\odot$	0	1	2	3	4	5
0	3	4	5	0	1	2
1	4	5	0	1	2	3
2	5	0	1	2	3	4
3	0	1	2	3	4	5
4	1	2	3	4	5	0
5	2	3	4	5	0	1

  Since every element generated under $\odot$ is an element of the set, there is closure under $\odot$
  Identity element is 3
  5, 1 and 4, 2 are inverse pairs and 0, 3 are self-inverse so every element has an inverse.
  $(a \odot b) \odot c = (a + b + 3) + c + 3 = a + b + c + 6$
  $a \odot (b \odot c) = a + (b + c + 3) + 3 = a + b + c + 6$
  Therefore associative.
  Since the four axioms of being a group are satisfied, G forms a group under $\odot$

  b $\{3\}$, $\{1, 3, 5\}$, $\{0, 3\}$

  c $G = (\langle 2 \rangle, \odot)$
  or $K = (\{1, 2, 4, 5, 7, 8\}, \times_9)$
  Produce a mapping of G to K, e.g.
  $3 \mapsto 1$
  $0 \mapsto 8$
  $1 \mapsto 4$
  $2 \mapsto 2$
  $4 \mapsto 5$
  $5 \mapsto 7$
  As there is a one-to-one mapping between the elements of G and the elements of K which preserves the group operation, $G \cong K$

6 a Since $ex = xe = x$ for all x

  b 3 does not divide into 8 so
  no, she is not correct.

  c $d^2 = a$, $d^4 = c$,
  $d^8 = e$
  Since period of d is 8, d is a generator and group is cyclic. Rotations have period 2 or 4 and reflections have period 2, hence no element of order 8, hence not isomorphic.

7 **a** $(x \cdot y) \cdot z = (x + y - 1) + z - 1 = x + y + z - 2$
$x \cdot (y \cdot z) = x + (y + z - 1) - 1 = x + y + z - 2$
Therefore associative.

b $x \cdot 1 = x + 1 - 1 = x, 1 \cdot x = x$ hence 1 is the identity.
$x \cdot x^{-1} = 1 \Rightarrow x + x^{-1} - 1 = 1 \Rightarrow x^{-1} = 2 - x$, and conversely
$x \cdot (2 - x) = x + 2 - x - 1 = 1$
$2 - x$ is an integer, therefore elements have inverses
$x + y - 1$ is an integer therefore closed.
Hence P forms a group under $\cdot$

c No
since inverse $2 - x$ is not a positive integer for all $x > 1$
For instance the inverse of 3 is -1, which is not a positive integer.

Index

A

abelian groups 140
addition
    modular arithmetic 112–13
    principle of counting 127
alternating sums 106
angles in semi-circles 3–4
arcs 3–4, 56–64
areas 65–71
Argand plane 9–13
arguments 9, 11–12, 34–5
associativity 97, 139
auxiliary equations 32–6, 38–9

B

back substitution 119–20
Bézout's identity 108–10, 119, 122–3
binary operations 139–42, 144–5, 149
bisectors 2, 7

C

calculators
    combinatorics 127
    diagonal matrices 93, 96
    recurrence relations 27, 33–5, 39
Cartesian equations
    arc lengths 56, 60–1
    loci 4
    objects in w-plane 11–12
    surface areas 65–6, 69
Cayley tables
    groups 138–9, 141–2, 145
    isomorphism 149–52
    subgroups 145
Cayley–Hamilton (C–H) theorem
    83–90
characteristic equations
    diagonal matrices 92, 98
    eigenvalues/vectors 78, 83–9
C–H see Cayley–Hamilton theorem
circles
    equations 4–5
    loci 2–5, 7
    regions bounded by loci 7
    transforming Argand plane 9–10, 12
closed form solutions 21–7, 29, 40
closure condition 138–9, 144–5, 147
codes for locks 126
coincidental roots 36
combinations
    combinatorics 125–6, 129
    groups 138–9, 142, 146
    subgroups 146
combinatorics 125–30
commutativity 140
complementary functions 35–9
completing the square 5, 7
complex numbers
    complex plane 1–18
    complex roots 34–6
    eigenvalues 79
    loci 2–8
    transforming Argand plane 9–13

cones 65
congruence equations 119–24
    simplification 123
    subtracting integers method 122
congruency
    congruence equations 119–24
    congruence modulo n 112, 116
    'is congruent to' sign 112
constants 23–4, 26, 33–4, 36–7
coprime integers 110
cyclic groups 141, 152

D

definite integrals 51
determinants 78–81, 84–5, 91
diagonal matrices 91–9
dihedral groups 141–2
direction of vector 78
distinct roots 36
division 106–11
    divisibility rules for integers 106, 115–16
    division theorem 107
    modular arithmetic 113, 115–16

E

eigenvalues/vectors 78–90, 91–6, 98
element of group, definition 138
elements of sets 129–30
empty set 129–30
equations
    auxiliary 32–6, 38–9
    characteristic 78, 83–9, 92, 98
    circles 4–5
    congruence 119–24
    parametric 57–8, 60–1, 66–7, 69–70
    polar 57–8, 60, 62, 67–9
    quadratic 32–3
    roots of 32–6
    simultaneous 23, 26–7, 34–5, 37, 40
    see also Cartesian equations
equilateral triangles 141–2
Euclid's algorithm 106–11, 119–20, 122–3

F

Fermat's little theorem 117
Fibonacci sequence 32
financial recurrence relations 20
first-order recurrence relations 20–31
    closed form solutions 21–7, 29
    general form 24
    homogeneous 23–4
    non-homogeneous 23–5
    proof by induction 29
    special case 24
frustums 65

G

generator elements 141–2
geometric series 22
greatest common divisor 107
group theory 137–58
    axioms 139, 142
    definition of group 139
    groups 138–48

    isomorphism 149–52
    subgroups 144–8

H

Hamilton see Cayley–Hamilton
highest common factor (hcf) 107–10,
    119–23
homogeneous recurrence relations 23–4,
    32–3, 35, 39
hyperbolic identities 60–1, 69

I

identities, trigonometric 53, 60–2, 68–70
identity elements 138–40, 144–7, 149–52
identity matrices 78, 84
indefinite integrals 51
index laws 114, 117
induction, proof by 29, 40, 97, 130
inequalities 7
initial conditions 20–1, 29, 32–40
inspection methods 67, 70
integers see number theory
integrals 38, 51
integration
    arc lengths 56–64
    by parts 50–4
    surface areas 65–70
inverses
    elements of groups 138–9, 144–7
    matrices 94
    multiplicative 120, 122–3
    self-inverse elements 138, 145, 147, 150–2
isomorphism 149–52

L

Lagrange's theorem 146–7
least positive residue modulus p 117
like terms 37, 41
limits 51, 60, 62, 66
lines of symmetry 141
loci 2–8
    complex numbers 2–8
    regions bounded by loci 6–7
    transformations to planes 10
lock coding 125

M

magnitude of eigenvector 80, 82, 95, 98
major arcs/sectors 3
matrices 77–104
    diagonalisation 91–9
    eigenvalues/vectors 78–90, 91–6, 98
    orthogonal 93–6
    square 78, 81–2, 94, 97
    symmetric 93–4, 97
minor arcs/sectors 3
modular arithmetic 112–24
    congruence equations 119–24
    congruency 112, 116, 119–24
    divisibility rules 115–16
    general rules 113
    group theory 139
    power rule 113–14
    properties 112

modulus 4–5, 11–12, 34–5
multiples 109–10, 117
multiplication
    modular arithmetic 112–13, 116, 120,
        122–3
    multiplicative inverses 120, 122–3
    principle of counting 127
    subgroups 144–5

N
natural numbers 115–16
non-empty groups 144–5
non-homogeneous recurrence relations
    23–5, 32, 35–6, 39–40
non-parallel eigenvectors 83
non-singular matrices 87
non-trivial subgroups 144–5
normalised eigenvectors 80, 82, 93–6, 98
normalised vectors 80
number theory 105–36

O
one-to-one mapping 149–51
order of element of group 140
order of group 140, 146–7
orthogonal eigenvectors 93–6
orthogonal matrices 93–6

P
parametric equations
    arc lengths 57–8, 60–1
    surface areas 66–7, 69–70
particular integrals 38
period of element of group 140, 146, 152
permutations 125–7, 138–40
perpendicular bisectors 2, 7
polar equations
    arc lengths 57–8, 60, 62
    surface areas 67–9
polygons 141–2, 146
polynomials 25–6, 88
population growth/decline 20–1
powers
    matrices 97–8

modular arithmetic 113–14
    of ten 115
prime numbers 117
probability rules 127
product rule 57
proof by induction 29, 40, 97, 130
proper subgroups 144, 147
proper subsets 129
Pythagoras' theorem 56

Q
quadratic equations 32–3
quotients 107

R
real complex components 11–12
real numbers 144–5
recurrence relations 19–48
    first-order 20–31
    second-order 32–41
reduction formulae 50–5
    integration by parts 50–4
    splitting the function 51
regions 6–7
regular polygons 141–2, 146
relations, recurrence 19–48
relatively prime integers 110
remainders 107, 113, 117
revolutions of areas 65–71
roots of equations 32–6
rotational symmetry 141–2

S
scalars
    scalar products 93–4, 96
    see also eigenvalues/vectors
second-order recurrence relations 32–41
    general solutions 33–40
    homogeneous 32–3, 35, 39
    non-homogeneous 32, 35–6, 39–40
    particular solutions 35–7, 39
sectors 2–3
self-inverse elements 138, 145, 147, 150–2
semi-circles 3–4

sequences 20–1, 23, 25–7, 32
sets 129–30, 141
simultaneous equations 23, 26–7, 34–5,
    37, 40
singular matrices 78
square matrices 78, 81–2, 94, 97
subgroups 144–8
subsets 129–30
substitution methods
    arc lengths 60, 62
    back substitution 119–20
    surface areas 67, 69–70
subtraction, modular arithmetic
    112–13
sum of geometric series 22
surface areas 65–71
symmetry
    abelian groups 140
    groups 140, 141–2, 146
    modular congruence 116
    regular polygons 141–2, 146
    symmetric matrices 93–4, 97

T
transformations 9–13
transpose of matrix 94
triangles, equilateral 141–2
trigonometric identities 53, 60–2, 68–70
trivial subgroups 144, 146–7
truncated cones 65

U
unit vectors 80

V
vectors 78–90, 91–6, 98
volumes of revolution 65–6

W
w-plane 9–12

Z
z-plane 9–10